Epidemic Diseases in Aberdeen and the History of the City Hospital

I. A. Porter and M. J. Williams

Retired Consultant Bacteriologist, The Regional Laboratory, Aberdeen City Hospital and Retired Consultant Physician, Aberdeen Royal Infirmary

ABERDEEN HISTORY OF MEDICINE PUBLICATIONS No 2

Published by
Aberdeen History of Medicine Publications
Northern Health Services Archives
ARI Woolmanhill
Aberdeen
AB25 1LD

Epidemic Diseases in Aberdeen and the History of the City Hospital
I. A. Porter and M. J. Williams

Aberdeen History of Medicine Publications No. 2

First published 2001

ISBN: 0 9527713 1 4

Series Editors:
Alexander Adam, Aberdeen Medico-Chirurgical Society
David F. Smith, History Department, Aberdeen University
Fiona Watson, Northern Health Services Archives

Previous publication:
'To the Greit Support and Advancement of Helth', 1997

Printed by Polestar Scientifica Aberdeen Ltd.

Dedication

This book is dedicated to all those who served the sick in the City Hospital and in particular to the many who spent the greater part of their working lives in that institution.

Some, both men and women, as a consequence of their devotion to their calling, gave their own lives. We honour them.

About the Authors

Dr Ian A. Porter graduated from Glasgow University MB ChB in 1945 and obtained his MD in 1960. After service with the RAF he started his career in bacteriology with Professor C. Browning in Glasgow and then worked for eighteen months with Professor J. Cruickshank in Aberdeen in the university department of bacteriology. He then briefly returned to Glasgow until appointed lecturer in bacteriology in the University of Durham, later becoming senior lecturer in the University of Newcastle as it became. After thirteen years he became consultant bacteriologist of the Ayrshire area laboratory service. He returned to Aberdeen in 1968 when appointed consultant microbiologist in the City Hospital laboratory and became consultant-in-charge of the laboratory service there in 1978, a post he held until his retirement in 1983. He is author of *Alexander Gordon, M.D., of Aberdeen, 1753–99* (1958).

Dr M. J. Williams was born in Aberdeen and studied medicine at Aberdeen University graduating with honours in 1954, proceeding to MD in 1965. Following resident posts at Aberdeen University and two years' service in the RAMC, he was appointed registrar and later senior registrar to Aberdeen General Hospitals. From 1961 to 1968 he was lecturer in materia medica and therapeutics in the University of Aberdeen. In 1968 he was appointed consultant general physician, with special interest in metabolic diseases, to the Aberdeen hospitals. He was in charge of Wards 2 and 3 at the City Hospital, moving to the Aberdeen Royal Infirmary in 1980. He was consultant-in-charge of the Aberdeen Diabetic Clinic from 1983 until his retirement in 1994. He is author of *J. J. R. Macleod: the co-discoverer of insulin* (1993).

Contents

Appendices

List Of Illustrations
(between pages 146-147)

Acknowledgements

Many individuals helped trace material. Fiona Watson, archivist to Northern Health Services Archives gave ready access to material in her possession and drew our attention to relevant material in other departments. Miss Cripps of the Aberdeen City Archives allowed access to the Public Health Minute Books and other volumes in her possession. Mr Alexander Adam, Honorary Librarian to the Aberdeen Medico-Chirurgical Society permitted us to borrow bound volumes of the publications of Dr J. Parlane Kinloch and Dr John Smith in the Society's possession and also other volumes and files of relevant newspaper cuttings. Staff at the Aberdeen Central Library, the Aberdeen University Special Collections and Archives and the Aberdeen University Medical School Library were all helpful. The late Dr Robert Fraser kindly gave permission for extensive use to be made of his unpublished manuscript - 'Memories of the City Hospital'. Many colleagues patiently answered several queries. Drs C. C. Smith, James Friend, Norris Rennie, David Reid, Tom Reid, Peter Smail, John Stowers, Hugh Galloway and Lewis Gillanders all provided or confirmed facts. Mr H. Norton, formerly Divisional Operational Services Manager of Aberdeen General Hospitals Division kindly provided information on recent developments and some future plans for the City Hospital site. Mrs Nan McKay, superintendent radiographer at the City Hospital, gave information on past developments in the radiology department there and drew our attention to the site of the 'anniversary tree' planted in 1977. Sister Rosemary Nixon provided details of some proposed developments on the site. Mr Bain, previous administrator at the City Hospital, did much work in obtaining personal reminiscences and information from previous members of staff, relatives and friends of the hospital. Unfortunately it has not been found possible to include much of this material in this publication.

Permission to reproduce photographs was freely given by several individuals or organisations. The photograph of the entrance to the City Hospital and administration block (Plate 2A) and the view of the inside of one of the wards (Plate 4B) were kindly provided by Northern Health Services Archives. Mr Adam, Honorary Librarian, Aberdeen Medico-Chirurgical Society, provided the photographs of Dr Francis Ogston, Dr W. J. R. Simpson, Professor Matthew Hay and Dr J. Parlane Kinloch in

Plate 8, the photograph of Dr John Christie in Plate 9, and of Dr John Smith in Plate 10. The photograph of Dr Ian MacQueen was obtained from Aberdeen Journals Ltd and is reproduced by permission of Eric Stevenson, assistant editor, *Press and Journal*. The photograph of Dr Theodore Thomson was reproduced by permission from the obituary published in *The Lancet*, March 18, 1916, p. 647 and the BMJ Publishing Group gave permission to reproduce the obituary photographs of Dr H. W. Rutherford (*British Medical Journal*, 1988, vol. 297, p. 551) and of Dr E. G. Barnes (*British Medical Journal*, 1996, vol. 313, p. 107). All the other photographs of senior medical staff at the City Hospital in Plate 9 were copied from University of Aberdeen Class of Medicine souvenirs with the permission of the University of Aberdeen. Drs James Friend and C. C. Smith provided the other photographs of the City Hospital in Plates 3, 4 and 5. While every effort has been made to secure permission to reproduce material used in this book, in a few cases it proved impossible to trace an appropriate person or persons. Apologies are offered to anyone who thinks they should have been acknowledged and they are invited to contact the authors or the publishers of this book.

All the photographs were prepared in the Photography Department of the Department of Medical Illustration of Aberdeen University Medical School and all the Figures were prepared by David Adams in the Graphics Section of the same department. Mr Keith Duguid, director of the Department of Medical Illustration kindly gave us permission to use these facilities. The skill and patience of his staff is gratefully acknowledged. Some of the early drafts of this history were typed by Miss Nora Findlay at the City Hospital while all the further work and the final draft was cheerfully and skilfully prepared by Miss Margaret Nimmo (now Mrs Symonds). The referencing format was the work of the editors of Aberdeen History of Medicine Publications.

Generous financial contributions towards the cost of production and printing were provided by the Trustees of the Guthrie Fund of the Scottish Society of the History of Medicine, and also from the endowment funds of the Grampian Health Board, Grampian University Hospitals NHS Trust, and Grampian Primary Care NHS Trust, and Aberdeen City Council. This assistance is gratefully acknowledged. The views expressed in this volume are entirely those of the authors.

Preface

The City Hospital on Urquhart Road, was Aberdeen's Fever or Isolation Hospital. The Infection Unit and the other specialties which developed there have all now been moved to the main hospital site at Foresterhill. The continued existence of the hospital is in fact in doubt and so it is appropriate to give an account of its origin, development and achievements.

The reasons put forward for the building of a permanent epidemic hospital at Cuninghar-Hill in the 1870s were sound, and remained so until the 1950s. Since then infectious diseases have for all practical purposes disappeared – at least in the number and severity of cases – although the Aberdeen typhoid outbreak of 1964 and the outbreak of *E. Coli* infection in Lanarkshire in 1996 are a sharp reminder of what can still happen in a modern society when there is a breakdown somewhere in the system of hygiene.

The need for the extensive provision of hospital beds for the isolation and treatment of epidemic and infectious diseases such as smallpox, cholera, typhus, typhoid, diphtheria, scarlet fever, poliomyelitis and puerperal fever has passed. The requirement for many beds for tuberculosis is no longer with us. As a result, many fever hospitals throughout the country have closed, but others have been adapted for the treatment of other diseases and for the care of the elderly sick. The City Hospital was not exempt from these changes and, as can be seen in the pages which follow, the diseases with which it dealt at one time were replaced by others.

Infections still occur in the community and patients with certain bacterial or viral diseases still require admission to hospital for investigation and treatment. Many such patients are severely ill and require the highest standards of medical care for their survival. It is now accepted that 'Infection Units' are better placed in the immediate environs of a major hospital with ready access to the full panoply of modern diagnostic and laboratory techniques.

So it has been in Aberdeen. Both the paediatric and adult infection units, along with chest medicine and the other medical specialties which developed at the City Hospital, are all now based on the Foresterhill site, either in the Royal Aberdeen Children's Hospital or in Aberdeen Royal Infirmary (Grampian University Hospitals NHS Trust).

The time is opportune to tell briefly the achievements of the hospital at Cuninghar-Hill, to put on record its successes and its failures, to note the devotion of its staff over the years and the esteem in which it was held by the citizens of Aberdeen and the surrounding counties over many decades.

January 2001

Chronology of the City Hospital

1867	Public Health (Scotland) Act. Local authorities given power to build hospitals for infectious diseases.
1873	Town Council agree to build Epidemic Hospital at Cuninghar-Hill.
1876–8	Construction of initial hospital buildings.
1877	First patients admitted.
1886	Hospital renamed 'The City Hospital'.
1887	The 'City Hospital Scandal' takes place.
1893–5	Major extensions – two wards and administration block enlarged, new laundry and porter's lodge built.
1898–9	Nurses' home extended.
1908–10	Further extensions, and alterations to wards.
1910	TB patients admitted.
1913–14	X-ray apparatus installed.
	TB dispensary (forerunner of chest clinic) started, with early laboratory facilities.
1917	Out-patient facilities for VD.
1920	Opening of main City Hospital laboratory.
1928	Further hospital extensions approved.
1931–2	New wards and new nurses' home opened.
	TB dispensary and x-ray department moved to central administration block.
1940	Opening of new isolation cubicle block in Wards 9 and 10.
1947	National Health Service (Scotland) Act.
	North-Eastern Regional Hospital Board set up.
1948	NHS introduced. City Hospital taken over by Secretary of State.
1950	TB department re-named the chest clinic.
	Closure of VD out-patient clinic.

1956	Ward 4 becomes general medical ward.
1959	Piped oxygen installed.
1960	Opening of rheumatology (physical medicine) unit in Ward 1.
1963	Liquid oxygen plant installed (first in Aberdeen).
1964	Aberdeen Typhoid Outbreak.
1965	Ward 6 becomes geriatric ward.
1966	Cessation of designated beds for TB.
1968	Expansion of general medicine into whole of Ward 2 and half of Ward 3.
1977	Centenary of the City Hospital.
1980	General medical units (Wards 2, 3 and 4) moved to Aberdeen Royal Infirmary.
1981	Wards 7 and 8 demolished. Portakabin unit for infection opened adjacent to Ward 9.
1982	New 30-bed geriatric unit (Ward 5) opens.
1987	New 60-bed geriatric/psychogeriatric unit (Wards 7 and 8) opens.
1990	Paediatric infection unit moves to Royal Aberdeen Children's Hospital.
1991	Opening of new AIDS unit in Ward 10.
	Opening of second 60-bed geriatric unit (Jasmine Park).
	Regional laboratory moves to university departments at Foresterhill.
1994	Chest beds move to ARI.
	Adult infection unit moves to ARI.
	Rheumatology unit moves to ARI.
1997	Chest clinic moves to ARI.
2001	? Future of City Hospital.

Chapter One

Plagues and Pestilences

From the beginning of recorded history, there is evidence that man has speculated on the nature and cause of diseases and, in particular, epidemic diseases. Explanations have never been lacking as to why plague or other pestilences should strike at this city or that and kill some individuals, while sparing others. However, it is only in the last 130 years or so, during which time the existence of micro-organisms has been demonstrated and the key part they play in bacterial and viral diseases appreciated, that there has been some clearer understanding of the causation and evolution of epidemic diseases.

Over the centuries many reasons were given as to why epidemics started and persisted. One of the most widespread and earliest-held beliefs was that disease was the result of the evil influences of supernatural powers. These powers, it was held, could be exercised by living persons, by the spirits of the dead or by superhuman beings. Such beliefs were not confined to the population of Britain or Europe, but were to be found amongst most peoples inhabiting the earth. In China, for example, it was thought that diseases were the work of devils who took possession of the body and could be cured when these invaders had been evicted by the application of charms, incantations and other superstitious practices.[1] In ancient Egypt disease was attributed to a spirit entering the body and exercising its harmful influence. To treat a patient it was necessary first to discover the nature of the spirit and then either drive it from the body or destroy it. Someone knowledgeable in magic, expert in reciting incantations and skilful in the making of amulets, was employed for this purpose. Drugs and special diets were then given to counteract the effects produced by the spirit in the body.[2]

In the Old Testament there is little concerning demonology but the practice of the magic arts is condemned. However, in the New Testament there is much more about demonology and although witchcraft and idolatory are denounced, the theory that disease is caused by evil spirits and can be treated by exorcism is accepted. There are numerous references to this procedure in the Gospels.[3] Belief in demons persisted throughout the centuries, from classical times into the period of Christian civilisation, down to the eighteenth century and perhaps even later. Thus we find a compendium of anti-demonological procedures, *Malleus Malificarum* or the *Hammer of the Witches* published in 1489 with the approval of the Pope. In

Scotland also, belief in demons was accepted and witches were put to death. As late as 1727 the last witch was burned at the stake.[4]

So far the belief that disease was due to the influence of evil spirits has been considered. There was another belief, however, similar in that it also conceived of a world ruled by supernatural forces, but differing in that it interpreted disease as being an expression of the wrath of a righteous God. In this latter case disease was considered to be a punishment for sin. This concept of the causation of disease was held especially by the Semitic people. Thus, in the Old Testament, there are many references to disease occurring as a result of sin and being the punishment of God, a belief which became an accepted part of the Christian doctrine. Incantations, amulets and sacrifices were of no value in the treatment of disease. The wrath of God could not be appeased by such measures.[5]

The doctrine of contagion, namely that certain diseases could be passed from one individual to another, also appears early in history. In the Old Testament there is a very clear conception of contagion, and based on it is a programme of isolation and disinfection. In the writings of the classical historians there is also a clear recognition of the fact that epidemics were spread by direct contact between the sick and the healthy.[6]

The great pandemic of bubonic plague in the sixth century provided further stimulus to the belief that it was a contagious disease. In 1348, when another pandemic of plague began, there was a widespread acceptance of the doctrine of contagion. By the fifteenth century medical men on the continent of Europe had developed a clear and logical theory of epidemiology. They realised that a disease such as plague was highly contagious and could be spread from the sick to the healthy. Moreover, infection appeared to be associated with objects and places used by those sick of this disease. It was believed that infection was a corruption of the air; that it arose from decomposing organic matter, from unburied dead bodies, from marsh lands and putrid water, and was associated with certain atmospheric conditions such as heat and dampness. The occurrence of great pandemics of disease was brought about, it was thought, by the malign conjunction of the planets and fixed stars, accompanied by other unusual phenomena such as earthquakes, falling stars and generally unseasonable weather. There was another factor which was believed to be of importance in determining if a particular person would be struck down by infection during an epidemic, namely, the individual constitution.[7] In the sixteenth century the view was put forward that diseases could be spread by direct contact between individuals by means of inanimate objects such as clothing or personal possessions, or through the air. This spread involved the passage of small infected particles from affected persons to others, but since their existence could not be demonstrated this theory received little attention at that time.[8]

Not all the factors identified as causes of epidemics were considered of equal importance by different authorities. Many of the factors such as weather, earthquakes and the stars could not be avoided, but infection might be. Thus great stress was placed on isolation and on quarantine. Although isolation had been practiced as far back as Biblical times the practice of quarantine was apparently established by the Venetians in the fourteenth century. Officers were appointed by the city to oversee public health and to ensure the isolation of infected ships, goods and people who arrived in Venice. A quarantine station was established in Ragusa in 1377 and all visitors who had come from places suspected of having plague were detained for a period of 40 days outside the city. Houses in which plague victims had lived were aired and fumigated, household goods were placed in the sun and washed while articles of little value were burned.[9]

'The Great Sanitary Awakening'[10]

Reference has already been made to the belief that decomposing matter could be a source of infection. It follows from this that if such material could be avoided the chances of acquiring infection would be greatly reduced. This view was expressed by King James VI and I in 1608 in a letter to the Convention of Burghs in Scotland about the laying down of middens or 'fulzie' on the streets. This practice, he said, was 'nocht only uncumlie and uncivill, bot lykwayis verie dangerous in tyme of plague and pestilence, and verie infective of itself'.[11]

In the middle of the nineteenth century, the 'great sanitary awakening' occurred and was based on the belief that disease was generated by filth. From 1850 onwards, a great effort was made by the sanitary reformers to clean up the masses of decomposing matter and refuse which abounded in the streets and near the habitations of the citizens of all the towns and villages in the United Kingdom. At the same time the importance of a pure water supply was demonstrated by John Snow (1813–58) and William Budd (1811–80). The introduction of cleaner water supplies resulted in a marked reduction in the incidence of typhoid and cholera.[12]

The Place of Micro-Organisms

Although many important observations on the nature and incidence of epidemic diseases had been made over the centuries the important facts as to their true cause had still to be uncovered. For such discoveries to be made science had to advance. The first important step forward was that taken by Antoni van Leeuwenhoek (1632–1723), a linen draper in Delft whose hobby was the making of simple microscopes. He was the first to observe micro-organisms, which he did in rain, sea and pond water, and in 1683 gave an unequivocal description of bacteria.[13] Over the years, using improved microscopes, others repeated and expanded his work, and observed bacteria and other microscopic creatures. However, it was not until 1839 that a disease of the human skin, favus, was shown to be caused by a fungus.[14]

The credit for establishing beyond doubt the role of micro-organisms in infectious diseases belongs to the French chemist, Louis Pasteur (1822–95). Between 1857 and 1863 he laid the foundation of modern microbiological technique, made many important discoveries and realised the far-reaching significance of his own findings. He was able to show how to prevent the spread of anthrax among cattle by immunisation and used similar methods to protect man against both anthrax and rabies. He demonstrated that lactic and butyric acid fermentations were the work of bacteria, that the fermentations involved in the production of beer and wines were the work of yeasts and that there was a relationship between the type of micro-organism involved and the type of fermentation produced.[15]

The professor of surgery at Glasgow University, Joseph Lister (1827–1912), heard of Pasteur's work on fermentation. At this time virtually all wounds suppurated, and the mortality after surgery was frightening. Lister considered that if micro-organisms caused fermentation they might also cause suppuration in wounds; and if there was an absence of micro-organisms in wounds, they might heal cleanly without the formation of pus, and without risk to the lives of the patients. As a result of this reasoning, Lister introduced in 1865 his antiseptic technique which involved the use of carbolic acid in the washing of wounds, in the spraying of the air of the operating theatre and in the application of protective dressings to wounds. In this way he achieved a striking reduction in post-operative sepsis and mortality and opened up the way for the advance of modern surgery.[16]

In 1870 Robert Koch (1843–1910), a German general medical practitioner, followed up the work which had already been done on anthrax. Koch was able to grow the organisms associated with this disease in artificial culture and to reproduce the disease by injecting the culture into animals. During the last quarter of the nineteenth century, Koch and his pupils, many of whom became world-famous, identified the causative organisms of tuberculosis, cholera, typhoid and diphtheria, and many other major infections of man and animals.[17] The age of microbiology had arrived.

It is pertinent to note here the contribution made to microbiology at this time by Dr Alexander Ogston (1844–1929) of Aberdeen, who later became professor of surgery at Aberdeen University. Ogston had been so stimulated by Lister's work on wound infection that he undertook further investigations of the subject in a small laboratory that he had built at the rear of his house in Union Street. These investigations consisted of examining the pus obtained from abscesses from patients. Ogston grew from many of the specimens small round micro-organisms, cocci, which he named *Staphylococci*. He was able to grow the staphylococci in pure culture and found that such cultures, when inoculated into guinea-pigs and white mice, produced abscesses. His findings were first made public in 1879. This was one of the major contributions to bacteriology which came from Britain at this period.[18] Ogston's name will appear later in this history as Assistant Medical Officer from 1868–72, at a time when plans for the building of an epidemic hospital were being discussed.

Over the centuries the mystery of epidemic diseases had persisted. Gradually pieces of the jigsaw puzzle were uncovered, fitted together, and a picture revealed. Observations made in different places at different times and discoveries made by workers in many different fields – by philosophers, poets, clerics and chemists – were brought together and found not to be contradictory as had first appeared, but to form a unity. It is we, in the twentieth century in particular who have benefited so greatly from the thoughts, observations and exertions of our forebears in that plagues and pestilences of the past ceased to exist and to terrorise the majority of the human race as they once did.

In the 124 years since 1877 when a permanent hospital for epidemic diseases was built in Aberdeen, the morbidity and mortality from these diseases has altered dramatically. This is part of the story of the City Hospital.

References to Chapter One

[1]   R. Porter, *The Greatest Benefit to Mankind*, London, Harper Collins, 1997, p. 151.

[2]   H. Sigerist, *A History of Medicine vol. 1, Primitive and Archaic Medicine*, New York, Oxford University Press, 1951, pp. 267–96.

3   A. R. Short, *The Bible and Modern Medicine*, London, Paternoster, 1953, pp. 109–23; C. E. A. Winslow, *The Conquest of Epidemic Disease: a Chapter in the History of Ideas*, New Jersey, Princeton University Press, 1943, pp. 3–34.

4   D. Hamilton, *The Healers*, Edinburgh, Canongate, 1981, pp. 80–4.

5   Winslow, op. cit., pp. 35–9.

6   W. Bulloch, *The History of Bacteriology*, London, Oxford University Press, 1938, p. 4.

7   L. I. Conrad, 'Arab-Islamic Medicine' in W. F. Bynum and R. Porter (eds), *Companion Encyclopedia of the History of Medicine*, London, Routledge, 1993, pp. 684–6; Porter, op. cit., p. 124; V. Nutton, *The Western Medical Tradition*, Cambridge, Cambridge University Press, 1995, p. 146.

8   Bulloch, op. cit., pp. 10–12.

9   D. Guthrie, *A History of Medicine*, London, Nelson, 1958, p. 127.

10 Winslow, op. cit., chap. XII 'The Great Sanitary Awakening', pp. 236–66.

11 J. H. F. Brotherston, *Observations on the Early Public Health Movement in Scotland*, London, Lewis, 1952, p. 79.

12 Guthrie, op. cit., pp. 388–9; Winslow, op. cit., pp. 271–286.

13 Bulloch, op. cit., p. 26.

14 Porter, op. cit., p. 430.

15 Bulloch, op. cit., pp. 59–62, 212–3, 247–51.

16 Hamilton, op. cit., p. 222–4.

17 Bulloch, op. cit., pp. 207–10, 237.

18 I. A. Porter, 'Sir Alexander Ogston (1844–1929)' in G. P. Milne (ed.) *Aberdeen Medico-Chirurgical Society. A Bicentennial History 1789–1989*, Aberdeen, Aberdeen University Press, 1989, pp. 179–189.

Chapter Two

Major Epidemic Diseases in Aberdeen before 1880

Plague

It is relevant as well as of interest to our story of the development of an epidemic hospital, to learn of the early outbreaks of epidemic diseases as they affected Aberdeen and the surrounding areas. An account may be constructed from Charles Creighton's *History of Epidemics in Britain*, which was first published in 1894, and from other sources. Creighton draws on documentary evidence for the occurrence of plague, mainly from the *Extracts from the Council Records of the Burgh of Aberdeen* and *Selections from the Records of the Kirk Session, Presbytery and Synod of Aberdeen*, published by the Spalding Club. The earliest source mentioning plague dates from 1401 and the disease appeared time and time again up to the middle of the seventeenth century. On 17 May 1498, the inhabitants of Aberdeen were warned by proclamation of certain measures to be taken to preserve the town from the pestilence. The principal precaution instituted was a guard of citizens at each of the four gates during the day, and the gates to be 'lockit with lockis and keis' at night.[1] Whether or not the plague actually struck Aberdeen in 1498 is not clear, but certainly in 1500 plague did affect the city. From the *Council Records* we learn that plague probably did not strike again until 1514. On 24 April that year various orders were made at Aberdeen against a disease that appears to have been the plague. These orders were for 'keeping of the town from strange sickness and specially this contagious pestilence renowned in all parts about this burgh'. The watching of the gates was again put into practice as it had been in 1498 against persons 'coming forth of suspect places where this violent and contagious pestilence reigns'. Lodges were erected on the Links and the Gallow-hill where infected or suspected individuals were detained for 40 days. In the following year, 1515, sixteen persons were banished from the town for a year and a day for disobeying the orders; again in 1530 these orders were renewed 'for evading the contagious pestilence reigning in the country'. In March 1546 a house in Aberdeen was 'shut up for the pest' and there are evidences of a continuance of this disease in August, October and December in Aberdeen and in certain other parts of Scotland. On 11 October 1546 there is noted in the *Council Records* that the St Nicholas 'braid silver' was given for the support of those sick of the pest.[2]

The absolute immunity of Aberdeen from plague in the second half of the sixteenth century is notable. Although plague ravished the rest of Scotland, no case occurred in Aberdeen. The *Council Records* for 1603 contain the entry, 'It has pleasit the guidness of God of his infinite mercy to withhauld the said plague frae this burgh this fifty-five year bygane'. The reasons for this immunity are not clear, but there is no doubt about the rigour with which the city put into operation its decrees against the plague. In May 1585, when many places in Scotland were suffering severely from plague, the magistrates of the city had erected three gibbets:

> … ane at the mercat cross, ane other at the brig of Dee and the third at the haven mouth, that in case ony infectit person arrive or repair by sea or land to this burgh, or in case ony indweller of this burgh receive, house or harbour or give meat or drink to the infectit person or persons, the man be hangit and the woman drownit.[3]

In October 1644 the Scottish Covenanters attacked Newcastle-upon-Tyne and on their return north of the border, plague which they had brought with them broke out in Edinburgh, Perth and other places. Infection reached Aberdeen in April 1647, having been carried, it is reported, by a woman from Brechin. The plague was still raging in Aberdeen in September and, even as late as November 1648, there were still a few cases. The number of deaths from plague in Aberdeen was estimated at 1,600 and, in addition, there were 140 in the nearby fishing villages of 'Futtie' and 'Torrie' on either side of the mouth of the Dee. This great loss of life occurred despite the usual rigorous measures which included the removal of infected persons to huts on the Links and at Woolmanhill, a cordon of soldiers to prevent their escape, a gibbet for those breaking the magistrates' orders and 'clengers' for the infected houses.[4]

Such a calamitous outbreak of infection was costly to the town and when the public funds were exhausted in supplying support for the inhabitants who were infected, the magistrates, of necessity, had to ask the county landowners for assistance. The expense incurred for the relief of the inhabitants during 1647 amounted to over £5,800 (Scots) and is given in the Treasury and Guildry Accounts for Aberdeen. It includes the expense of burying the dead and the costs of the gibbet, 10 fathoms of rope, rosen, vinegar, medicines and meal, and the services of the clengers who looked after the sick in the huts used as hospitals and who prescribed such remedies as were available.[5]

This severe epidemic of plague in 1647–8 was the last to occur in Scotland for many years, indeed, until the beginning of the twentieth century. However, the memory of this disease lingered long and the knowledge of its destructive abilities was not readily forgotten. The dismay that the threat of plague evoked is shown in a proclamation made by the provost of Aberdeen in November 1720, after he heard that plague was in the Isle of Man. Two months earlier, the Lord Justices had proclaimed that quarantine was to be imposed upon ships arriving from the Mediterranean, Bordeaux, the Bay of Biscay or the isles of Guernsey, Alderney, Sark or Man. The provost of Aberdeen now affirmed that the 'Justices of Peace and other Officers and Ministers of Justice' were commanded to ensure that no goods from ships from any of the places mentioned were to be landed. He warned that persons coming ashore from such ships might 'prove highly detrimental to the health of His Majesty's people'. Furthermore, for anyone to 'buy, receive or to take in their custody any goods clandestinely and unduly run and imported' would put the health of the individual and the community at risk and incur 'His Majesty's highest displeasure'.[6]

Although plague disappeared from Aberdeen and was to be rare in Scotland after 1648 there were numerous other major infectious diseases to trouble the populace.

Cholera

The most virulent of the water-borne diseases, cholera has been endemic in India for centuries, its true home being the delta of the Ganges. It became epidemic in Bengal in 1817, and British troops in this region suffered severely from the disease. In subsequent years it spread slowly but relentlessly north-west to Afghanistan and through Russia to reach Moscow in 1830, and thereafter steadily ravaged the whole of Europe. From Hamburg in Germany, where the disease appeared to be particularly virulent, it was carried to Britain where the first cholera death occurred in Sunderland, in October 1831. Most parts of the country were thereafter involved and 4,000 deaths were recorded in London alone.[7]

The cholera epidemic brought a degree of panic to the population of Britain. The authorities, being aware for months of the steady progress of the disease across Europe, had taken steps to try and prevent it reaching Britain. However, despite all attempts by quarantine regulations and other means, cholera arrived and established itself in this country. Great efforts were made to deal with and limit this dreaded disease, but it moved northwards into Scotland and on 18 January 1832 the first cases appeared in Musselburgh. Thereafter the infection spread through most of Scotland. Glasgow and the surrounding districts were affected by the end of February, and Dundee by April. Aberdeen and the northern counties remained free of the disease in the early part of the year but by August it was clear that the infection was likely to strike at any time.[8]

Boards of Health had been set up in most towns in the country to combat this infection. The Boards had very wide powers to carry out any measures that were considered important in preventing the spread of cholera. Action taken included the cleaning and lime-washing of stairs, passages and closes, and the removal of rubbish and filth from ashpits and privies. Thus, for example, any insanitary conditions could be dealt with immediately. Boards had the power, if necessary, to impose a levy on the citizens to raise funds to pay for the cost of any such work. However, much of the money available to the Boards of Health came from voluntary subscriptions.

Aberdeen set up a Board of Health in late 1831. In February 1832 it gave notice of an intention to raise £2,000 to pay for measures to combat cholera, and in the third week of August, called a public meeting to confirm its powers to spend the money then collected. The Board reckoned that the probable cost to the city of dealing with the expected epidemic would be in the region of £4,500, but this was not accepted by the meeting. At another meeting a few days later, a revised estimate of £3,400 was given. Of the £2,000 that had already been raised by voluntary subscriptions, £1,400 still remained and the Board suggested that a levy of £2,000 should be made on the citizens to make up the total to their estimate. This was rejected, the Board being told to spend the remainder of the money they had in hand before asking for further money, either from subscriptions or by levy![9]

Cholera appeared in the vicinity of Aberdeen during the last week of August and was reported in the *Aberdeen Journal* of 5 September 1832 as follows:

> It is with much concern that we have at length to announce the appearance of cholera in this neighbourhood. It commenced on Monday the 27th [August] and up to yesterday morning, at 10 o'clock, according to the official daily report published by the Board of Health, there had been 20 cases and 8 deaths: of these, 18 cases and 7 deaths have occurred at Cotton [near present-day Woodside], and 2 cases and 1 death at Old Aberdeen.
>
> We need not here reiterate what we have so often told our readers, as to the necessity of taking every due precaution to ward off this malady, or to mitigate its virulence, should it reach them. Cleanliness of person, and of residence; moderation in diet; temperance in the use of ardent or fermented liquors; the absence of

all unnecessary alarm; ... these are the specifics which we should recommend – seconded, as they readily will be, in every case of need, by the skill and attention of the medical profession, whose services should be called for on the slightest appearance of any of the premonitory symptoms of the disease.[10]

For a time the infection seemed to be confined to Old Aberdeen and Cotton but it spread to the city by the end of September. The *Aberdeen Journal* reported on 17 October as follows: 'We regret to perceive, from the official report that the number of cases in this city has received a considerable accession during the week'. Since their last item on the issue, there had been thirteen new cases and nine deaths, and a total of 69 cases and 28 deaths so far. Thirty cases and fourteen deaths had occurred in Aberdeen.[11] A fall in the number of new cases was apparent in the middle of November but a week later a further report told of 21 fresh cases of the infection, fifteen of which were from Footdee Square.[12]

Further information concerning this 1832 epidemic of cholera is given in the *Report of the Sanatory* [sic] *Condition of the Poor of Aberdeen*, prepared by Drs Alexander Kilgour and John Galen in 1840. They give the total number of cases of cholera in Aberdeen as 260 and the number of deaths as 105. Of this number, they say that 56 cases occurred in the fishing village of Footdee containing 56 houses with a total population of 480 inhabitants. This village, which consisted of two squares of houses, was so deficient in drainage as to call for strong remonstrations from the Board of Health to the magistrates and Town Council who were the landlords![13]

The initiative that gave rise to the Boards of Health when it appeared that the cholera might invade the country from the Continent, was soon lost when the cholera epidemic was over. The Boards were soon dismantled, although there is little doubt that through their efforts to improve the sanitary conditions, particularly in the poor parts of the towns, they achieved much in mitigating the effects of the epidemic and curtailing its spread. If such Boards had not been disbanded the whole public health movement might have become an effective power for good health, some 40 to 50 years before it eventually did so.

But cholera did not disappear forever. It returned again in 1848–50, but at that time there were relatively few cases in Aberdeen – less than 40 – although more cases occurred in the county.[14] Much more severe was the third epidemic that affected the whole country in 1853–4. In Scotland alone, 6,000 deaths are believed to have occurred. On this occasion Aberdeen was badly affected, there being 303 cases between August and December 1854, of which 200 died. A cholera hospital was set up for the treatment of those individuals who could not be treated adequately at home due to lack of bedding, the poor state of their dwellings, or the lack of any proper person to attend to them. A house of reception was opened at Porthill at the beginning of September, and another was opened in Footdee. These reception houses provided sleeping accommodation and food for the families of the victims. As in previous epidemics great attention was paid to cleaning up the city.[15] A further outbreak occurred in 1866 when there were at least 136 cases and 64 deaths between August and December.[16]

In 1868 the Aberdeen Royal Infirmary Committee informed the local authority (at this time the Police Commission – see page 22–3) that they would not in future admit cholera patients to the Fever Hospital where they had formerly been treated. In 1871, in order to prevent the subsequent importation of cholera from abroad, new powers were given to the Medical Officer to inspect foreign vessels arriving in the port. A special sub-committee was set up to consider where any cases should be accommodated and treated. The Town Council decided to use a building in the City Poor House as a temporary cholera hospital and despite objections from persons working at Aberdeen harbour, a temporary wooden building was built at the beach to accommodate any definite or suspected cases of cholera in seamen. This was erected by October 1871 at a cost of £86 - 5d.[17] However, the Infirmary managers later relented and agreed to admit cases.[18]

Only five cases of cholera occurred in 1872 and despite alarm in 1873 when there was a significant outbreak in Hamburg and other Baltic ports with which Aberdeen traded, no cases were found in ships arriving in the harbour. There were, however, a further nine cases in 1874 and four the following year. There were then three years clear until 1879 when two more cases were reported and then in 1880, the last significant outbreak in Aberdeen when seventeen cases occurred.

The causative organism – the comma bacillus or *Vibrio cholera* – was discovered by Koch in 1886. When working the previous year in Egypt and India, he had examined the faeces of 32 patients during life, and the intestinal contents at autopsy of another 62 patients who had succumbed to the disease. The comma bacillus had been found in all. He was, however, unable to reproduce the disease in lower animals by administration of the comma bacillus and so his conclusion that this organism was the cause of cholera, was initially challenged by others, but was later confirmed.[19]

Smallpox

Another epidemic disease that troubled the citizens of Aberdeen and the rest of Scotland was smallpox. One of the most infectious of all diseases, smallpox has probably existed since ancient times. Galen (AD 131–200) described a disease that may have been smallpox, but the Persian physician, Rhazes (AD 860–932), gave the first clear description. There is belief that the disease originated in Asia, spreading early to the Mediterranean and Africa, and in the middle ages to Europe. It was then carried by African slaves to the West Indies and the Americas and by seamen to all parts of the world.[20] Huge epidemics occurred causing enormous mortality, while the fortunate few who survived were left scarred and disfigured, and often blind. In Russia in one year, two million died, and in Africa and Asia whole populations were decimated.[21]

One of the earliest references to smallpox in Aberdeen is an entry of 12 August 1610 in the records of the Kirk Session, namely 'there was at that time a great visitation of the young children with the plague of the pocks'.[22] Between the seventeenth and nineteenth centuries there were many outbreaks of this disease with resultant high mortality. Children in the first few years of life suffered greatly from smallpox, mortality being very high. In the decade after the introduction of the compulsory registration of deaths in Scotland, that is 1855 to 1864, there were 10,548 deaths from smallpox, about two-thirds occurring in children under five years of age.[23]

Vaccination

It had been frequently observed that a person who had been fortunate to have a mild form of smallpox and survive, was unlikely to be at risk of a second attack. Although from early times deliberate inoculation of matter from what was hoped to be a mild form was found to bring protection, this seems not to have been done in Europe until the eighteenth century. The procedure, however, was not always successful, and its use could indeed trigger an outbreak. It was not until the closing years of the eighteenth century that Edward Jenner (1749–1823) experimented, in Gloucestershire, with a new safer form of inoculation, using infective material from another disease, cowpox.

Cowpox was known as a trivial condition, characterised by spots or pustules on the udders of cows and sometimes contracted by milkmaids through contact during milking. Country folk recognised that milkmaids who had had cowpox were resistant or immune to smallpox. Jenner, who occasionally gave live smallpox inoculations, noted they never 'took' in subjects who had had cowpox. He put forward a suggestion that cowpox inoculation would be a much safer method to protect against smallpox. Jenner's views met with scepticism from his medical peers, and after talking on the subject to a local medical society, he was actually threatened with expulsion, unless he kept his ridiculous views to himself!

Jenner then embarked on a series of experiments that would nowadays be deemed unethical. He inoculated a number of people with matter from the pustule of a patient with cowpox, and then subsequently inoculated them with matter from cases of smallpox, and found this had no effect. After further experiments, he submitted his results for publication to the Royal Society, but his paper was rejected. He therefore produced more data with similar results and eventually published these at his own expense in 1798. The initial response was discouraging, but gradually other doctors tried the method and it became accepted. The term vaccination was introduced for this form of inoculation. Jenner's pioneering work became fully accepted and the technique he introduced was used worldwide. It had an important bearing on the subsequent history of the disease. [24]

Vaccination in Scotland and Aberdeen

There is evidence that deliberate smallpox inoculation had been used in Scotland since 1721 but was entirely superseded by the procedure of vaccination from the early 1800s. Through ignorance or negligence, however, many children and adults were to remain unvaccinated and great epidemics of smallpox were to continue in Scotland for many decades.

The first vaccinator in the Aberdeen area was probably the Rev A. J. Forsyth of Belhelvie (1768–1843), who later attained fame as the inventor of the percussion lock that revolutionised the firearms industry. He had personally communicated with Jenner, and having learnt all the necessary details, vaccinated his first patient, a young girl in whose family smallpox had broken out. The procedure proved successful. [25]

A formal vaccine institution was opened in Aberdeen on 2 November 1803, partly endowed by a fund for promoting inoculation provided by a citizen before vaccination had been discovered. This work was later taken over by the General Dispensary, Vaccine and Lying-in Institution founded in 1823. A vaccinator, often a surgeon, was an official member of the staff of the Dispensary and the service was available to all the sick poor residing within the Dispensary boundary. For a time this service was restricted to the City and Footdee but was gradually extended as the City grew. [26] So it was with many other similar institutions throughout

Scotland. Moreover, in 1854, the Board of Supervision in Scotland ruled that Parochial Medical Officers were required to vaccinate all persons *gratis*. However, only about 20–25 per cent of infants were vaccinated at this time. Compulsory vaccination of infants was introduced in England in 1853 and in Scotland in 1864.[27]

Between 1860–81, there were four epidemics of smallpox in Aberdeen, the largest occurring in 1871–2. Whenever an outbreak occurred in England or even on the continent, Aberdeen was likely, sooner or later, to be involved, the contagion arriving either by land or water.[28] Initially such cases were admitted to the Infirmary and between 1858–70 there were a small number of cases recorded most years, with larger numbers in 1860 and 1863–4, causing 46 and 58 deaths respectively in these two outbreaks. The epidemic in 1871–2 was much larger. At the beginning of December 1871, when there were already twenty cases in the Royal Infirmary, the Infirmary managers forced the local authority to take responsibility for the problem, leading to the opening of accommodation at Mounthooly. There were 213 cases admitted, of which 45 died. During 1872 there was total of 132 deaths from smallpox in Aberdeen.

Typhus Fever

It is probable that typhus fever has affected mankind since ancient times and was in the past one of the great epidemic scourges of the world.

Particularly in the first half of the nineteenth century, typhus fever was a significant disease in Scotland and Aberdeen had its share of cases. Before 1865 the term typhus fever included typhoid fever as well as a number of other fevers. The clear differentiation between typhus and typhoid was made clinically in 1835 but almost three decades elapsed before the distinction was made in official returns. The fact that a number of different diseases were covered by the same term explains why 'fever' continued with a high prevalence over many years, why its death rate fluctuated widely in different years and why its epidemiology was so erratic in nature.[29]

An outbreak of typhus fever took place in Aberdeen in the years 1817–19. Although no figures are available of the total number of patients involved, it was so great that the Aberdeen Infirmary was unable to deal with them. The two fever wards at the Infirmary, each of eleven beds, were fully utilised. During the outbreak it became necessary to take over two buildings in the city for use as hospitals.[30]

A second outbreak of typhus fever occurred during the years 1831–

2. The fever accommodation at the Aberdeen Infirmary had been increased to 52 beds, by the addition of two more fever wards to deal with such a situation and to prevent the spread of infection to other patients in the Infirmary. The records of the Aberdeen Dispensary show that during these two years 2,704 cases of typhus were treated in this institution and of that number 57 died. During the years 1835–9 typhus was again prevalent in Aberdeen with 3,380 cases and 280 deaths – a mortality rate of 8.3 per cent.[31]

During the years 1863–6 there was a further outbreak of typhus fever and a smaller one during 1869. After this, the number of cases of typhus fever fell markedly and never again reached the high figures which had been so common during the first half of the century.[32] The causative organism, named the *Rickettsia prowazeki*, was first described by Henrique da Rocha-Lima in 1916. The name was chosen to honour an American doctor, Dr Howard T. Ricketts (1871–1910), who had died in 1910 whilst investigating the epidemiology of epidemic typhus and the related Rocky Mountain Spotted Fever.[33]

Measles

In addition to the major infections already discussed, there were many other infectious diseases that afflicted the population. Measles was one of the commoner. Now known to be due to a paramyxovirus, measles is a highly infective febrile disease characterised by a distinctive rash and catarrhal inflammation of the eyes and respiratory tract. Now a relatively benign disease of children, it was in the past more virulent and caused considerable mortality.

In 1808 an epidemic of measles affected the whole of Britain and appears to have been especially severe in Glasgow. During the months of May and June 1808, 259 and 260 children respectively died, this in a population of 100,000. At this time measles displaced smallpox as a killing disease in a city which had the reputation as being the worst city in the kingdom for smallpox.[34]

In Aberdeen, measles broke out in the spring of 1808 and here the disease is said to have had a greater mortality than had been noticed for a long time. Persons of all ages who had never had measles before, were affected and many adults were included in this outbreak. Few persons, it is said, escaped this infection who had been previously unaffected by it. A writer on the Aberdeen epidemic recorded 'I always observed that in full grown persons the eruptions were more numerous, quicker in appearing and longer in going off than in young subjects'.[35]

In 1882 W. J. R. Simpson, the Medical Officer of Health for Aberdeen, reported that during the preceding quarter of a century there had been three very large epidemics of measles and a number of small ones. He noted that by the early 1880s severe measles epidemics caused more deaths than the largest outbreaks of smallpox.[36] The mortality from measles began to fall in the 1870s but remained high well into the twentieth century.

Dysentery

Dysentery was another disease that was well known to the inhabitants of Scotland. There are records of outbreaks of the 'bloody flux' from the seventeenth to nineteenth centuries. This disease appears to have been in evidence for only a few years at a time and then to have died out, recurring sometimes as long as twenty years later. There were quite definite 'dysenteric periods'. One of those periods covered the years 1800 to 1803 when dysentery occurred in Glasgow, and the disease was not heard of again in this area until 1827.[37]

Aberdeen and the surrounding area also had outbreaks of dysentery. One that attracted a great deal of attention occurred in the fishing village of Footdee in 1789. The best account of this outbreak is given in a handbill issued on 16 June to elicit the support of the citizens of Aberdeen to succour the distressed families:

> An alarming account having been given of a putrid and infectious distemper prevailing in Footdee; to quiet the minds of the public, the following state of the fact is published by authority of a Committee of the Magistrates, Clergy, Physicians, and other Citizens, met on purpose to enquire into and use every possible means to put a stop to the evil.

> Since the month of February, a dysentery has raged very universally in the families of the fishermen of the place. During the winter, a certain degree of the same disorder was not unfrequent in Aberdeen, but where proper care was taken, and the conveniences of life not deficient, it was easily cured, and arose to no height; when it appeared among the fishermen in Footdee, who with their families amount to about one third of the inhabitants, in all not exceeding 550, the rest being chiefly sea-faring people or employed in shipbuilding, the progress of the disease has been very different. As in most other fishing towns in Scotland, there are dunghills of the most putrid materials collected in pits dug for the purpose

before every fisherman's door in the town, no inconvenience is felt
from this by the inhabitants of those houses when in health, as they
are universally accustomed to it; but during the prevalence of any
disorder that has the least putrid tendency, it never fails to prove a
most aggravating circumstance, as has often been experienced in
the very fatal progress of the small pox in fishing towns.[38]

The handbill went on to state that the association of the disease with the
peculiar 'habits and ways of life' of the fisher folk of Footdee meant that
there was no cause for general alarm. There was no evidence that the
disease 'could be communicated at a distance or by a slight intercourse with
the diseased' and all the physicians who had visited the sick remained
healthy.

From February to the beginning of June, ten had died in Footdee of
dysentery, eight of whom were fishermen or members of their families, and
two were women living close to them. On the last day that the committee
responsible for the handbill met, there were 27 ill. Thirteen of the worst
cases were housed in the local Battery, which had been converted into a
temporary hospital on the authority of the magistrates. With the assistance
of the committee, beds and other facilities had been provided. The handbill
concluded with an appeal for financial assistance:

> ... there is no doubt that the disease may be eradicated; but it will
> require time, and a considerable expense must be incurred, as after
> a seeming recovery, the patients are so liable to relapse, and the
> men for a long time so little in condition to provide for their
> families, that these must be assisted by contribution.
>
> These considerations it is hoped will awaken the feelings
> of a generous public, ever ready to afford liberal assistance in all
> calamitous cases, in behalf of an industrious, quiet, and necessary
> part of the community, and when a proper mode of application is
> fallen upon to raise the necessary supplies, may have the desired
> effect.[39]

In this chapter, the diseases that caused major epidemics in and
around Aberdeen have now been mentioned, but no reference has been
made to other infectious diseases such as diphtheria, scarlet fever and
whooping cough. These had also been present throughout the centuries
when the major epidemic diseases were taking their toll, but had been
dwarfed by them. It was only when diseases such as plague, cholera and
typhus had been overcome that the high morbidity and mortality of these

other infectious diseases were fully appreciated and steps were taken to combat them. These will be recounted in later chapters.

References to Chapter Two

[1] C. Creighton, *History of Epidemics in Britain*, vol. 1, London, Frank Cass, 1965 (2nd edition, orig. 1894), p. 361.

[2] Ibid., p. 362.

[3] Ibid., pp. 370–1.

[4] Ibid., p. 564.

[5] G. A. G. Mitchell, 'The Earlier Medical History of Aberdeen' in D. Rorie (ed.) *The Book of Aberdeen*, Aberdeen, Lindsay, 1939, pp. 17–18.

[6] '*Advertisement by the* Honourable *the* Justices of the Peace *of the Shire of* Aberdeen, *met at* Aberdeen *upon the Twenty first day of November, One Thousand Seven Hundred and Twenty* Years' contained in 'Documents relating to the City of Aberdeen, 1670–1819', Aberdeen City Archives.

[7] W. W. C. Topley and G. S. Wilson, *The Principles of Bacteriology and Immunity*, vol. II, London, Arnold, 1929, p. 1721.

[8] C. Creighton, *History of Epidemics in Britain* vol 2, Cambridge, The University Press, 1894, pp. 806–15.

[9] A. G. McEntegart, 'An earlier Aberdeen Epidemic – Cholera 1832', *Zodiac, a Journal of Aberdeen University Medical Society*, April 1965, pp. 26–8.

[10] *Aberdeen Journal*, 5 September 1832.

[11] *Aberdeen Journal*, 17 October 1832.

[12] *Aberdeen Journal*, 28 November 1832.

[13] A. Kilgour and J. Galen, *Report on the sanatory condition of the poor of Aberdeen*, sponsored by Aberdeen Town Council, 1840, p. 6.

[14] McEntegart, op. cit., p. 28.

[15] 'City Parochial Board Statistics of Cholera', *Aberdeen Free Press*, 8 December 1854.

[16] *Aberdeen Journal*, 23 January 1867.

[17] Aberdeen City Archives, Public Health Minute Book no. 1 (hereafter PHMB/1), October 1871.

[18] PHMB/1, September 1872.

[19] Topley and Wilson, op. cit., pp. 1722–3.

[20] P. Pringle, *The Romance of Medical Science*, London, Harrap, 1948, p. 48.

[21] Pringle, op. cit., p. 97.

[22] Creighton, op. cit., vol. 2, p. 434.

[23] Creighton, op. cit., vol 2, p. 622.

[24] Pringle, op. cit., pp. 97–107.

[25] Mitchell, op. cit., p. 19.

26   W. F. Croll, 'The Aberdeen Dispensary and Vaccine Institution' in D. Rorie, op. cit., pp. 50–2.

27   Topley and Wilson, op. cit., pp. 2207–8.

28   W. J. Simpson, *Health History of Aberdeen During the Past Quarter of a Century*, Aberdeen, 1883, p. 8.

29   W. H. Holmes, *Bacillary and Rickettsial Infections*, New York, Macmillan, 1944.

30   Kilgour and Galen, op. cit., p. 2.

31   Ibid.

32   Simpson, op. cit., p. 9.

33   Topley and Wilson, op. cit., p. 2207.

34   Creighton, op. cit., vol 2, pp. 652–3.

35   Creighton, op. cit., vol. 2, p. 652.

36   Simpson, op. cit., p. 7.

37   Creighton, op. cit., vol. 2, pp. 652–3.

38   'To the Public: Aberdeen, June 16, 1789', *Aberdeen Journal*, 22 June 1789.

39   Ibid.

Chapter Three

Hospitals for Isolation and Treatment of Epidemic Diseases in Aberdeen prior to 1877

Aberdeen, like most other towns in the country, had no separate and permanent hospital for infectious diseases until well into the nineteenth century. After the opening of the local Infirmary in 1742, it was a feature of almost every major epidemic that accommodation for the sick had to be sought in its wards. There is no difficulty now in accepting that a permanent epidemic hospital was at least desirable, if not necessary, when epidemics of smallpox, typhus and scarlet fever were breaking out with almost monotonous regularity. Many local medical men held this view around 1850, but it was not until later that the citizens and their elected representatives accepted it and steps were taken to provide such accommodation for the victims of epidemics.

There had been some earlier primitive facilities for certain infectious diseases. A Lepers' House had been built on the Lepers' Croft early in the sixteenth century, near to the highway known as the Spital connecting Old Aberdeen, then a separate burgh, with the city. Patients unfortunate enough to contract leprosy, which was particularly contagious and dreaded, were confined there, not for treatment, but to separate them from the healthy. It is reported that the last inmate of the Lepers' House was 'ane puir woman infectit with Leprosie' to whom the key was given in 1604, but it is believed that she died soon afterwards.[1] Leprosy had died out in this part of Scotland by the middle of the seventeenth century, and the building had become ruinous, although the remains were still to be seen in 1746. This is a good example of an isolation facility which outlived its usefulness and was allowed to fall into decay when the disease for which it was erected was no longer a problem.

Mention was made in Chapter 2 of the 'plague huts' built on several occasions during the sixteenth and seventeenth centuries on the Links and at Woolmanhill. Here again special isolation facilities were created for one particular disease, then epidemic in the country and greatly feared by all citizens. This accommodation, it should be noted, was provided by the Town Council. Plague vanished from Scotland after the middle of the seventeenth century, apart from a brief return in 1900.

The Aberdeen Infirmary, located at Woolmanhill, had opened in 1742 and gained its Royal Charter from King George III in 1773.[2] When cases of an epidemic disease appeared in the town, those who required isolation and hospital care were usually admitted to the 'fever beds' set aside there. If the outbreak was mild or with relatively few cases of disease and with little or no spread in the community, the small number of fever beds available was sufficient to meet the situation. However, when the outbreak was a severe one with spread throughout the town, the existing beds were inadequate to provide the necessary isolation and care. In such circumstances the citizens and Council were forced to take action. A temporary hospital would have to be constructed as quickly as possible or an existing building taken over and adapted to the requirements of a fever hospital at the least possible cost. An old factory in the Gallowgate was converted to provide space more than once.[3] On each occasion when the authorities had been stirred to action in the face of a severe epidemic or the threat of an epidemic, the action was not sustained. Once the immediate danger was over with the cessation of the epidemic and removal of the threat, their concern and interest abated. The building used might be sold and the furnishings dispersed. In a few years' time, with the development of another severe epidemic, the whole cycle would be repeated.

In the previous chapter reference was also made to the use of the Battery to give shelter to the victims of the dysentery epidemic at Footdee in 1789 and to the setting up of a temporary hospital for cholera victims in 1854. From 1875 there was also a fever hospital at Middlefield, run by the Woodside Commissioners of Police. This was just a cottage with eight small apartments. It was in regular but not constant use, mainly for smallpox cases, until closure in 1891, when Woodside was absorbed into Aberdeen and the residents could then be admitted to the City Hospital.[4]

As the city grew in size due to industrialisation, and as overcrowding increased, infectious diseases played an increasing part in the activities of the Infirmary. In 1832 the managers decided to build a new fever department as the first phase of a new larger hospital. This new fever department opened in 1833 and provided 60 beds. This was, however, still quite inadequate to cope with epidemics. In 1863 there was a major outbreak of typhus, continuing for three years and involving a total of 1,731 patients with a mortality of 13 per cent.[5]

Background to the Building of the Epidemic Hospital at Cuninghar-Hill

On 15 August 1867, the Public Health (Scotland) Act, passed by the Tory government of Disraeli, received the Royal Assent. This covered

53 pages, with 122 separate clauses dealing with a wide variety of public health matters, and gave the local authorities new powers and responsibility in this field. They were required to appoint a full-time Sanitary Inspector, to consider the appointment of one or more Medical Officers, and to provide appropriate office accommodation and suitable salaries. Local authorities were also given the power to build hospitals for patients with infectious or contagious diseases and to provide facilities for the disinfection of clothing, bedding and other articles. They were also allowed to remove persons with infective or contagious diseases from their homes and in the case of seaports, seamen with such diseases from their ships or vessels.

On 28 November 1867, the Commissioners of Police of Aberdeen held a special meeting to consider their duties as the local authority under this new legislation. It was decided to set up a Public Health Committee (PHC) to meet monthly, or more often if required, to execute remits made by the local authority. A legal agent would be appointed and a new post of Sanitary Inspector was created. They deferred decision on the appointment of a Medical Officer but agreed to revise the regulations on common lodging houses and to keep separate minutes. These recommendations were all approved and the committee as initially constituted had fourteen members, but was later reduced.[6] The Sanitary Inspector was appointed the next month, his duties detailed, and office accommodation provided at 33 Marischal Street. It was a whole-time post at a salary of £75 per annum. It was February 1868 before a decision on appointing a Medical Officer was taken and Professor Francis Ogston accepted the post in March.[7]

Francis Ogston, Medical Officer 1862–81

Francis Ogston (1803–87) was born in Aberdeen, the third son of Alexander Ogston, founder of a local soap factory. He obtained an MA from Marischal College and proceeded to medical training in Edinburgh, graduating MD in 1824. He set up in practice in Aberdeen, in 1831 became Police Surgeon, and in 1862 medical officer to the local authority (a post with a rather more restricted remit than that of Medical Officer under the 1867 Act). From 1839 Ogston served as lecturer, and from 1857 foundation professor, in medical logic and jurisprudence at Marischal College. In 1860, when Marischal fused with King's College to form the University of Aberdeen, this appointment was maintained.[8] After 1868, Ogston continued his duties as university professor and as Police Surgeon, and the post of Medical Officer under the new legislation involved much additional work. He was required to visit patients with suspected infections and to arrange for fumigation of their homes when appropriate. He also had to visit and inspect vessels arriving in the harbour from foreign ports to prevent the importation of infectious diseases from abroad. He was also to be intimately involved in the planning of the town's future epidemic hospital. He reported monthly to the PHC on numbers of cases of zymotic diseases, a new schedule of these having been prepared. The Royal Infirmary, General Dispensary, the City Parochial Board and the Old Machar Parochial Board had to provide the Medical Officer with returns monthly. The sum of £2 - 2s was paid yearly to each organisation for this work.[9]

Francis Ogston's salary was £43 - 10s per annum and there was no provision for extra fees, including those for the payment of a substitute.[10] He named his elder son, Dr Alexander Ogston, as his substitute to act in his absence. Alexander Ogston (1844–1929) also held a university appointment as assistant to his father as professor of jurisprudence. In addition, he was ophthalmic surgeon to the Royal Infirmary and later became full surgeon and regius professor of surgery at the University of Aberdeen. Alexander Ogston discovered the bacterium that was the major cause of wound sepsis and named this the *Staphylococcus*, work which was reported in classic papers published in 1881 and 1882. He was knighted in 1912.[11]

In December 1867, before Francis Ogston was appointed Medical Officer, the PHC considered building an epidemic hospital but soon abandoned the idea because of the lack of available funds, and it was to be ten years before this came to fruition after much argument and discussion. A pamphlet entitled *Remarks on the Necessity for Increased Fever Accommodation in Aberdeen*, published in 1873, provides much useful information on the struggle. The pamphlet, written by Dr J. W. F. Smith (later Smith-Shand), senior physician at the Royal Infirmary, was dedicated to the president and managers of that institution. It was compiled to inform the Infirmary Committee and other responsible citizens of the facts concerning outbreaks of epidemic diseases that had occurred in the town during the previous fifty years. It drew attention to the lack of hospital beds for the victims of these diseases. Although much good medical advice and encouragement had been given regarding the need for a permanent epidemic hospital, no effective steps to achieve this had been taken. For example, there had been a significant outbreak of smallpox in the area in 1871. As usual, the city had been unprepared and without adequate fever beds. By 1873, the situation had become quiescent, there being little in the way of epidemic disease at that time, and it appeared that the local authority might be in danger of forgetting that epidemics were likely to reappear, if not that year, then perhaps the following year. However, the members of the medical profession in Aberdeen, and in particular those on the staff of the Royal Infirmary, were no longer prepared to accept the procrastination, the lack of will and absence of action by the local authority with regard to the provision of a permanent epidemic hospital.[12]

Over the years from 1839 to 1872, the smallest annual number of cases admitted to the fever wards of the Royal Infirmary had been 132, comprising six different forms of contagious disease. In 1840, 1,207 cases of fever had been treated; in 1843, 1,344 patients had been admitted while in 1864, 1,048 cases were cared for, of which 897 had been typhus and 111 smallpox. J. W. F. Smith had been appointed a physician to the Infirmary in 1863 and was able to describe at first hand the conditions during the typhus epidemic over the years 1863–5:

> … while the entire accommodation for epidemic cases in the Fever Hospital proper, with its four wards consisted of 60 beds (the Infirmary itself had accommodation for 230 patients) – there were in the week ending 13 December 1863, 107 cases of typhus, 10 cases of smallpox, 29 ordinary medical and 60 surgical patients, making a total of 206 patients; and in the week ending 10 January 1864 there were 102 cases of typhus, 20 of smallpox, 36 ordinary medical and 59 surgical cases making a total of 217. When we consider the risks run by mixing in the same ward cases of typhus and smallpox, and the number of fever cases in the main building in the close vicinity of the surgical and medical patients it cannot be said that they got fair play in their struggle for life.[13]

Thus it would appear that during epidemics or occurrences of different fevers, accommodation was provided in the fever wards and then when these were full, in the wards normally occupied by medical and surgical patients. This, however, was clearly to the detriment of the medical and surgical patients already in the hospital.

One of the steps 'to effect a much needed reform in the management of the public health' following the 1863–5 typhus outbreak, was a special meeting of the Aberdeen Medico-Chirurgical Society at their Hall in King Street on 19 December 1867. The meeting was called by the President at the request of the medical officers of the Royal Infirmary and an account of it was given in the *Aberdeen Journal* of 25 December 1867. The purpose of the meeting was to consider 'the necessity for forming a Fever Hospital, or at any rate enlarging the accommodation for that purpose to a much greater extent than existed'. A letter from the physicians and surgeons at the Infirmary was read at the meeting. It detailed many of the difficulties, dangers and disasters that had occurred in the hospital during the typhus outbreak. A few extracts from this letter illustrate the conditions prevailing at that time:

> To meet the irrepressible demands for admission, children often had to be put two-a-bed; over and again convalescent adults had to be similarly mated ... the ordinary medical wards had to be set apart for fever cases. This arrangement continued for nearly twelve months. At the same time a proportional number of surgical beds had to be given up to the physicians ... the surgical work of the house was thereby crippled. Fever cases having been introduced into the main building, and having in fact come into it like a flood, typhus spread itself all through the entire house. In the medical and surgical wards alike, persons, ill of other diseases were attacked by typhus. Few, if any of the nurses attached to these wards escaped the disease, and several of them died. Other inmates afflicted were the resident physician's assistant and the matron. Several students attending the hospital, even if never entering the fever wards, took the disease and one died. Three of the physicians caught it and two died. Surgical operations deemed expedient could not be performed for fear of the patients operated on catching the infection. And good grounds there were for that apprehension, for already, several operated on were seized with typhus, and nearly all so seized died of it ... The evils referred to were experienced in an equal degree in the Hospital during the severe epidemic of 1847–48, and also in that of 1839–40, and in that of 1843–44. And it is absolutely certain that they will be experienced again, should nothing be done meanwhile towards meeting and encountering them. Effectively they <u>may</u> be met. All that is wanting is the <u>will</u> – the will of the community. Money will do it. Let the money be supplied without stint; and a skilled architect, acting under the guide of competent medical men will provide for Aberdeen such a Fever Hospital as shall completely answer the end view ... Let there be no jealousy in the matter as between this institution and that. Let the several Boards – Infirmary and Parochial – and let the public as well pull together.[14]

At this meeting, an extract relating to a fever hospital was read from a report which had been presented to the City Parochial Board on 15 Dec 1866. The authors of the report were Professor Francis Ogston, the Medical Officer, and Dr Beveridge, lecturer in pathology, pathologist to the Royal Infirmary, and secretary of the Medico-Chirurgical Society. It concerned the provision of a fever hospital for Aberdeen and detailed many of the aspects of epidemic diseases that needed to be considered when patients suffering from such diseases were admitted to hospital. The authors concluded their report stating 'we are strongly of the opinion that now is the time to set about it; and a portion of the money at the disposal of the Parochial Board could not be more usefully spent for the benefit of the sick poor and of the town generally than by contributing to the erection of a fever hospital'.[15] When this extract had been read, the meeting then resolved:

1. That in the opinion of this meeting, the only satisfactory mode of treating febrile diseases among the poorer classes, and of preventing their spread, is by affording such an amount of hospital accommodation as may enable the sick to be at once removed from their own homes, and the different diseases to be separated from each other.

2. That, in the opinion of this meeting, the accommodation presently afforded for this purpose in the Royal Infirmary is totally inadequate, not only for separating different diseases, but even for admitting the cases that occurred during an epidemic without overcrowding the wards, and so diminishing the chance of recovery, as well as needlessly endangering the safety of the attendants.

3. That considering the present time, when the town is comparatively free from fever, as the best for urging on the public at large the consideration of this question, the meeting resolves to press upon the public bodies concerned the necessity of taking active steps to provide suitable accommodation before the occurrence of another epidemic.

4. That copies of these resolutions be transmitted to the Town Council, the Police Commissioners, the Parochial Boards of St Nicholas and Old Machar and the Managers of the Royal Infirmary.[16]

Dr Beveridge passed this information to the local authority, leading to the discussions about the establishment of a fever hospital by the PHC in December 1867, earlier referred to on page 24.[17] During 1868 the matter was further considered at several meetings between the Infirmary Committee, members of the Parochial Board and the PHC. However, as mentioned earlier, nothing was achieved because of the lack of available funds.[18] The Infirmary medical staff therefore found themselves still burdened with the same old difficulties. Fortunately, however, the number of fever cases admitted from 1866 to 1870 was small, although there were always examples of patients dying who might not have died – being convalescent and almost ready to leave hospital when they fell victim to another fever from which they succumbed. Because of the restricted accommodation, cases of typhus, typhoid, scarlatina and smallpox were often put in the same ward with disastrous consequences.

Eventual Decision to Build an Epidemic Hospital

It required a major outbreak of smallpox during 1871–2, to force the local authority to action. An epidemic had started in England, the disease having been brought from the continent by refugees of the Franco–Prussian war. A small number of cases of smallpox occurred in Aberdeen in May 1871, but a few months later the PHC received correspondence from the managers of the Royal Infirmary, who were concerned about the demands on their accommodation in the event of any further significant outbreaks.[19] The matter was re-opened in December 1871 when twenty cases of smallpox were reported. The function of 'local authority' with respect to public health matters had recently passed from the Police Commissioners to the Town Council. The managers of the Royal Infirmary informed the Council that it was their responsibility to make arrangements for reception of the smallpox cases. The Medical Officer was detailed to arrange for the vaccination of all contacts and the PHC considered erecting a temporary wooden building near the Infirmary and renovating the old cholera hospital to house cases. It was decided, however, that these plans would be too costly and would take too long to implement. It was eventually decided to purchase an old disused match factory in Mounthooly.[20] The site was occupied in January 1872 and after rapid alterations, the establishment was certified fit to receive patients by Professor Ogston. There was accommodation for 40–50 patients with room for twenty more in an emergency. Ogston was detailed to take charge of the medical arrangements and was authorised to use one or more senior medical students as resident medical officers, and to engage appropriate nurses. The establishment opened on 17 February and two days later had admitted 35 cases. The outbreak continued until August with a total of 213 cases admitted. Consequent on this strain on resources, in June 1872 the local branch of the British Medical Association asked the local authority to reconsider the question of a permanent epidemic hospital. However, it was September before the PHC decided to set up a sub-committee to look into the matter.[21] This is of course a common administrative subterfuge designed to delay or avoid decision making, but in this case was to produce quick results.

In the interim there was dispute between Professor Francis and Dr Alexander Ogston and the local authority. Francis Ogston, the Medical Officer, had assigned his son Alexander, in his capacity as the Medical Officer's substitute, to look after the smallpox patients. Alexander later submitted a bill for fees totalling £472 - 10s but the local authority refused to pay, believing it was within the Medical Officer's terms of duty to have done this work, and that his substitute was not entitled to any separate remuneration.[22] A difficult situation then arose. Alexander resigned from his duties at the smallpox hospital and his father was asked by the local authority to take charge. The Medical Officer initially refused, but later relented, and agreed to take over until the epidemic ceased, which it did soon afterwards.[23]

Dr Alexander Kilgour was asked to adjudicate. He had been lecturer in medicine at King's College from 1839–49 and was a highly respected physician, being referred to as the 'Modern Sydenham'.[24] He recommended that £230 be paid to Alexander Ogston for his work. The local authority, one suspects with ill grace, was forced to agree and pay.[25] Probably related to this acrimony, Francis Ogston resigned from the post of Medical Officer on 23 August 1872.[26]

The PHC reconsidered the Medical Officer's duties and decided to amalgamate the post with that of Police Surgeon. The duties were all defined, occupying four and a half quarto size pages under 22 separate headings. The post was offered to Francis Ogston in November 1872, and after seeking clarification on some points, he formally accepted in January 1873. The remuneration was £63 per annum. It is of interest that at the same meeting as Francis Ogston accepted the post, the PHC had to consider a petition from twenty persons in the Gallowgate complaining of a bad smell emanating from his father's soap works in Loch Street. Family problems with the local authority continued! To obviate other frictions, however, Dr Patrick Smith was appointed as substitute rather than Ogston's elder son.[27]

In early 1873, Dr J. W. F. Smith was completing the pamphlet referred to earlier. At this time he stated the only fever accommodation existing in the Infirmary was two fourteen-bed wards. The old fever house had been demolished but a washing house at the Infirmary was being made ready for the reception of fever cases. This was to consist of two wards with thirteen beds in each giving total fever accommodation offered by the Royal Infirmary as four wards and 54 beds. Dr Smith made clear in his publication that the local authority possessed all the powers necessary to supplement the

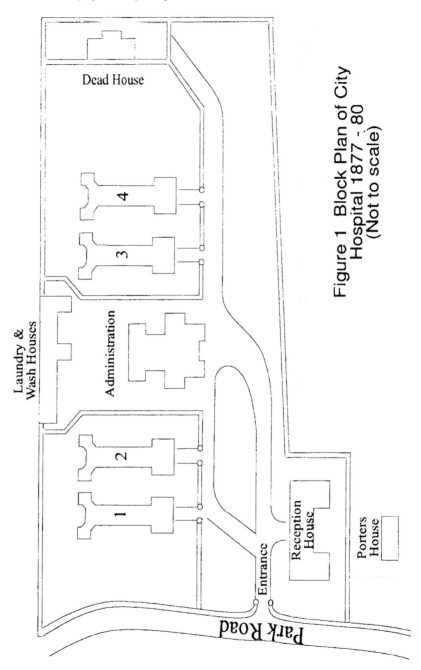

Figure 1 Block Plan of City Hospital 1877 - 80 (Not to scale)

work of the Royal Infirmary in the treatment of epidemic diseases. His plea for the establishment of an epidemic hospital was in fact to be answered. At about the same time, the PHC sub-committee formed to look into the matter decided that that such a scheme should go ahead and recommended a site at Cuninghar-Hill (rabbit hill – now the Broad Hill) adjoining the Links. There was a croft there of nine and three-quarter acres, on land belonging to Aberdeen University. It was confirmed that the University was willing to sell the land at a cost of £2,500, and Professor Ogston approved the site. Later in the year it was decided that the hospital need initially only occupy two acres, leaving room for expansion, and in the interim the unused land would be leased. The City Architect was detailed to draw up plans providing accommodation for not more than 100 patients. Various alterations were made, on grounds of cost, before final plans were approved and tenders for construction settled in April 1874. The final plan included four separate one-storey pavilions, accommodating 72 patients in all, with a separate small building known as the reception house intended for doubtful or contact cases.[28] There was also an administrative block, a small laundry, a disinfecting station and a 'dead house' (mortuary). Entrance to the hospital then was off Park Road. The whole site was enclosed by a high stone wall and the pavilions were separated from each other by walls seven feet in height. An outline plan of the hospital as finally built and as it continued until 1887 is shown in Figure 1.

It was at Professor Ogston's particular suggestion that the ward areas or pavilions were built of concrete, without any wooden floors or linings. There was strong suspicion that he was influenced in this decision by his son Alexander with his interest in antisepsis. This mode of construction allowed for the buildings to be literally hosed out as needed to maintain cleanliness. It was not intended that the hospital be continually in operation, but would just be opened at times of epidemics or when demand existed, and this view probably led to many economies with resultant problems which were to be a source of future trouble.

Because of its site and role, the hospital was initially known as Cuninghar-Hill Hospital or the Epidemic Hospital.[29] Its total cost, including that paid for the site, was £15,000. Dr Alexander Forbes was appointed as medical attendant and was to be paid £1 - 11s - 6d for each case treated.[30] The first patients, two cases of smallpox, were admitted in July 1877. A new era in the treatment of infectious diseases in Aberdeen had begun.

References to Chapter Three

[1] John Stuart (ed.), *Selections from the Records of the Kirk Session, Presbytery, and Synod of Aberdeen*, Aberdeen, Spalding Club, 1846, p. 34.

[2] I. D. Levack and H. A. F. Dudley (eds), *Aberdeen Royal Infirmary*, London, Baillière Tindall, 1992, pp. 9–30.

[3] Ibid., pp. 31–44.

[4] Aberdeen City Archives, Public Health Minute Book, no. 1 (hereafter PHMB/1), 21 December 1891.

[5] Levack and Dudley, op. cit., pp. 31–44.

[6] PHMB/1, 28 November 1867.

[7] PHMB/1, 10 March 1868.

[8] A. M. Millar, 'Ogston, Francis'. in L. Stephen and S. Lee (eds), *Dictionary of National Biography*, vol. xiv, London, Oxford University Press, 1973, pp. 946–7.

[9] PHMB/1, 16 March 1868.

[10] PHMB/1, 17 February 1868.

[11] I. A. Porter, 'Sir Alexander Ogston (1844–1929)' in G. P. Milne (ed.). *Aberdeen Medico-Chirurgical Society. A Bicentennial History 1789–1989*, Aberdeen, Aberdeen University Press, 1989, pp. 178–89.

[12] J. W. F. Smith, *Remarks on the Necessity for Increased Fever Accommodation in Aberdeen*, Aberdeen, Brown, 1873.

[13] Ibid.

[14] *Aberdeen Journal*, 25 December 1867.

[15] Ibid.

[16] Ibid.

[17] PHMB/1, 31 December 1867.

[18] PHMB/1, 15 June 1868.

[19] PHMB/1, August 1871.

[20] PHMB/1, January 1872.

[21] PHMB/1, 16 September 1872.

[22] PHMB/1, 19 August 1872.

[23] PHMB/1, 17 August 1874.

[24] J. Marnoch, 'Aberdeen Doctors' in J. Scott Riddell (ed.), *BMA Aberdeen 1914. Handbook and Guide to Aberdeen*, Cheltenham, Burrow, 1914, pp. 100–106.

[25] PHMB/1, September 1872.

[26] PHMB/1, 23 August 1872.

[27] PHMB/1, February 1873.

[28] M. Hay, 'The City Hospital' in Riddell, op. cit., pp. 52–7.

[29] Aberdeen City Archives, Public Health Minute Book vol. II (hereafter PHMB/2), 15 November 1875.

[30] PHMB/2, April 1877.

Chapter Four

The Epidemic Hospital 1877–87: Years of Trials and Tribulations

The opening of the new epidemic hospital coincided with a time of crisis. Before it was ready there was a large outbreak of typhus in the city and in October 1876 the managers of the Royal Infirmary notified the local authority that their wards designated for such cases were full. At a special meeting of the Public Health Committee (PHC) on 1 November 1876, it was decided, as a temporary expedient, to re-open the accommodation in Mounthooly earlier used for smallpox. Eighteen beds were accordingly prepared and used.[1]

In early 1877 Professor Francis Ogston, the Medical Officer, was asked to try to increase the incidence of vaccination in Aberdeen, in view of an outbreak of smallpox in London. He was empowered to engage another practitioner and three medical students to help with this task. Despite their efforts, two cases of smallpox occurred in July 1877 and were the first patients admitted to the new Epidemic Hospital.[2] It was early the next year before a further pavilion was ready, which initially admitted patients with typhus fever and later patients with scarlet fever. At this time, the Royal Infirmary still admitted patients with zymotic diseases to their fever wards, having 24 beds for cases of typhoid and 28 for typhus. They also had accommodation for up to ten patients with scarlet fever and seven with erysipelas.[3] In December 1878, Professor Ogston obtained permission for his younger son, Francis jr. (known as Frank) to act as his substitute. As with the earlier arrangement when Alexander Ogston had acted as the Medical Officer's substitute, there was no additional salary.[4]

Dr Forbes, the medical attendant to the Epidemic Hospital, died suddenly on 30 August 1880, and in December, Professor Ogston resigned from his post as Police Surgeon and Medical Officer of the local authority. In early 1881 the PHC considered the vacancies created, and decided to restructure the different posts that it controlled. A new position, to be entitled Medical Officer of Health (MOH) for the City, was to encompass the duties of Medical Officer of Health, Police Surgeon, medical attendant at the Epidemic Hospital, medical attendant at the gas works, examiner of the quality of gas, and inspector of dairies, cow sheds and milk shops. The post would be whole-time at a salary of £300 per annum. The conditions of employment were carefully drafted, the post advertised and a shortlist of applications considered in June. The application of Francis Ogston jr, who had been assistant to his father, was unsuccessful. Dr W. J. R. Simpson was elected by a majority and accepted the post on 27 June 1881.[5]

William John Ritchie Simpson, Medical Officer of Health 1881–6

Simpson was to hold the post in Aberdeen for just five years before leaving to become MOH in Calcutta where he established a reputation as a physician and pioneer in tropical medicine. Born in Glasgow, he had taken his MB CM in Aberdeen in 1876 and his MD in 1880. He decided on a career in public health and obtained his Diploma in Public Health (DPH) in Cambridge the same year, and then served as deputy MOH for East Kent. After leaving Aberdeen, he stayed twelve years in Calcutta and then became professor of hygiene at King's College, London and lecturer in tropical hygiene at the London School of Tropical Medicine. He was elected FRCP in 1899, made CMG in 1909 and received the honour of knighthood in 1923.[6]

Two years after his appointment in Aberdeen, Simpson was granted permission to teach public health at the university. His workload at the hospital and elsewhere steadily increased and in November 1883, he applied for an increase in salary from £330 to £380. This was approved and it was agreed that the following year it would be further increased to £430.[7]

The city at this time was expanding rapidly. The population had increased from 63,228 to 105,003 between 1841 and 1881 and was still growing. The workload in the Royal Infirmary had also increased considerably and in April 1885 the managers notified the Town Council that, at the earliest possible date, they wished to discontinue admitting patients suffering from infectious diseases, for whom the local authority was legally responsible. Simpson told the Public Health Committee, which at the end of 1883 had been reconstituted as a Public Health Committee of the Town Council, that additional nursing staff would be required at the Epidemic Hospital to cope with the extra demand. He recommended the appointment of a properly qualified head nurse to be responsible for the nursing arrangements. They would also need a complement of under-nurses and a cook, and various alterations at the hospital were advised.[8] The committee visited the hospital and recommended that the concrete floors in three of the pavilions should be covered in wood and the inside walls lined with varnished wood to a height of four feet. The entirely concrete structures had been found rather forbidding. Some improvements in the mortuary were also approved.[9] In December 1885 the PHC re-visited the hospital to check on the improvements made. They also appointed Miss

Mary Thomson as head nurse, who was provided with a salary of £40 per annum and board and lodgings. She had been head nurse at Barnhill Hospital, Springburn in Glasgow.[10]

Dr Simpson resigned from his post on 15 March 1886. The PHC took the opportunity of reconsidering and redefining the new appointee's role. It was decided that the MOH would cease to be inspector of dairies, cow sheds and milk shops and medical attendant at the gas works. He would, however, continue to be Police Surgeon, examiner of the quality of gas, and medical attendant at the Epidemic Hospital. He would be required to work full-time and would receive remuneration of £300 per annum. It was also agreed that the MOH would cease to be head of the Sanitary Department, which would become the responsibility of the Chief Sanitary Inspector acting in conjunction with the MOH. However, an amendment was passed reversing the latter decision. The duties of MOH were carefully detailed, but in respect of the role of medical attendant to the Epidemic Hospital it was decided he 'shall attend to the treatment of patients and take whole medical charge and responsibility'.[11] The omission of any mention of administrative responsibilities was to lead to problems. It was also decided that in future the hospital would be called the 'City Hospital' and that representatives of the PHC would visit the hospital weekly. It is doubtful whether the latter decision was implemented. Dr Theodore Thomson was appointed MOH in May 1886 and was to take up his post on 1 June.[12] This was Thomson's first appointment in public health.

Theodore Thomson, MOH 1886–8

One of a large family, Thomson was born at Belhelvie, Aberdeenshire, where his father was a minister. He obtained his MA at Aberdeen University in 1877 and studied medicine at Edinburgh and London, qualifying MD at London in 1882. He was to obtain his DPH at Cambridge in 1888.[13] His appointment as MOH in Aberdeen was his first such post and he was to hold the position for less than two years. It was to prove an unhappy period for the hospital whose reputation, which in the public eye had never been good,[14] was to be brought into serious question.

Soon after Thomson's appointment, he reported on some deficiencies in the hospital and on the need for more accommodation, but before any action was taken, complaints of a more serious nature surfaced. There were complaints of patients being sent home in a verminous state and the Aberdeen United Trades Council lodged a document listing many serious charges. It claimed that 'beds were swarming with lice', that there was 'an utter want of cleanliness', a 'shortage of adequate clothing for patients' and a 'want of proper variety of food supplied to those convalescent'. Furthermore, persons were being employed as nurses 'whose character and habits made them totally unfit for that position' and there was a 'want of proper supervision over the nurses and inmates'. The PHC considered these allegations on 16 August 1886. It was noted that the hospital had been intended only for intermittent emergency use but because of the action of the Infirmary managers earlier that year in refusing admission to most zymotic cases, the hospital was now in constant usage. Steps had already been taken to have the hospital thoroughly equipped and put in an efficient state and it was felt that most of the complaints were out of date and had already been addressed.[15] Later, however, improvements in the heating and hot water supply at the hospital were agreed and the purchase of a new disinfecting machine at a cost of £285 was arranged.[16] In November 1886 an appeal for 'cast-off clothing for patients', by F. Maitland Moir, convenor of the Public Health Committee, was published in the local press and evoked a good response.[17]

In late December 1886 there was also a complaint from the parents of a boy who had been in hospital with scarlet fever, alleging maltreatment by other inmates. On investigation, it was found that two older boys, who had also been patients, had plunged the complainant's son, aged three and a half years, into a cold bath. The conduct of the officials at the hospital in having allowed this to happen was condemned.[18]

In January 1887, Thomson arranged for Dr James MacKenzie Booth[*] to act as his substitute and asked the PHC to consider extensions to the hospital from 64 to 115–120 beds and the purchase of an ambulance. Until then patients – even those with smallpox – had to be carried to the hospital in a covered stretcher by a couple of porters. The same porters brought infected clothing and bedding for disinfecting in a small hand van. The extensions requested were to be costed, and in the interim, £422 was to be spent repainting, repairing and improving various structures.[19] Before any action could be taken, however, there were more serious complaints.

The first intimation of this was an article in the *Evening Gazette* of 7 March 1887, entitled 'Alarming Occurrence at the City Hospital'. A young female patient, a probationer nurse at the Sick Children's Hospital, had been admitted to the City Hospital with suspected typhus. On 24 February, despite having a high fever and possibly being delirious, she had

---

[*] James MacKenzie Booth (1855–1919) MA 1875, MB CM 1877, MD 1886. Consulting surgeon, Aberdeen Royal Infirmary 1904. Previously lecturer and senior lecturer in clinical surgery.

been left alone in a room with an unguarded fire. She had got up, wrapped in her blankets, and had fallen into the fire, receiving dreadful burns, leading to her death some days later.[20] The matter was picked up by all the other local papers – *Aberdeen Free Press*, *Evening Express* and *Aberdeen Journal* – all of which carried reports on the ensuing days. Further unpleasant facts emerged as letters from the victim's aunt and father were published. The affair developed into a major local scandal.

The City Hospital Scandal

The full facts were as follows. The probationer nurse was Annie Laing, a farmer's daughter aged twenty from Conon Bridge in Ross-shire. In early February she had been involved in nursing typhus patients at the Sick Children's Hospital, and two weeks later herself became fevered and unwell. She was seen by Dr Garden, the surgeon there, and was thought to have contracted typhus. Typhus was highly contagious and was often accompanied by high fever and delirium, requiring special nursing supervision. She was initially kept in quarantine at the Sick Children's Hospital, but on Monday 21 February, for the safety of other patients, was transferred to the City Hospital. She was seen there the following day by Dr Thomson who did not think she had typhus, and two days later, although she was still markedly febrile, he removed her special 'typhus nurse'. Laing was then transferred to a small room adjoining the measles ward, the girl having previously had this condition. The accident occurred in this small room, which had an unguarded coal fire, and which was separated from the measles ward by several yards of outdoor courtyard. At night, these two areas were covered only by an untrained ward maid. On the night of 24 February, the patient, when alone and unsupervised in her room, had got up and then fallen into the fire, sustaining severe burns. She was only discovered some time later. After a few days, she died in terrible pain. [21]

Further unsavoury facts emerged in the ensuing days. On 10 March, the *Daily Free Press* published a letter from Miss Mart Laing, the deceased girl's aunt, a qualified nurse and former hospital sister and matron, who lived in Forres. The day before the tragic event, she had travelled to Aberdeen in response to a telegram from the girl's father. She had telegraphed ahead to a cousin, who was a medical student in Aberdeen, asking him to seek Dr Thomson's permission for the aunt to stay in the hospital and nurse the girl. This request had been refused. On her arrival, the aunt saw the head nurse and made a similar request, but in her own words, 'the matron was inexorable' and said such a suggestion was out of the question. The aunt was only permitted to speak to the girl through a closed window and half-open door for fifteen minutes. The fatal accident occurred that evening. The aunt was thereafter allowed to stay with the girl until her death.[22]

On 23 March, the *Gazette* published a letter from a lady who was staying at the hospital at the time of the incident, looking after her two children who were patients in the measles ward. This was the ward covered at night by the ward maid responsible for Annie Laing in the adjacent but separate room. The mother stated that at 2 am on the night of the tragedy, she had got up to give one of her children a drink and had seen the ward maid lying on top of a bed. She could not certify that the maid was asleep, but recorded that the maid made no response to the mother having got up to attend to her child.[23] The inference was clear.

On 9 March, in advance of the letter in the *Gazette*, the PHC had held an urgent meeting to consider the incident. Members expressed disquiet that the accident had not been brought to their attention at the time it occurred. Dr Thomson lamely replied that he had intended reporting the occurrence at the next routine meeting. According to the press reports 'plain language was used by some members'. Full reports on the incident were called for, and a sub-committee of three members formed to investigate.[24] This was, however, overtaken by events.

On 16 March at a meeting of the Aberdeen United Trades Council the affair was the sole item on the agenda. The Council was probably still smarting from the rebuff they had received the previous year and the atmosphere was clearly hostile. The president reported that he had been overwhelmed by demands for 'something to be done to get the institution put on a proper footing'. The whole management and organisation were felt to be defective and a full independent investigation of the hospital by some government official was demanded. It was also suggested that the full facts should be collected and put in the hands of local MPs to bring to the attention of the Lord Advocate in the House of Commons. It was felt that if the press had not reported the incident, it would have been hushed up. There was also open criticism of Dr Thomson. The law permitted him to remove patients to hospital even from good home circumstances and it was said 'his orders were often ridiculous'. Many cases of infectious diseases were said to go unreported because of 'want of confidence in the hospital'.[25] The matter was also featured in *The Scotsman* the following day. There was only a rather brief initial reference to the Aberdeen incident, however, the opportunity being taken to level criticism at some of the Edinburgh hospitals![26]

A meeting of the sub-committee set up by the PHC was delayed by the illness of one of the members, and in the face of increasing public outcry, fuelled by the press, it was decided that the full PHC should consider the matter. Several meetings were held in late March to take evidence from all those involved. Dr Thomson, it was reported, was 'under examination for 1½ hours'.[27] Before these investigations were complete, however, the *Free Press* on 26 March carried a detailed and highly critical report by a 'Special Commissioner', who had visited the hospital that day, finding that the 'surroundings were dismal and the main entrance was barred'. Entrance was gained through a side gate, down a lane past dilapidated houses, and eventually through a house where the inmate was 'in a dirty unhygienic state'. A detailed description of the layout of the hospital followed and it was noted that the ground between the pavilions was partly of uneven unkempt grass but largely of potatoes! The reception block was first visited and was deemed to be a 'disgrace'. The rooms were low, damp and dirty, with litter in all corners. Windows were broken and stuffed with paper. The wards were little better. The concrete construction was noted, with the comment 'a more unsuitable material for a hospital could not be found'. Ventilation was defective, the bed sheets inferior and toilet facilities inadequate and filthy. The nursing staff was detailed and considered to be quite inadequate. The hospital `ambulance' was inspected and found to be an 'ordinary cab of somewhat venerable appearance'! The article concluded by asking 'how had things gone so terribly wrong'? It was noted that Dr Thomson, shortly after taking office, had reported the problems but 'nothing had been done'. Finally, it was suggested that if the hospital 'is to retain, or if you prefer regain public confidence, major expenditure is required'. The staff needed to be materially increased and there was a plea for a resident medical officer. The article occupied two and a half columns and was clearly heavy censorious criticism. Both the PHC and the Town Council were felt to bear the burden of responsibility.[28]

The PHC report was completed at the end of March. Initially marked 'Private and Confidential', it soon appeared in full in the press. The facts of the incident were confirmed. Although the head nurse was considered most at fault, it emerged that Dr Thomson had only seen the girl once a day after the accident, and he did not accept responsibility for the administration of the hospital. The head nurse had spoken to Dr Thomson several times about the nursing shortage and other problems but she had not felt it proper to report directly to the PHC. Thomson, however, had never relayed her anxieties. Members of the sub-committee felt his explanations 'unacceptable'. Despite the fact that the original contract referred only to the

MOH's medical rather than administrative role at the hospital, members clearly felt it was Thomson's duty to manage the hospital. The committee was highly critical of Thomson's conduct and agreed that the whole system of management required 'speedy and urgent reform'. Bowing to public demand and outcry they agreed to an outside assessment and called on the superintendent of Edinburgh Royal Infirmary, deputy surgeon-general Charles H. Fasson, to visit and report on all aspects of the hospital.[29]

In early April, two questions on the subject were asked in the House of Commons. The Lord Advocate replied that the local procurator fiscal, in the ordinary course of his duties, had made a full enquiry and reported there was no case for criminal prosecution. It was agreed that a grave indiscretion had occurred but that as an independent outside assessment of the hospital had been arranged, no further steps were envisaged.[30] The local press continued to feature almost daily columns on the matter. By now the tone of the headlines had changed from 'Alarming Occurrence at the City Hospital' to 'The City Hospital Scandal'. Editorials stressed that the main question was how 'to obviate any similar occurrence in the future'.[31] Further skeletons emerged from the closet. In early April the Town Council was served with a writ from a John Thain claiming damages of £150 for alleged improper treatment of his daughter while in the hospital.[32]

The ward maid involved in the incident had not worked at the hospital from the day of the accident and the head nurse offered her resignation on 2 April 1887.[33] On 13 April Fasson agreed to make his enquiry and submitted his report to the PHC on 22 April. It was full of condemnation and was soon quoted extensively in the local press. He felt that the hospital as an institution was an 'utter failure'. Although the site was excellent, the grounds were disgraceful, and he thought that some small houses abutting on the boundary wall should be removed. In Fasson's opinion, the walls separating each pavilion were also unnecessary and impeded the free circulation of air. The ventilation and heating arrangements of the wards were unsatisfactory. He did not like the concrete construction and recommended various alterations and remedies. The bath and latrine accommodation also required attention. The reception block was altogether unfitted for the treatment of patients. Fasson stressed that there was an urgent need for additional accommodation because, as presently constituted, the hospital could only treat two classes of disease at any one time. He recommended three additional pavilions of 24 beds each. These could be considered as the 'City Hospital', and used for cases of measles, scarlet fever and whooping cough, while the existing pavilions, after refurbishment, could be retained as the 'Epidemic Hospital'. The MOH's role should be clearly defined and extended. He should have powers to order all classes of individuals with contagious diseases, who did not have proper accommodation at home, to be removed to the hospital – 'rich and poor alike'. Fasson also recommended the appointment of a resident medical officer who would work under the supervision of a visiting medical officer (presumably the MOH), the latter having sole administrative charge of the establishment. The nursing establishment also needed to be increased and their efficiency improved. He suggested the use of probationer nurses, taken in rotation from the other hospitals in Aberdeen. In epidemics, extra demands for beds could be met by erecting temporary wooden framed buildings 'with the walls filled with sawdust to keep warm'.[34]

Some prejudices were revealed. Fasson disapproved of male nurses! He objected to the reception block. He felt that patients with the same disease should be treated under same roof (presumably he was assuming that each block would have separate male and female wards and was not suggesting mixed wards). He approved of medical students visiting. He felt this would improve the standard of care but recommended that it be restricted to postgraduate students (which did not seem a very practical suggestion).

The PHC readily accepted many of the recommendations. They agreed to improve the existing buildings as already planned, to replace the reception house with a new building on Park Road, to improve the grounds and to plant trees. It was agreed in principle that extensions were required but no funds were immediately available, and the cost involved was to be investigated. They also agreed in principle to having a resident medical officer and in the meantime decreed that the MOH should visit twice daily. A new head nurse had already been appointed on the understanding that if she proved satisfactory, the post would be upgraded to that of matron. The sub-committee had been fortunate in obtaining the services of Miss Bothwell who had been trained at the original Nightingale school and was formerly head nurse at Aberdeen Royal Infirmary. Her appointment to the City Hospital was ratified on 16 May. Her salary was £60 increasing to £75 per annum when upgraded to matron. There was also to be a sufficiency of under-nurses.[35]

Despite the open criticism of their work, neither Dr Thomson nor any of the members of the PHC felt obliged to resign. A scapegoat had been found in the form of the previous head nurse. Thomson continued in post, but on 19 December 1887 tendered his resignation, having been appointed

MOH in Sheffield. It seems likely that his departure was related to the earlier tragic accident, but no lasting damage was done to his career. He served as MOH for Sheffield for four years with distinction and established a reputation as an efficient administrator. He was asked to join the Local Government Board as a medical inspector in 1891 and continued in this service until he retired due to ill health in 1913. He was a delegate to many international sanitary conferences and contributed to the control of spread of smallpox and enteric fever. He received a CMG in 1905 for his services to the Colonial and Foreign Offices. He died at the early age of 57.[36]

At the end of 1887, the fortunes of the City Hospital (it had been decided to retain this name for the whole institution) were clearly at a nadir. Although major improvements had been agreed, finances were limited, and these changes would take time to implement. The task of restoring public confidence in the institution fell to the next MOH, Matthew Hay.

References to Chapter Four

[1] Aberdeen City Archives, Public Health Minute Book vol. II (hereafter PHMB/2), 1 November 1876.

[2] PHMB/2, 16 July 1877.

[3] PHMB/2, 17 August 1878.

[4] PHMB/2, 11 December 1878.

[5] PHMB/2, 20 June 1881.

[6] Obituary, W. J. R. Simpson, *British Medical Journal*, 1931, vol. 2, p. 633; Simpson, Sir William John Ritchie, *Concise Dictionary of National Biography 1901–1970*, Oxford, Oxford University Press, 1982, p. 610.

[7] PHMB/2, 30 November 1883.

[8] Aberdeen Central Library, Town Council Minutes (hereafter TCM), 19 October 1885.

[9] TCM, 21 January 1884.

[10] TCM, 21 December 1885.

[11] TCM, 15 March 1886.

[12] TCM, 17 May 1886.

[13] Obituary, T. Thomson, *British Medical Journal*, 1916, vol. 1, p. 469.

[14] Aberdeen Medico-Chirurgical Society, News Cutting File 1886–1887, (hereafter NCF 1886–87), p. 97: *Free Press*, 17 March 1887.

[15] TCM, 16 August 1886.

[16] TCM, 18 August 1886.

[17] NCF 1886–87, 'The City Hospital – An Appeal', *Aberdeen Free Press*. November 1886.

18   NCF 1886–87, p. 47: 'Charges against the Aberdeen City Hospital', *Evening Express*, 29 December 1886.

19   TCM, 17 January 1887.

20   NCF 1886–87, p. 88: 'Alarming Occurrence at the City Hospital', *Evening Gazette*, 7 March 1887.

21   Ibid.

22   NCF 1886–87, p. 90: Mart. Laing, *Daily Free Press*, 10 March 1887.

23   NCF 1886–87, p. 106: Annie Henderson, letter to the editor, *Gazette*, 23 March 1887.

24   NCF 1886–87, p. 88: 'The Alarming Occurrence at the City Hospital', *Evening Gazette*, 9 March 1887.

25   NCF 1886–87, p. 98: 'The Alleged Burning at the City Hospital', *Free Press*, 17 March 1887.

26   NCF 1886–87, p. 98: 'City Fever Hospital', *The Scotsman*, 17 March 1887.

27   NCF 1886–87, p. 100: *Express*, 22 March 1887.

28   NCF 1886–87, p. 110: Special Commissioner, *Free Press*, 26 March 1887.

29   TCM, 4 April 1887: Public Health Committee Report, 30 March 1887.

30   NCF 1886–87, p. 130.

31   NCF 1886–87, p. 119: 'City Hospital scandal', *Free Press*, 31 March 1887.

32   NCF 1886–87: 'The City Hospital–Action against the Council' *Free Press*, 6 April 1887.

33   TCM, 18 April 1887.

34   C. H. Fasson, *Report to the Town Council*, Aberdeen, Cornwall, 1887.

35   TCM, 16 May 1887.

36   Obituary, T. Thomson, op. cit.

Chapter Five

The City Hospital in the Matthew Hay Era 1888–1923

Professor Matthew Hay was to be the longest serving and most distinguished holder of the post of MOH. He fulfilled the task with outstanding administrative capacity and scientific skill of the highest order for no less than 35 years. During this period, the City Hospital, where he was also medical officer in charge, was raised to the highest standard. There were to be several extensions and major new developments and he was also a major instigator in the development of the other hospitals in Aberdeen to their present high standard. Bureaucratic ineptitude, however, almost deprived the city and the hospital of his great drive and talents.

In February 1888, the Public Health Committee (PHC) considered proposals for filling the post vacated by Dr Thomson. The convenor of the committee proposed that the MOH should be asked to live at the hospital and act as a resident medical superintendent. Most members felt this would be impractical and proposed instead that the MOH should be asked to visit twice daily, while being non-resident but in medical control of the hospital. This amendment was carried and the convenor resigned! The shortlist of applicants was considered in March. Hay, who had unsuccessfully applied for the post in 1886, was again one of several applicants. Some committee members felt that as he was already professor of medical logic and jurisprudence at the university, he should not be considered.[1] Fortunately this motion was overruled by the Town Council and he was duly appointed. The end result was to the hospital's and the city's good fortune.

Hay was born at Slamannan in Stirlingshire on 27 December 1855 and had a prosperous childhood and upbringing. His father was a colliery proprietor and his mother the daughter of a wealthy ship owner. He was the eldest of six children. He was educated at Dollar Academy and then took up the study of medicine at Edinburgh University. He had a brilliant undergraduate career, winning the majority of the undergraduate prizes, and graduated MB CM with first class honours in 1878 and was awarded the Ettles prize as the most distinguished student in his year.[2] His career plans were initially uncertain. In 1876 he had designed the plans for an iron foundry that the family had acquired and he might have abandoned medicine to become a captain of industry.[3] He decided, however, to devote his life to medicine and became demonstrator in materia medica in Edinburgh. He proved himself a brilliant energetic researcher with around twenty publications during the next six years. His particular interests were in the actions and therapeutic uses of the saline cathartics, on which he published a short monograph in 1884,[4] the action and uses of nitrites and nitrates in angina, and the toxicology of certain alkaloids. During his vacations, Hay extended his knowledge by working on the continent at centres in Strasbourg, Berlin and Munich. He obtained his MD in 1881, with honours and a gold medal. He also received the triennial Goodsir memorial prize, which is awarded for the best original monograph on an anatomical or physiological subject.

Hay was destined for a distinguished career and in 1883, at the age of 27, he applied for and was appointed to the chair of medical logic and jurisprudence (forensic medicine) in Aberdeen, following Francis Ogston's retirement. A year later, he was invited to become professor of pharmacology at Johns Hopkins University at Baltimore, then the leading medical school in North America, but he declined this invitation because of family commitments. Hay was to occupy the chair in Aberdeen for 43 years, besides taking on many other duties. Because of his forensic expertise Hay figured as an expert witness in many causes célèbres of the time. One of the most noteworthy was the Ardlamont murder trial or Monson case in which his testimony played a major role, leading to a verdict of 'not proven'.[5]

In 1886 Alexander Dyce Davidson, the professor of materia medica at Aberdeen University, died suddenly of a cerebral haemorrhage. Hay was asked by the Senatus to take responsibility for teaching that subject until a successor could be appointed, and he gave his first lecture just a week after Dyce Davidson's demise.[6] The appointment of John Theodore Cash to the chair of materia medica the next year relieved him of this additional burden. Cash, who was to have an important influence on the development of the science of pharmacology, held the chair until 1919.[7]

Hay was also responsible for the teaching of public health and forensic medicine and was noted as a brilliant lecturer. Despite the fact that the classes in forensic medicine were held at eight o'clock in the morning during the summer term, to accommodate the needs of law students, he received many testimonials to his abilities as a lecturer. He was notably kind to his students and gave financial assistance to many.[8]

Early Developments at the City Hospital under Hay's Leadership

As mentioned earlier, the City Hospital had an unsavoury reputation and patients would only agree to go there under duress, but shortly before Hay's appointment as MOH in 1888, the PHC had begun some improvements. A wooden pavilion was constructed and furnished at a cost of £1,062.[9]

The question of a resident medical officer was also under discussion but was deferred when Hay was appointed.[10] Hay became medical attendant with whole medical charge and administrative responsibility for the hospital and was required to visit twice daily. Dr Alexander McGregor was appointed as substitute MOH to stand in for him in his absence. A book was provided for the medical officers to record their visits. Various other improvements took place as funds became available. The drainage and water supply were replaced, a new entrance on Urquhart Road constructed, new steam heating to the wards installed, a new ambulance with rubber tyres obtained, and trees and shrubs planted in the grounds. Heating was also for the first time provided for the nurses' accommodation.[11]

In March 1889, the university requested facilities for medical students to visit the City Hospital.[12] An earlier request seems to have led to no action.[13] On this occasion it was agreed, however, with some restrictions imposed at Hay's request. Only senior students would be allowed to attend and they could only attend on two days a week. In addition, there were never to be more than eight students at a time, a fee of one guinea per student would be paid by the university, and a record of attendance kept.

In late 1890 it was agreed to admit patients from the Aberdeen District of the County Council, and in 1890–91 there was a great demand for accommodation at the City Hospital. The population served was then 141,000 including the District Council area, which contributed about 20,000. At times a temporary medical assistant was engaged.[14]

The reputation of the hospital gradually improved. Following Aberdeen Town Council's decision to adopt the 1889 Infectious Diseases (Notification) Act from 1 April 1891, applications were accepted from Kincardine County Council and from Banchory to have patients from their areas admitted.[15] At the same time Aberdeen County Council suggested to the Town Council that Hay might take on the then vacant position of Medical Officer of Health for the county. This was not deemed by the PHC to be a satisfactory arrangement.[16]

In 1893 major extensions costing nearly £14,000 came into operation. Two of the original central pavilions were enlarged, providing 16 additional beds each, and two new detached pavilions were built. One of these, constructed of wood, was solely for smallpox cases, while the other was used initially as a reception-house and then, owing to an increase in diphtheria and typhoid patients, was continuously occupied by such cases. The wards were fitted to accommodate 146 adult patients, exclusive of about 70 to 80 cots for children. There was also a rearrangement and enlargement of the administration block, providing ample and excellent accommodation for nurses. A clock and bell were added in 1899, transferred from the old water house in Broad Street.[17] This had been erected in 1766 as the central reservoir for the town water supply, draining water from springs at Gilcomston and Fountainhall. The clock had been placed at its front by a copper company in 1767, followed two years later by the bell. This Broad Street reservoir was superseded by the introduction of Dee water in 1866 and the building had thereafter been used as a store.[18] A lodge was built beside the new hospital entrance on Urquhart Road, an office for the medical officers' use was built beside one of the pavilions, and improved washing room facilities were provided. The new buildings were of granite with wood panelling or dadoes on the walls and hardwood flooring. The earlier concrete construction, although functionally useful, had proved aesthetically unpleasing and had received much adverse criticism.[19]

There was some concern that the wooden interiors might predispose to retention of the common zymotic infections in the crevices or seams. Under stress of circumstances, pavilions had to accommodate all kinds of cases including smallpox and typhus. However, never once was the infection of one set of cases conveyed to the succeeding set. Between successive occupations, there was always an interval of several days during which the ward was fumigated or sprayed with disinfectant, well aired and sunned, and the walls, floors and furnishings all carefully washed with soap and disinfectant solutions.[20]

The citizens of Aberdeen and their representatives still had reservations about the hospital, however. In January 1892, there was a complaint regarding possible maltreatment of a patient at the hospital. This was thoroughly investigated and was not substantiated. The claim appeared to have been malicious. The PHC reported that the management of the hospital was 'thoroughly efficient'.[21] Two years later, Aberdeen United Trades Council again lodged complaints with various allegations of mismanagement. After investigation, the PHC again felt these were unsupported and they again recorded tribute to the zeal and efficiency of Professor Hay in improving the facilities.[22]

Further Developments in Staffing, Management and Accommodation

The question of having a resident physician was re-opened and in

September 1894, Dr W. E. G. Duthie of Woodside was appointed. He was to act under the 'instruction and supervision of Dr Hay'.[23] Duthie resigned from the post on 31 August 1895 and was replaced by Dr James Fletcher MB CM, DPH. Consequent on the appointment of a resident physician, the MOH's contract was altered, so that he was now required to visit just once instead of twice daily, unless circumstances required otherwise. The salary of the resident physician was initially £50 per annum, with board and lodgings, but was increased in 1897 to £75 and then in 1900 to £100.[24] (In June 1898 the title was changed to resident medical officer.) Dr James S. Laing, who was appointed in March 1897, died in post on 6 July 1902, but subsequent medical officers resigned after short periods in post and so in 1906 it was stipulated that the holder must occupy the position for a minimum of twelve months. The occupant of the post under the new arrangement was an Edinburgh graduate, Dr A. G. Anderson, who should not be confused with the Aberdeen physician who became Sir A. G. Anderson.[25]

In view of various alterations and extensions and the increasing size and workload of the hospital a separate City Hospital committee reporting to the PHC was set up early in 1895.[26] This consisted of six members and met fortnightly. The following year, a visiting sub-committee was formed to visit the hospital monthly and the next several years saw regular expenditure on repairs and repainting and further minor alterations and extensions. Attention was also given to improving amenities for patients and their visitors. More shrubs and trees were planted, eight gas lamps placed in the grounds, garden seats provided, a smoking room built and swings for visitors' children erected. In August 1896 new visitors' regulations were drafted, approved and printed on a visiting card. Visitors had to speak to their relatives through closed windows and children under the age of 15 were not admitted. Visitors were only allowed to enter wards if patients were dangerously ill, in which case special permission would be given. Then they had to wear a 'wrapper' provided, have no personal contact with the patient, and wash their hands and face before leaving.[27]

Miss Bothwell, the first official matron, had had to retire in June 1896 because of ill health and was given a pension of £20 per annum. The following month, Miss Margaret Frater was appointed matron at an increased salary of £70 per annum, further increased in 1899 to £85.[28] Miss Frater was from Tarves and had trained in nursing at the Edinburgh Royal Infirmary. In June 1898, the expenditure of £4,650 was agreed to enlarge the administration block to provide extra staff accommodation and small reception and departure rooms for hospital patients. The extension provided accommodation for 53 staff, including the matron, the resident medical officer (RMO) and 30 nurses.

In 1898 the managers of the Royal Infirmary informed the Town Council that they would no longer admit cases of erysipelas to the Infirmary. One of the pavilions at the City Hospital was designated to take such cases pending the provision of new accommodation.[29]

Facilities for Smallpox

In the 1890s, cases of smallpox were admitted to a special pavilion, kept for this purpose and fenced off from the other wards. Over the years, there were several requests from the district council committees of country areas asking if their smallpox patients could be admitted to the City Hospital, but these requests were always rejected. It was agreed, however, to admit patients with other infectious diseases if desired.[30]

In March 1901, the PHC had to consider a circular from the Local Government Board consequent on a smallpox epidemic in the south. In the Board's view, smallpox patients should not be admitted to the wards or pavilions of a hospital in which patients with typhus, scarlet fever or other infectious diseases were housed. They believed each area should have its own separate smallpox hospital.[31] Hay did not feel this necessary, but a few months later the PHC said in a response to an enquiry from Aberdeen District Committee, that if the Town Council decided to proceed with the erection of a smallpox hospital, they would be willing to consider collaboration.[32] However, nothing came of this and the smallpox pavilion at the City Hospital continued in use with regular repairing, repainting and upgrading as required.[33]

In 1920 there was a further outbreak of smallpox in the North-East of Scotland, and the question of providing special separate hospital accommodation for patients with this disease again arose. After discussion, it was agreed that it would better if such cases were not admitted to the City Hospital. A proposal was adopted that Summerfield Hospital, which was the fever hospital of Aberdeen District of the County, should be adapted and used for this purpose.[34] Smallpox cases, however, continued to be admitted to the City Hospital for several more years, until the final outbreak in this region in 1930.[35]

Facilities for Tuberculosis and the Development of Laboratory Services

In 1906 there was an approach from the Parish Council about providing special sanatorium facilities for patients with tuberculosis (TB). A special group was set up to look into this matter.[36] However, the demands on the hospital generally were increasing at this time and in October 1907, when Hay reported on the existing accommodation for patients and staff, a variety of deficiencies were identified. Extensive expansions and alterations were agreed, but no firm conclusions had yet been reached on the question of facilities for TB. Additional adjacent ground had been purchased, and it was decided to enlarge two of the existing pavilions, to construct a new one for skin diseases and to extend the administration and reception block. It was agreed that if there were to be special facilities for TB at the hospital, an additional pavilion at the east end of the site could be built. The cost of the initial extensions was to be £10,500, plus £1,550 for a TB pavilion.[37]

The extensions were completed and opened for use in November 1910. In the event, a TB pavilion was not built, but one of the old wards was reconstructed and enlarged, with open wooden balconies, to provide accommodation for 36 adult patients, mostly with pulmonary TB, and a few children with non-surgical TB.[38]

In 1913 it was decided to put up a new building for patients with infective skin diseases, with an improved disinfecting station for verminous persons, and to convert and equip the current skin disease ward, which was a two-storey block, as a TB dispensary (where out-patients would be seen). Consequent on this development, the post of assistant medical officer, with special reference to TB was created. He would be in charge of TB cases, assisted by the RMO, and would also be responsible for the TB dispensary. Dr George S. Banks, an Edinburgh graduate, was appointed to this new post in August 1913.[39]

The new arrangement also allowed for the expansion of the hospital's laboratory services. The importance of new techniques in bacteriology for the diagnosis and management of infections had first been raised in 1898 by Hay, who pointed out that cholera, diphtheria, typhoid fever and tuberculosis could all now be diagnosed precisely. Bacteriological methods could also be used in the examination of foods, milk and water. A special sub-committee had been set up to consider the matter and arrangements were made for this work to be done under the supervision of the professor of pathology at Aberdeen University. The Town Council provided the salary for a special assistant and an annual sum to meet outlays. This proved satisfactory, but Hay believed if would be better for the local authority to establish a laboratory of their own.[40]

In 1910 a small room in the basement of one of the pavilions at the City Hospital was altered and equipped at a cost of £15 to serve as a small laboratory for bacteriological purposes, to give quicker results and to supplement the service provided by the university.[41] The rising number of tuberculosis admissions markedly increased the workload and a laboratory attendant was appointed. A new larger laboratory space was then created in the TB dispensary, and the detached building, with a direct entrance from Urquhart Road, was termed the Tuberculosis Institute at the City Hospital and opened in April 1914.[42]

The lower floor of the TB Institute was occupied by a commodious waiting room, four cubicles for patients undressing, a consulting room with a small examination room attached, a small dispensary room, storage space for records and a private office for the tuberculosis medical officer. The upper storey was not fully occupied. Two rooms were equipped as the laboratory and there was also a dark room for the x-ray apparatus that had just been installed.[43] A special tuberculosis sub-committee was also formed to oversee work in this field.

By 1914 the hospital had accommodation for 70 TB patients, 48 in the reconstructed ward and 22 in the lean-to shelters which had been designed by Hay, as will be discussed later. No heating was provided in the TB wards except in dressing rooms and bathrooms.[44]

The City Hospital in 1914 and Wartime Developments

By 1914 the size, staffing and workload of the hospital had vastly increased over the first quarter century of Hay's tenure of the post of MOH. Because of the steadily increasing demands it had been decided, in August 1913, that there should be two RMOs at the City Hospital, a junior and a senior appointment.[45] In addition, Dr J. Parlane Kinloch was appointed to the new post of deputy MOH in April 1914. The administration of the hospital was running smoothly and its reputation had been greatly enhanced. The visiting committee had steadily reduced the frequency of their visits from monthly to quarterly, a clear sign of confidence in the administration.[46]

Hay described the hospital in 1914, in an article written to mark the annual BMA conference held that year in Aberdeen, just before the outbreak of war.[47] Hay reported that in 1913 the average daily number of patients undergoing treatment had been 264, with a total of 3,050 patients admitted. The year had, however, been very busy with outbreaks of diphtheria and scarlet fever (see Chapter 6). Despite the absence of a separate smallpox hospital, Hay said a vigorous scheme of vaccination or re-vaccination of other inmates had always prevented the spread of the disease to other patients. The total capital cost of the hospital to that time, inclusive of site, had been about £65,000.[48]

World War I was to have a major disrupting effect on the hospital. New building and developments were delayed although a new motor ambulance was obtained in early 1915.[49] In the early years of the war, several of the younger medical staff left to the join the RAMC and Hay himself served as a lieutenant colonel in the Sanitary Service in the Territorial Branch of the RAMC.[50] Despite increasing the salary it proved impossible to fill the post of Senior RMO because of the shortage of young doctors. In September 1915 when Dr James Chalmers resigned from the post to join the RAMC, the deputy MOH, Dr Kinloch, had to take over his duties. When Dr Banks, an earlier resident who had become the tuberculosis medical officer in 1913, joined the RAMC, this work was also covered for a period by Kinloch, before he himself left for the war. After Kinloch left, Dr Lucas, the superintendent of the private Nordrach-on-Dee Sanatorium at Banchory, covered the TB work, helped by Dr Bruce West who had been discharged from the RAMC on health grounds. West was made assistant physician at the City Hospital and in 1918 was promoted, with a salary increase, to assistant tuberculosis officer.[51]

The war years also saw a considerable increase in the incidence of venereal disease (VD) and government legislation passed in 1916 made local authorities responsible for providing facilities for early diagnosis and treatment, although government sources would meet three quarters of any expenditure on such a scheme.[52] As a temporary measure the laboratory premises in the TB Institute were altered and used as an out-patient treatment centre for VD. This was to continue in successful use for many years. There were also extensive discussions with the managers of the Infirmary as to how facilities for VD might best be provided. The outcome is described in Chapters 7 and 8.

Post-War Developments

A major development in the early post-war years was an extension to the laboratory services at the City Hospital. Although limited laboratory facilities had been in place at the TB Institute, the majority of the City Hospital's bacteriological work was carried out by the university bacteriological department at the Royal Infirmary, under Theodore Shennan, professor of pathology and consultant pathologist to the City Hospital. Hay had always favoured having full laboratory facilities on site. After much discussion this finally came to fruition in 1920 and all the bacteriological services provided by Shennan's university department were transferred to the City Hospital from 1 January of that year.[53] As new building was not possible at the time, the laboratory was confined to the upper floor of the TB Institute and this space became even more cramped in 1923, when the Town Council appointed a whole-time chemist and city analyst who also required accommodation. The laboratory was responsible for all the bacteriological work of the City Hospital and also that from medical practitioners in the city and North-Eastern region.

In 1920 Dr John Smith was appointed to spend half his time in the wards and clinic dealing especially with TB cases, and half his time in the laboratory under the supervision of Dr Kinloch, who had returned from war service to resume his post as deputy MOH. In practice, however, Kinloch provided little supervision and two years later the duties were adjusted, and Dr Smith placed in charge of the laboratory.[54]

The post-war years were a period of increasing work and responsibility for Hay. The Town Council had become responsible for maternity and child welfare schemes and so in 1919, an assistant MOH was appointed to supervise this work. Hay's salary was later increased to £877-10s per annum.[55]

Throughout his whole term of office as MOH, Hay produced monthly and quarterly reports which were sent free of charge to all medical practitioners in the city, medical officers in surrounding districts and the chief cities of Scotland, and to the Scottish Board of Health. It was decided in 1921, that these should continue although their production clearly involved a lot of labour.[56]

In November 1922, Hay intimated his resignation as MOH on health grounds. The Town Council asked him to defer this, and gave him leave of absence, but despite spending several months abroad, his health remained poor, and he finally resigned on 14 May 1923. He had held office for 35 years. The Lord Provost paid personal tribute to his work for which the Council was extremely grateful. He was granted a retirement allowance of £550 per annum.[57]

In addition to his university duties and arduous work as MOH, Hay indulged in many other activities. He was a member of Aberdeen University Court from 1889–1926, and represented the university on the Carnegie Trust for the Scottish Universities from 1901–20, and on the General Medical Council from 1919–24. He was an external examiner in forensic medicine to several British universities. In addition he was a member of the Medical Research Committee (now Council) from 1913–16 and served on many other national and local medical bodies. He was a governor of

Aberdeen Technical College and a member of the Joint Committee of the Rowett Research Institute. He was also a prominent member of the BMA and president of the section of medical jurisprudence at the Aberdeen conference in 1914. He received the degree of LLD from both Edinburgh and Aberdeen and was made an honorary fellow of the Royal College of Physicians of Ireland.[58] Considering his many national as well as local contributions, it is surprising that he never received a knighthood or comparable honour.

Despite his innumerable activities Hay is best remembered locally as the 'father' of the Aberdeen Joint Hospital Scheme. At the end of World War I, the Maternity Hospital, Sick Children's Hospital and Royal Infirmary were all on separate sites and in poor states of repair. The accommodation they provided was inadequate for their growing needs. It is generally acknowledged that the scheme of having new hospitals built on a peripheral site was born in the fertile mind of Hay. It has also been recorded that Hay spent his Sunday mornings tramping the outskirts of Aberdeen looking for a suitable site, and that he himself selected the slopes of Foresterhill as the ideal location.[59] Ashley Mackintosh, then professor of medicine, was an enthusiastic advocate of the scheme and presented the proposals at an historic meeting of the Aberdeen Medico-Chirurgical Society on 20 February 1920. In addition to providing a new Infirmary, a new Sick Children's Hospital and accommodation for the university clinical departments, there were plans to build a tuberculosis hospital of 150–200 beds and joint services such as heating and laundry. There were to be many hiccups before the scheme came to final fruition in the late 1930s, and along with many other changes, the proposal for the tuberculosis hospital disappeared. Matthew Hay's major contribution to this scheme is rightly commemorated by a plaque in the entrance concourse in the Phase I extension of Aberdeen Royal Infirmary.

In 1926 Hay retired from the professorship of forensic medicine, as the subject had become known, and the chair went out of being. His remaining years were marred by ill health and his attending physician later recorded that despite Hay's training in pharmacology, he had an inordinate faith in drugs, his bedside table always being littered with medical samples which he would try simultaneously, regardless of whether they might have opposing actions.[60] He died at his home in Rubislaw Terrace in Aberdeen on 30 July 1932 at the age of 78.

References to Chapter Five

[1] Aberdeen Central Library, Town Council Minutes (hereafter TCM), 20 February 1888.

[2] 'Hay, Matthew', *Who was Who 1929–1940* (vol. III), London, Adam & Charles Black, 1967, p. 612; Obituary, Matthew Hay, *British Medical Journal*, 1932, vol. 2, pp. 332–3.

[3] L. A. Wilson, 'Matthew Hay (1855–1932)' in G. P. Milne (ed.), *Aberdeen Medico-Chirurgical Society. A Bicentennial History 1789–1989*, Aberdeen, Aberdeen University Press, 1989, pp. 190–8.

[4] M. Hay, *An experimental investigation of the physiological action of saline cathartics*, Edinburgh, MacLauchlan & Stuart, 1884.

[5] Obituary, Hay, *British Medical Journal*, 1932, op. cit.

[6] Hay's full lecture notes on materia medica are in the possession of the Aberdeen Medico-Chirurgical Society. See M. Williams, 'Matthew Hay's Lectures on Materia Medica given at Aberdeen University 1886–87', *Proceedings of the Royal College of Physicians of Edinburgh*, 1998, vol. 28, pp. 407–13.

[7] W. J. Dilling, 'John Theodore Cash' in W. D. Simpson (ed.) *The Fusion of 1860*, Edinburgh, Oliver and Boyd, 1963, pp. 270–1.

[8] A. G. Anderson, 'Matthew Hay' in ibid., pp. 273–5.

[9] TCM, 16 January 1888.

[10] TCM, 19 March 1888.

[11] TCM, 30 October 1892.

[12] TCM, 6 March, 10 April 1889.

[13] Aberdeen Medico-Chirurgical Society, News Cutting File 1886–87: 'Health of the Town', *Free Press*, 19 April 1887.

[14] TCM, 10 December 1890, 5 October 1891.

[15] The Act made it compulsory to notify various listed infectious diseases.

[16] TCM, 10 April 1891.

[17] TCM, 2 May 1899.

[18] R. Anderson, 'Broad Street 1833' in *Aberdeen in Byegone Days*, Aberdeen, Aberdeen Daily Journal, 1910, p. 15.

[19] TCM, 22 September 1892.

[20] M. Hay, 'The City Hospital' in J. Scott Riddell (ed.), *BMA Aberdeen 1914. Handbook and Guide to Aberdeen*, Cheltenham, Burrow, 1914, pp. 52–7.

[21] TCM, 13 January 1892.

[22] TCM, 19 February 1894.

[23] TCM, 5 September 1894.

[24] See Appendix 3 for a list of those holding this post up till 1913.

[25] TCM, 16 April 1906.

[26] TCM, 21 January 1895.

[27]   TCM, 17 August 1896.

[28]   TCM, 20 October 1899. For Miss Frater see Appendix 2.

[29]   TCM, 31 August 1898.

[30]   TCM, 16 April 1901.

[31]   TCM, 13 March 1901.

[32]   TCM, 25 June 1901.

[33]   TCM, 21 June 1920.

[34]   TCM, 9 June, 11 August, 29 October 1920.

[35]   Annual Report of the Medical Officer of Health for Aberdeen for 1930, pp. 32–4.

[36]   TCM, 18 December 1905.

[37]   TCM, 5 October 1908.

[38]   TCM, 19 December 1910.

[39]   TCM, 4 August 1913.

[40]   Annual Report of the Medical Officer of Health for Aberdeen for 1907, p. 32.

[41]   TCM, 15 May 1910.

[42]   TCM, 21 April 1913; Annual Report of the Medical Officer of Health for Aberdeen for 1914, p. 61.

[43]   TCM, 31 October 1913.

[44]   Hay, 1914, op. cit.

[45]   TCM, 18 August 1913. See also Appendix 4.

[46]   TCM, 20 September 1915.

[47]   The BMA next returned to Aberdeen just before the World War II, in 1939.

[48]   Hay, 1914, op. cit.

[49]   TCM, 15 February 1915.

[50]   Obituary, Hay, *British Medical Journal*, 1932, op. cit.

[51]   TCM, 17 December 1917, 17 June 1918.

[52]   TCM, 19 June 1916.

[53]   TCM, 19 January 1920.

[54]   TCM, 2 Oct 1922.

[55]   TCM, 4 Oct 1920.

[56]   N. J. Logie, 'History of the Aberdeen Joint Hospital Scheme and Site' in Milne, 1989, op. cit., pp. 155–78.

[57]   TCM, 21 May 1923.

[58]   'Hay', *Who was Who*, 1967, op. cit.; Obituary, Hay, *British Medical Journal*, 1932, op. cit.; Wilson, 1989, op. cit.

[59]   Wilson, 1989, op. cit.

[60]   Anderson, 1963, op. cit.

Chapter Six

Infectious Diseases in Aberdeen and the City Hospital to 1923

Development of Notification

Voluntary notification of certain designated infectious (zymotic) diseases was introduced in Aberdeen in early 1868. Initially, only the medical officers of the Royal Infirmary and the Aberdeen General Dispensary made returns.[1] In March 1868, the medical officers of the City Parochial Board and the Old Machar Parochial Board were also asked to participate, and over the following months, other associated parishes of the city were included.[2]

From an early stage, the Medical Officer had given monthly summaries of these notifications to the Public Health Committee (PHC). These were then printed, but unfortunately few remain in existence. In subsequent years, however, the Medical Officer of Health also produced annual figures, and included those from earlier years for comparison, so that information is available from 1871, apart from the year 1881, for which data cannot be traced. Mortality data was also recorded in Scotland on a national basis from 1855, and much useful information on the Aberdeen trends was contained in a paper given in April 1882 by Dr W. J. R. Simpson, the MOH, to the Aberdeen Philosophical Society. This was subsequently published as a monograph entitled *Health History of Aberdeen During the Past Quarter of a Century*.[3] Simpson gave mortality data for all the major zymotic diseases in Aberdeen from 1858–81, and later MOH reports gave information on annual incidences and mortality for each disease, with many additional useful facts.

In 1878 the local authority issued a circular to all medical practitioners in the city and to the medical staffs of the Infirmary and Dispensary. This announced that 2s 6d (12.5p) would be payable for each case of zymotic disease within the city boundary notified without delay to the Sanitary Inspector. The only classes of zymotic disease then included in the scheme were smallpox, measles, scarlatina (scarlet fever), diphtheria, typhus fever and enteric fever (typhoid). The medical staff of the parochial boards were paid an annual fee for such notifications.[4]

In 1889 the Infectious Disease (Notification) Act was passed, permitting MOHs throughout the country to introduce compulsory notification schemes for a listed number of infectious diseases. It was not, however, until 1891 that the PHC recommended to the Town Council that the Act should be fully adopted by the Council. The initial notification to MOHs was the responsibility of the head of the affected family or the medical practitioner involved. The Act was adopted on the advice of Matthew Hay, who knew from personal experience that many cases of infectious diseases in the city were not being attended by a medical practitioner, and so were less likely to be notified.[5] He considered it essential to have knowledge of *all* the infective cases if there was to be success in grappling with the different outbreaks. The Town Council agreed to bring this Act into local operation from 1 April 1891.[6] The prime responsibility for notification now lay with the householder, although medical practitioners continued their arrangements as before, so that a scheme of dual notification was in place. The adoption of the Act also extended the list of notifiable diseases to include membranous croup (diphtheria), erysipelas, relapsing and continued fevers and puerperal fever. Whooping cough and measles, which were not specifically mentioned in the Act, were later included nationally, although, in Aberdeen, notification of measles had been included in the circular issued by the local authority in 1878. Compulsory notification of these two diseases was discontinued in early 1903, but the MOH then introduced a scheme of voluntary intimation.[7] Thereafter, there must have been many cases of whooping cough and measles that remained unreported.

In subsequent years, the list of notifiable diseases was gradually extended. Epidemic cerebrospinal meningitis (meningococcal meningitis) was added in 1908, and acute poliomyelitis (infantile paralysis) and ophthalmia neonatorum in 1913. Chickenpox was made temporarily notifiable for a period of one year in 1914 in an attempt to prevent cases of smallpox being misdiagnosed and perhaps missed. This was repeated in 1920 when there was an epidemic of smallpox in Glasgow, with fear of its spread throughout Scotland. Pulmonary tuberculosis (TB) was made compulsorily notifiable in 1912 and all other forms of TB in 1914. This disease will be dealt with in detail in the next chapter. Other diseases were also steadily added. In 1919 dysentery, acute primary and influenzal pneumonia, malaria and trench fever joined the list.[8] As will be seen later, these changing regulations had a considerable influence on the workload of the City Hospital.

Infectious Diseases and the City Hospital

For the first ten years of its existence, the hospital had only been opened intermittently as required for certain epidemics. No detailed figures

Figure 2A Annual admissions to City Hospital 1887–1923

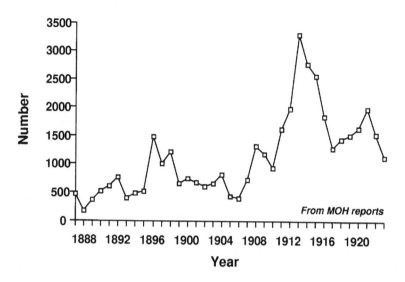

Figure 2B Deaths at City Hospital 1887–1923

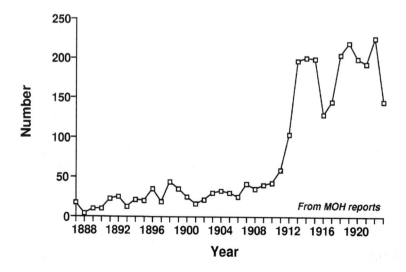

for the number of admissions or deaths during this period are available. From 1887, however, the hospital was in continuous use. Figure 2A shows the steady increase in the annual admissions to the City Hospital for the period 1887–1923, with a peak of 3,050 cases in 1913 when there were major outbreaks of scarlet fever and diphtheria. From 1908 onwards, with just one exception, there were always over 1,000 admissions a year and often in excess of 1,500. Part of the steady increase in later years was related to the regular admission of cases of TB after 1911. The number of deaths per annum over the same period is shown in Figure 2B. Up until 1910 this was not unduly high, averaging 3–4 per cent but increased considerably after 1911 as many of the TB cases being admitted were patients with advanced pulmonary disease for whom little could then be done.

An account will now be given of the common individual infections contributing to the workload, starting with the 'major infections': plague, cholera, smallpox, typhus fever and typhoid fever.

The Major Infections

Plague: Aberdeen remained free from this dreaded affliction, but there was fear of a recurrence in 1900 when there was an outbreak in Glasgow. The MOH drew up a memorandum on the symptoms of the chief varieties of the disease and distributed this to all medical practitioners in the city. Special precautions were taken with ships from plague-infected countries and the Sanitary Department attempted to clear all unnecessary refuse. Widespread destruction of rats, which were then the known vector, was also instituted. The city was spared. Concern returned in 1910 when there was a small outbreak in Suffolk, and rats in that area were found to be carrying the disease. The MOH and Sanitary Department again instituted an assault on Aberdeen's rats, particularly near the harbour, and advice was given on making buildings as far as possible 'rat-proof'. Any dead rats were also examined bacteriologically, but no evidence of the disease was found.[9]

Cholera: This dread disease never returned to Aberdeen after the outbreak in 1880 mentioned in Chapter 2 but when outbreaks occurred abroad, the regulations regarding the inspections of ships were periodically re-imposed. All such vessels were visited by the MOH or his deputy, the crew checked and the ship's water tanks emptied, disinfected and refilled with water from the city supply.[10] These arrangements proved their worth.

Smallpox: The large outbreak in 1872 noted in Chapter 2 was the last major epidemic of this disease in the city, although there was a minor outbreak with 41 cases in 1887.[11] Thereafter just occasional numbers were to be recorded for several more decades.

Since its opening in 1877, cases of smallpox in the city were admitted to one of the pavilions of the Epidemic Hospital. On two occasions in the 1890s, single cases of smallpox occurred among the patients in other pavilions. After this, whenever a smallpox patient was admitted, it became standard practice to enquire into the vaccination status of all other patients at the hospital. Vaccination or re-vaccination would then be performed on all who were unvaccinated, or who were more than twelve years from the time of their last vaccination. No further instance of smallpox among the ordinary fever cases occurred. When not in use, the smallpox pavilion, after thorough airing, cleaning and disinfection, was used for other types of fever case, and no case of smallpox was recorded as a result of this practice.[12]

In theory, smallpox should have been fully preventable by vaccination after the publication of Jenner's work in 1798. However, as mentioned in Chapter 2, vaccination in Scotland was only compulsory from 1864 and in many instances the procedure was not done adequately. Experience had shown that re-vaccination around puberty was essential, but was not a common practice. There was also a vocal anti-vaccination lobby. In 1876, when smallpox reappeared in England and there were worries of it reaching Aberdeen, the Medical Officer was asked to study the incidence of vaccination in the parts of the city where he was likely to be received. Of 406 persons visited, 206 were found to be unvaccinated or improperly vaccinated. Only 106 of the latter agreed to attend the Dispensary or their medical attendant for the procedure, and a proportion of these probably defaulted.[13] In other words only 50 per cent of the group at greatest risk were adequately protected. As recorded in Chapter 3, the smallpox outbreak of 1872 was the final stimulus to the building of the Epidemic Hospital at Cuninghar-Hill, where one of the pavilions was regularly used for smallpox cases. Indeed the hospital was sometimes referred to in the community as the 'Smallpox Hospital', which probably contributed in part to its early unsavoury reputation with the populace. But after the outbreak in 1887, only 29 cases of smallpox were admitted to the hospital during the next twenty years.[14]

In 1907 the Vaccination (Scotland) Act enabled parents to avoid having their children vaccinated simply by making a statement of conscientious objection. A survey done by Matthew Hay showed that as early as 1908 the number of unvaccinated children was already higher than it had been before the Act. Even among those vaccinated, the procedure did still not appear to have been done adequately and Hay warned of the dangers of a considerable further epidemic in this inadequately protected group.[15] Fortunately, this did not occur and Aberdeen was free of the disease for six years, but in 1914 there was a small outbreak of six cases, with one fatality. The original case was of a lad who returned to Aberdeen while working as assistant steward on a vessel that had come from Almeria in Spain. He had taken ill during the voyage but the attack was so mild and the eruption so slight that smallpox was not even suspected until his father and brother became ill, and smallpox was diagnosed. His mother was also unwell and all contacts were immediately seen and vaccinated or re-vaccinated. Another case occurred nearly two weeks later in a woman who ran a nearby small shop. It was discovered that she had visited the stricken family the day before their removal to hospital. Her illness tragically proved fatal. An additional case appeared among a group of post-graduate students training for the Diploma in Public Health, to whom Matthew Hay had demonstrated the cases. Hay only allowed students who were properly re-vaccinated to enter the ward, but the victim had not been properly re-vaccinated, contrary to what he had claimed. Fortunately his illness was mild.[16]

A further small outbreak, involving eight patients, occurred in 1918. It started in a local military hospital and all the subsequent cases were directly traceable to the first victim, a wounded soldier who had been evacuated from France. All recovered. A single case occurred in 1923, contracted in another part of the country. Regular surveys of the number of one-year-old children who remained unvaccinated were carried out. This fluctuated over the years but was still averaging around 10 per cent, which was deemed a greater number than desirable.[17]

Typhus Fever: As mentioned in Chapter 2, Aberdeen's official returns until the 1880s included typhoid fever and other fevers under the heading of 'Fevers' but typhus was probably numerically the most important.

Yearly death rates for 'Fevers' in Aberdeen for the period 1858–81 are shown in Figure 3A, which clearly illustrates the major epidemic of 1863–6 and the smaller outbreak during 1869 mentioned in Chapter 2. The number of cases occurring thereafter fell markedly, although it was to remain a significant problem for many decades and contributed to the workload of the Epidemic Hospital. The first patients with this disease were

(Infections and the City Hospital to 1923)

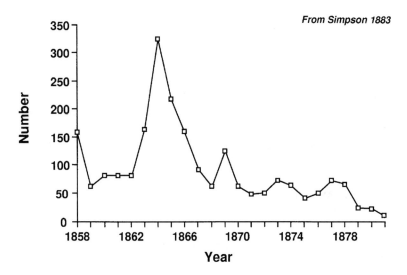

Figure 3A 'The Fevers'
Yearly death-rate per 100,000 population 1858–81

From Simpson 1883

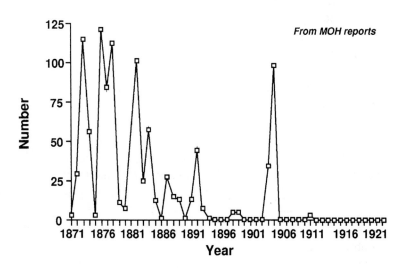

Figure 3B Typhus
Annual incidence in Aberdeen 1871–1923

From MOH reports

admitted there in February 1878.[18]

The annual reported incidence of typhus in Aberdeen for the period from 1871–1923 is shown in Figure 3B. Between 1887–99 a total of 124 patients with this disease were admitted to the City Hospital. There were no cases in the next four years but an epidemic which began in late 1904 and continued until mid-April 1905 taxed the energies of the Public Health Department. Clinically, the disease is abrupt in onset with high fever, headache and marked weakness. After a few days, a flat pink rash appears, first on the upper trunk, then spreading over the entire body but usually sparing the face. The spots later darken and with severe illness become haemorrhagic. There is often an accompanying dry cough with fast respiration and the pulse is rapid and weak. The temperature remains high, and during this period the patient is prostrated and may be delirious. With recovery, the temperature falls after 13–16 days and mental and physical powers rapidly return. In fatal cases, hyperpyrexia may develop, with circulatory and kidney failure.[19] Figures 4A and B, which are two representative cases admitted to the City Hospital during this epidemic, illustrate these features.

There was a total of 131 cases with 22 deaths. With only a few exceptions, it was possible to correlate all the cases with one family, although the original source remained obscure. Eight members of the hospital staff involved in caring for the patients were infected, of whom one, the ambulance driver, died. Matthew Hay studied the cases in the epidemic intensely, and was the first to postulate that typhus might, like malaria, be conveyed by insects. Hay thought body vermin were responsible but unfortunately settled for the wrong insect by incriminating the flea. He noted that every case of typhus seen had flea-bites, and that although some patients when presenting were free themselves of body vermin, all at the probable time of infection had been in contact with vermin-infested patients. He quoted many details of individual cases to support his theory.[20] In 1911, however, Charles Nicolle (1866–1936) and his associates showed that the body louse, *Pediculus corporis*, was in fact the responsible vector.[21] The city was free of the disease for five years until 1911, when three cases, all in the same family, appeared. The only person in the family to escape was the mother who had suffered from the disease in early life. The source of the infection was not ascertained. This was the last experience of the disease in the city although in the 1960s one of us (MJW) personally saw in Aberdeen a case in a Polish seaman off an Eastern Block factory ship.

Figures 4A and 4B. Illustrative Cases of Typhus Fever

A. Fatal Case: Mrs M.D. Age 48. Illness commenced 17 Jan 1905. Admitted 18 Jan. Rash appeared 20 Jan. Died 28 Jan.

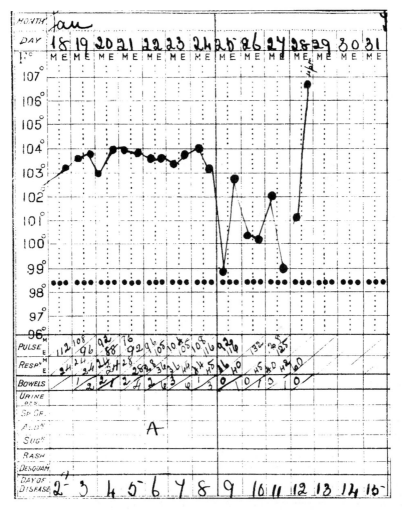

Notes

18 Jan	Slight headache. Body covered with insect bites but no rash discernible.
20 Jan	Rash appearing on shoulders and chest. Patient feels worse.
23 Jan	Considerable prostration. Slight cough.
25 Jan	Collapsed. Pulse weak.
27 Jan	Rash distinctly haemorrhagic.
28 Jan	Large bruises on lower extremities. Respirations rapid. Confused. Twitching of face and limbs. Hyperpyrexia. Died 5 pm.

B. Non-Fatal Case: Mr A. McM. Age 17. Labourer. Illness commenced 5 Feb 1905. Rash appeared and admitted 7 Feb. Discharged 23 March.

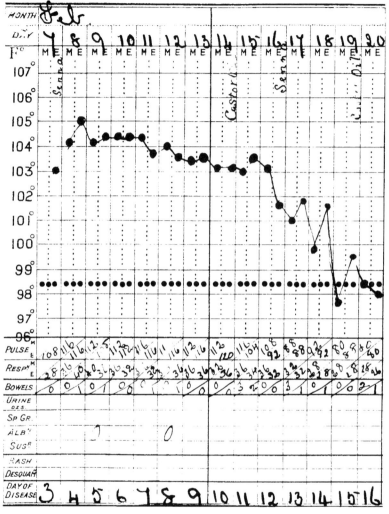

Notes 7 Feb   Face flushed. Violent headache. Tongue coated. Macular rash, profuse on shoulders and arms.

         9 Feb   Delirious.

        11 Feb   Rash now petechial (haemorrhagic).

        14 Feb   Rash fading.

        16 Feb   Rash almost gone: delirium continues.

        18 Feb   Deaf and stupid!

        26 Feb   Much better.

       23 Mar   Discharged

Typhoid Fever: Although cases of what were probably typhoid had been described since the time of Hippocrates, it was not clearly distinguished from other types of continued fever. The disease was eventually named typhoid because of its similarity to typhus, and, as stated earlier, cases of typhoid fever were included in returns for the latter disease before 1865.

The distinction was not really fully established until Sir William Jenner (1815–98) published a book in 1850 *On the Identity or Non-Identity of Typhoid and Typhus Fevers.* By numerous detailed clinical and post-mortem examinations Jenner showed that the lesions in the Peyer's patches of the small intestine and in the mesenteric glands were specific to typhoid and never found in typhus.[22] The term enteric fever was introduced in 1869 to emphasise the difference, but never achieved popularity, and typhoid fever has remained the preferred name. It was William Budd, a practitioner in Devon, who, in a book published in 1873, clearly established how the disease was spread from the faeces of a patient in water, food or fomites, such as clothing and bedding. Karl Eberth (1835–1926) observed the responsible organism in 1880, and five years later it was isolated from the faeces by Richard Pfeiffer (1858–1945), and also isolated and studied by Georg Gaffky (1850–1918).[23]

Overcrowding and poor standards of hygiene and sanitation predispose to typhoid fever and it shares with cholera a pre-eminent position among water-borne diseases. In the past, huge epidemics have spread among soldiers. In the Boer War, of a total of just over 200,000 British troops, 57,684 suffered typhoid and there were 8,022 fatalities from the disease.[24]

The reported annual incidence of typhoid in Aberdeen in 1871–1923 is shown in Figure 5. The numbers in the early years are certainly an underestimate, as many cases were unreported. Clinically, the illness is of gradual onset with non-specific features, and lasts about four weeks. There is loss of appetite, tiredness, weakness, headache, aches and pains and fever. During the first week, the temperature steadily rises, headache increases and patients usually have a non-productive cough. Nose bleeding is common. There is vague abdominal discomfort and tenderness and usually constipation unless the initial infection was heavy, when diarrhoea occurs. During the second week, the fever is higher and sustained and patients become obviously ill, profoundly weak, and lethargic. Diarrhoea is common, the stools may contain blood, and the pulse rate is characteristically slower than expected. The abdomen is distended and often tender, and the spleen commonly palpable. Distinctive pink, slightly raised skin lesions – 'rose spots', sparse in number – frequently appear on the chest and abdomen. In uncomplicated cases, after about four weeks, the temperature slowly subsides, but the patient remains weak and convalescence is slow. The mortality rate was around 10 per cent. Death could occur from profound toxaemia or intestinal perforation or haemorrhage, which were most likely during the second or third week of illness.[25]

Figure 5 Typhoid
Annual incidence in Aberdeen 1871–1923

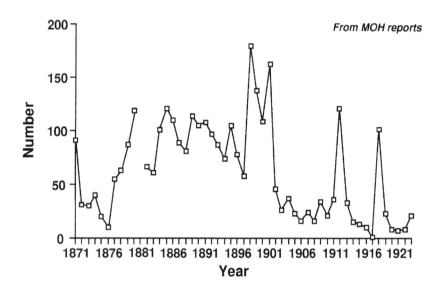

In January 1884, Dr Simpson reported on an outbreak involving 25 persons in thirteen families which he believed was due to infected milk as had been reported elsewhere in the country.[26] All the families involved obtained their milk from the same farm, and on visiting it, he found an uncovered burn or ditch nearby, which was contaminated by the overflow from a nearby school cesspool and manure from adjoining fields. This polluted water was being used to wash cans, pails and dishes in the farm, and even to dilute the milk! Having also ascertained that the excretions from a typhoid patient had earlier been put into a drain linked to the burn, he felt that this proved adequate explanation for the outbreak. Further selling of milk from the farm was barred. Matthew Hay reported another outbreak from infected milk, involving eighteen cases, in October 1898, and a few months later further outbreaks involving twelve and 25 cases occurred.[27]

Hay stated that this series of epidemics was unprecedented in the records of the Public Health Department and pointed to an unusual prevalence of typhoid among families of dairy-keepers and farmers.[28] He noted that many cases of typhoid were not correctly diagnosed and so proper precautions were not taken. All infections conveyed by milk, whether typhoidal, scarlatinal, tubercular or diphtheritic, could be totally prevented by boiling milk but local custom was against this. Hay observed that milk was the only animal product which was not cooked before being consumed, and that in countries like India, where milk was universally cooked, consuming it raw appeared to be as barbarous as the consumption of raw flesh. The main objection to boiling was that it altered the taste. This could be obviated by sterilising milk by heating it to a temperature below the boiling point and Hay felt that it would be cost-effective for the municipality to sterilise *all* milk in this fashion. He correctly predicted that such a scheme would eventually be universal in the country and concluded by 'fain wish[ing] that Aberdeen had the distinction and advantage of leading the way'.[29] Unfortunately this was not to be.

Many other outbreaks related to milk were described in subsequent years. In 1907 Hay was involved in the investigation of a huge epidemic from this source in Peterhead, which continued for almost three months, and produced nearly 300 cases.[30] Early isolation of infected patients seemed essential to limit the spread of the disease throughout the family and to others. A similar epidemic in Aberdeen in 1918 involved 97 cases and was definitely established as due to infected milk. An unrecognised case had occurred in the farmer's wife who continued to take part in milking operations when unwell. At the time of the Aberdeen outbreak she was still excreting typhoid organisms in her faeces. Fourteen of the 97 cases died.[31]

Hospital admissions: Figure 6 shows the number of cases of the 'major infections' – smallpox, typhus and typhoid – admitted to the City Hospital during the period 1887–1923. During this period all cases of smallpox and typhus in the city were admitted to the City Hospital, but the number of typhoid cases is well below the overall incidence, as typhoid patients were more often admitted to the Royal Infirmary or Sick Children's Hospital. In total, the major infections formed only a small part of the hospital workload, apart from the transient increase in typhus cases during the outbreaks of 1892 and 1904–5, and typhoid in the epidemics of 1901, 1912 and 1918.

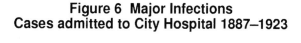

Figure 6 Major Infections
Cases admitted to City Hospital 1887–1923

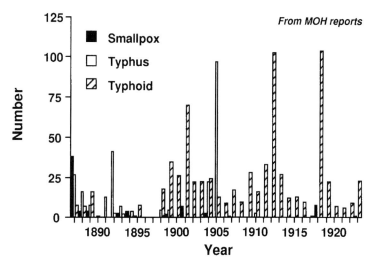

The Other Common Zymotics

Measles, whooping cough, scarlet fever and diphtheria were also common diseases. They were all generally less feared than the 'major infections' but were a much more common cause of death.

Measles: The mortality rates from measles for the period 1858–81 are shown in Figure 7A. Measles appeared to occur in outbreaks every two to three years and Dr Simpson noted that the disease caused more deaths than occurred with the largest epidemics of smallpox.[32] In December 1884, Simpson expressed concern at the increasing number of cases of measles at that time and the level of mortality, and a list of precautions to limit spread was issued. Financial penalties were threatened if the precautions were disregarded, and at times the infant departments of schools were closed to limit spread. This condition remained highly prevalent, although the number of deaths had fallen since the 1870s, and Simpson thought this was related to a decline in the number of cases as a result of improved health education. Schools, he believed, were the main source of spread, and teachers had been encouraged not to allow sufferers to return too soon to school.[33] The

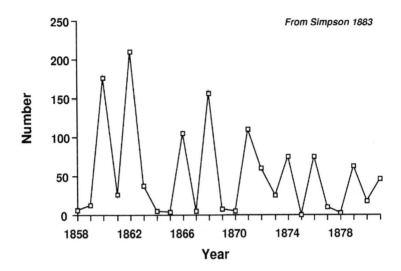

Figure 7A Measles
Yearly death-rate per 100,000 population 1858–81

From Simpson 1883

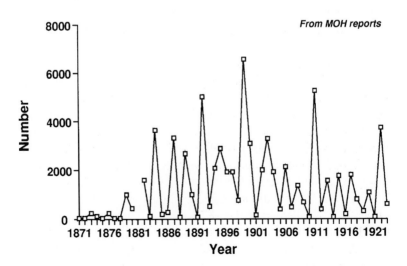

Figure 7B Measles
Annual incidence in Aberdeen 1871–1923

From MOH reports

condition was, however, to remain highly prevalent. Figure 7B shows the annual incidence from 1871–1923, with massive outbreaks in 1892, 1899 and 1911, that in 1899 being the largest with 6,527 reported cases. The mortality rate remained high well into the twentieth century.

The mortality rate from measles was highest in children under two years of age and low in those over five. Thus in the ten years up to 1900, there were altogether 4,883 cases of measles notified among children under two years of age and of these, 495 died, or about one in every ten cases. At ages above five in the same period there were 10,318 cases with only 39 deaths, or about one in 260.[34] No scheme for the protection of children in the vulnerable age group then seemed practical. In 1910, when Matthew Hay reported on the problems posed by measles, he felt there was a need for public education on the danger of this disease, and also whooping cough. Measles and whooping cough were much less feared than scarlet fever, although this fear of scarlet fever was no longer warranted. Only a small number of cases of measles were admitted to the City Hospital, preference being given to cases of scarlet fever and diphtheria because of limitation of beds. In the further epidemics that occurred in 1917 and 1922 Hay arranged for a ward to be set aside for measles cases. He was concerned that measles was causing more deaths in infants than the other diseases. Among infants from unsuitable home circumstances, the mortality rate among those admitted was much lower than among those who stayed at home.[35]

Whooping Cough: Whooping cough, or hooping cough as it was earlier called, is an acute respiratory illness that classically affects infants and young children. The descriptive name derives from the distressing prolonged inspiratory effort that follows a prolonged bout of coughing. The condition has been recorded since the sixteenth century. The great English physician, Thomas Sydenham (1624–89), gave the alternative name 'pertussis' to any illness accompanied by violent coughing but this term later came to be used as an alternative for this distinctive epidemic disease.[36]

Dr Simpson's mortality data for the period 1858–81 (Figure 8A) shows that the condition was endemic, with some year-to-year variation, and although the annual number of deaths was not great, it ranked high among the causes of death in children. It seems to have been even commoner in later years, as shown in Figure 8B, with a peak reported incidence of 3,645 cases in 1902, one of four years when there were over 2,000 cases. In 1880, when the disease caused 50 deaths in a period of three months, the local authority issued a memorandum on precautions to be

Figure 8A 'Hooping Cough'
Yearly death-rate per 100,000 population 1859–81

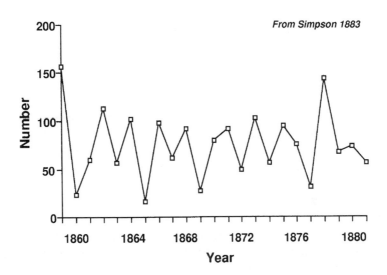

From Simpson 1883

Figure 8B Whooping cough
Annual incidence in Aberdeen 1871–1923

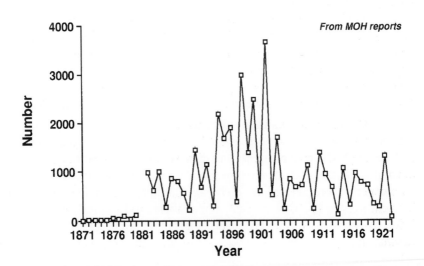

From MOH reports

taken to limit spread, and imposed financial penalties for breaches. It recommended that when whooping cough occurred in a family, the remaining children should not be sent to school or allowed to mix with their neighbours.[37] As mentioned in the introductory section of this chapter, whooping cough had been notifiable in Aberdeen since 1891, accounting for the apparent upsurge in numbers at that time, as shown in Figure 8B. Dual notification, whereby both the medical attendant and parent had to notify the disease, commenced in August 1891 accounting for the considerable increase in incidence thereafter. In 1900 Matthew Hay asked Dr Laing, resident medical officer at the City Hospital, to prepare a report on the prevalence of and mortality from whooping cough in Aberdeen. This was incorporated in the MOH's annual report for 1902. Like measles, the mortality rate from whooping cough was particularly high in those under the age of two, about 20–25 times as high as in those over five. In the ten years ending 1900 there were altogether 4,819 cases under two years of age with 548 deaths, or about one in every nine cases; and 4,040 cases above five years of age with 20 deaths, or one in 202. No scheme for adequate protection seemed then feasible.[38]

The apparent decline in incidence after 1903 was due to the fact that, from that time, whooping cough ceased to be compulsorily notifiable. Relatively small numbers of cases of this disease were admitted to the City Hospital as mothers were generally reluctant to have their very young children admitted. In addition, such children would need to stay in hospital for around six weeks, and the bed numbers available did not permit this.[39]

Scarlet Fever: This infection is now known to be due to Group A streptococcal infection in the tonsils or pharynx with strains of the organism which produce a specific toxin – the erythrogenic or scarlatinal toxin – resulting in the characteristic diffuse bright red rash from which the condition gets its name.

Scarlet fever had been recognised in earlier centuries, but it was first clearly described and given its name by Thomas Sydenham in 1666.[40] The responsible organism, *Streptococcus pyogenes*, was discovered by Ottomar Rosenbach (1851–1907) in 1884, and Hugo Schottmueller (1867– 1936) in 1903 was the first to show that certain strains produce a distinctive haemolysin when cultured on blood-agar, leading to the use of the term haemolytic streptococcus. Detailed classification followed the work of Rebecca Lancefield (1895–1981) and others in the 1930s.[41]

Poor socio-economic conditions and overcrowding predispose to scarlet fever, and the disease is spread by droplet infection. Death could occur in the acute stage whilst sequelae such as nephritis or rheumatic fever with resultant kidney disease or heart damage were major problems. Yearly death rates per 100,000 population for the period 1859–81 (taken from Dr Simpson's paper) are shown in Figure 9. A major outbreak in 1859–61 caused 750 deaths, and after a lull of three years a further epidemic lasting five years from 1865–66 caused about 400 deaths. The highest mortality was found among the lower social classes living in poor conditions. From 1875 the mortality rate fell. Experienced physicians of the time considered the disease had become less virulent but Simpson thought that improved sanitary conditions in the city from that time were a major factor.[42] Figure 10 shows the annual reported incidence from 1871–1923 and, as will be seen, Dr Simpson's views were not really supported, as further huge outbreaks were to recur, with peaks of 1,676 cases in 1896 and a record 1,873 in 1915.

Figure 9 Scarlet Fever
Yearly death-rate per 100,000 population 1859–81

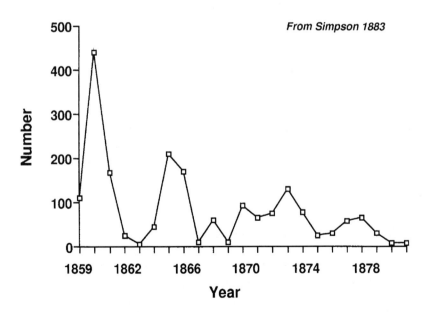

The first patient with scarlet fever admitted to the Epidemic Hospital arrived in July 1878.[43] The condition had in fact been epidemic in Aberdeen since 1877 and in early 1878, the local authority, concerned because by then there had been over 500 cases, issued a memorandum with reference to precautions to be adopted to attempt to check its spread. People were reminded that the condition was very infectious and that the patient remained infectious for some weeks during the phase of characteristic 'skin peeling'. Isolation was recommended, everything removed from the sick-room was to be disinfected and the room itself, and all its contents, disinfected after recovery. Financial penalties ranging from £5 to £20 were imposed for various breaches of these regulations.[44] These regulations were reissued in 1885.

Figure 10 Scarlet Fever
Annual incidence in Aberdeen 1871–1923

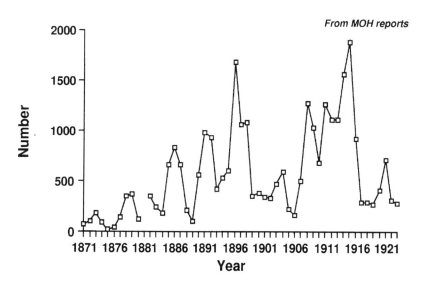

As shown in Figure 10, there was a huge outbreak of scarlet fever in 1896–8. In 1898 Hay reported on a 'milk epidemic', identified in April that year causing 49 of the cases. The outbreak was traced to one farm which was the sole supplier to five different milk shops in town from which all those involved had obtained their milk. When the farm was visited, no specific infection was identified in any of the cows or in the persons employed or living there although some had earlier had symptoms of sore throat. Although no proof was obtained, it was thought likely that one or more of those in the farm household with sore throats may have had mild scarlet fever. Certainly when the supply of milk from the farm in question was temporarily suspended, the outbreak from this source ceased.[45] Later in the year another small outbreak, in Holburn district, was thought to be due to a similar train of events.[46]

Another huge epidemic occurred in 1908 and continued until 1916, but the disease then was much milder than before and the case fatality fell from around 3.6 per cent to 1.2 per cent during the epidemic. The number of cases who required removal to hospital also fell. During the 1913–22 decennium, the disease remained common with an average of 584 cases admitted to the City Hospital each year. The case mortality, however, remained low, around 3.8 per cent.[47] Immunisation against this disease was not introduced in Aberdeen until 1925.

Puerperal Fever: Although not numerically common, puerperal or childbed fever, a complication following the delivery of a child, was dreaded by women because of its frequently fatal outcome. The condition merits consideration because of an important local contribution to our understanding of this disease.

In 1795, Dr Alexander Gordon (1752–99), physician to the Aberdeen Dispensary, a well-trained and able obstetrician, published *A Treatise on the Epidemic Puerperal Fever of Aberdeen*, his findings made during an outbreak of puerperal fever over the years 1789–92. Based on his careful records, Gordon provided the first overwhelming evidence of the contagiousness of puerperal fever, showing that a doctor, student or midwife carried the disease from one obstetrical case to another.[48]

In a paper published in 1843, Oliver Wendell Holmes (1809–94) again drew the attention of the medical profession to the contagiousness of puerperal fever and quoted the work of Alexander Gordon. However, it is Ignaz Semmelweiss (1818–65) who is usually credited with this discovery, having independently shown, in 1847, that puerperal fever was transmissible by doctors and medical students to recently-delivered women. He had noted that the disease was commonest in wards attended by medical students, many of whom had come direct from the dissecting room. Puerperal fever, he asserted, was caused by the conveyance to the pregnant women of putrid particles from the dissecting room through the agency of examining fingers. By compelling all his students to wash their hands in disinfectant before examining pregnant women, he markedly reduced the mortality rate. His findings were, however, scorned by his peers and he was hounded from Vienna to Budapest, where he died a lonely disillusioned man.[49]

Puerperal fever was not made notifiable in Aberdeen until 1891. In previous years, the MOHs several times remarked on the alarming number of monthly deaths from this cause, pointing out the nature of its spread and the means of prevention. A relationship with erysipelas was also noted by Hay.[50]

Figure 11 shows the annual number of cases and deaths for the years 1897–1923. As it affected women in their prime and left a new-born child motherless, it had a devastating effect on the unfortunate family. On average there were 10–12 cases a year with an unusual high of 24 in 1914. The condition accounted for some half of all maternal deaths. The situation was to remain unaltered until the advent of chemotherapy in the 1930s.

Figure 11 Puerperal Fever
Total annual cases and fatal cases 1897–1923

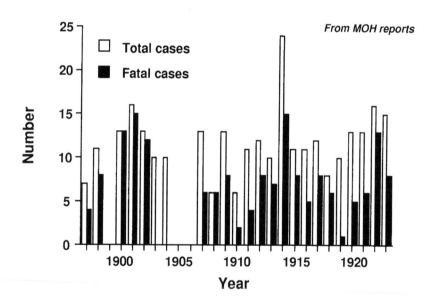

Erysipelas: Now known to be due to Group A streptococcal skin infection, this condition most often affects the face or head although any part of the body may be involved. The condition is usually of abrupt onset with high fever and shivering followed quickly by the appearance of a zone of redness and swelling, most frequently around the bridge of the nose. This spreads with a sharply defined raised edge and the involved area is intensely red, hot, painful and glistening. Before the introduction of antibiotics the illness lasted about 7–14 days. A relationship with scarlet fever and puerperal infection had been recognised even before the bacteriological cause was discovered. Erysipelas was common in the past and a frequent reason for admission to the City Hospital. The mortality rate was relatively low and the disease attracted comparatively little attention from the MOH compared to those already mentioned. There was rarely any special comment on erysipelas in the annual or other reports.

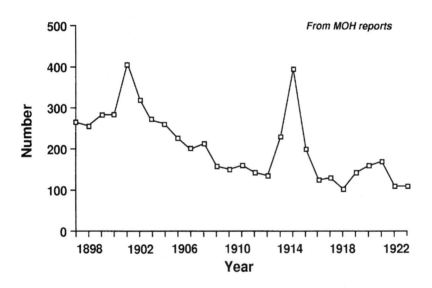

Figure 12 Erysipelas
Annual number of cases 1897–1923

The annual number of notifications for this disease in 1897–1923 is shown in Figure 12. There were often 100–200 cases each year with occasional outbreaks affecting double that number. In earlier years, sufferers had been admitted to the Royal Infirmary but the managers refused to admit such cases after 1898. For a short period they were admitted to the Poor House before arrangements were made for their admission into the City Hospital. Only the more severe cases, usually in poorer households where proper attention could not be given, were admitted.[51]

Poliomyelitis: Poliomyelitis, or infantile paralysis, was not common during this period but is included here because of its later importance. Although poliomyelitis was not compulsorily notifiable in Scotland until 1926, in Aberdeen notification was made obligatory by the Town Council from 12 May 1913.[52] A viral disease, spread by human contact, it was probably world-wide in distribution but only seemed to become epidemic during the first half of this century especially in the highly-developed countries of Western Europe and North America. The illness can take several forms. Inapparent infection can occur producing an antibody response conferring immunity without producing symptoms. An abortive form produces non-specific symptoms without neurological symptoms. In non-paralytic poliomyelitis there are signs of central nervous involvement and meningitis without paralysis. The major illness or paralytic poliomyelitis can cause flaccid weakness of one or more muscle groups with predilection for the limbs, or can give rise to an overwhelming paralytic illness with bulbar involvement leading to death from respiratory failure.[53]

Figure 13 Poliomyelitis
Annual number of cases of 1913–23

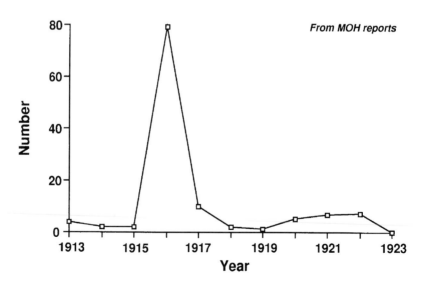

The annual number of cases reported in Aberdeen from 1913–23 is shown in Figure 13. These were generally small but in 1916–17 there was a considerable outbreak, producing 79 cases in the first year and ten in the next. All the patients were under fifteen years of age and 43 were less than two years old. This was characteristic of the disease then and it was the reason for its alternative name – infantile paralysis. No non-paralytic cases were identified, probably because of lack of any specific diagnostic test at this time. As soon as the outbreak became evident, a circular letter was sent by the MOH to all medical practitioners asking them to be on the lookout for cases in their practice. Almost all cases were admitted to the City Hospital. The disease was generally mild in this Aberdeen outbreak and there were only four deaths, all the fatal cases involving bulbar paralysis in children under the age of one year. In a few cases the paralysis was slight, clearing within a week. In others, however, it was more pronounced and continued longer. For the 75 cases that were left with some degree of paralysis, special clinics were arranged with expert surgical, electrical and massage services. Five years later a follow-up study showed that 54 had recovered completely, while the remainder were said to be steadily improving. Aberdeen was lucky compared with New York where a concurrent epidemic involved over 8,000 persons with a more severe form of the disease, the case mortality being 24 per cent.[54]

Diphtheria: World-wide in distribution, this infection, which is spread by droplet infection, was first identified as a clinical entity by Pierre Bretonneau (1771–1862) in France in 1826. The disease most commonly affects the throat with severe local pain and fever. After a few days the characteristic greyish-white membrane, due to exudate, forms on the affected area. This may spread downwards to involve the larynx with resultant laryngeal obstruction leading to severe breathlessness from obstruction of air entry into the lungs, and this was commonly fatal without special treatment in infants and young children. Severe toxaemia also occurs and powerful toxins produced could have severe effects on the heart and nervous system, and death from heart failure was also common. In 1883 Edwin Klebs (1834–1913) described a bacillus on the diphtheritic membrane but did not produce convincing evidence of its aetiological relevance. The following year Friedrich Loeffler (1852–1915) isolated and intensely studied the organism, proving its role. Officially known as the *Corynebacterium diphtheriae* because of its club-shaped morphological appearance, it is often known as the Klebs-Loeffler bacillus.[55]

In the period 1861–81 diphtheria does not seem to have been a common disease in Aberdeen, although whether this was related to incorrect diagnosis or under-reporting is not clear. Mortality rates for the period are

Figure 14A Diphtheria
Yearly death-rate per 100,000 population 1861–81

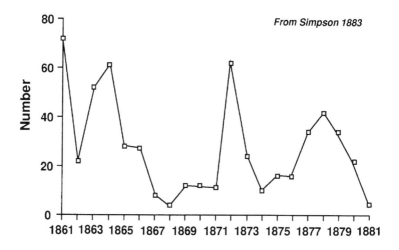

From Simpson 1883

Figure 14B Diphtheria
Annual incidence in Aberdeen 1871–1923

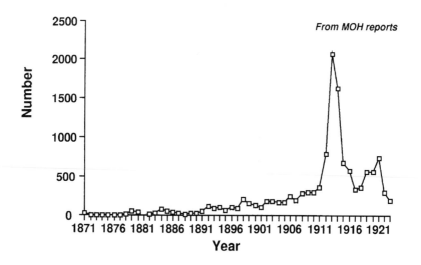

From MOH reports

shown in Figure 14A. Dr Simpson thought it was a country rather than a town disease, believing that stinking middens, undrained land and the filthy surroundings of farms favoured the condition.[56] Certainly the reported incidence for the period 1871–1923 shown in Figure 14B suggests that it remained uncommon until 1912 when a major outbreak started, with a peak incidence of 2,062 cases in 1913. The incidence then fell, apart from a less dramatic upward trend from 1917, and a smaller peak in 1921.

The use of diphtheria antitoxin, an artificially-produced agent which neutralises diphtheria toxin when injected, was first described by Emil von Behring (1854–1917) in 1890, and its use extended rapidly in all civilised countries. In his monthly report for March 1898, Hay described the antitoxin as 'one of the most substantial gains ever achieved by medicine in the domain of therapeutics'.[57] As it had to be used very early for full effect, Hay stressed the need for early diagnosis of any suspected case by calling a doctor as soon as possible. The value of this treatment was re-emphasised in Hay's annual report for 1900. Of the 128 cases reported that year, 82 had been removed to the City Hospital where all except the mild cases were treated with antitoxin. Although many cases were severe, with several requiring tracheostomy, the mortality was only 7.3 per cent. This contrasted with a mortality rate of 52 per cent for those treated at home where antitoxin was rarely used.[58] Matthew Hay repeatedly urged the local authority to supply free antitoxin to medical practitioners in the city, but it was not until 1906 that this advice was heeded. A circular letter was then issued to all city doctors stating that a free supply of diphtheria antitoxin with a syringe could be obtained either from the Public Health Office or at the City Hospital, the latter of course being always open. Instructions on use were also included.[59] Utilisation of this service remained poor, however, and the mortality rate, especially among patients admitted during the later stages of the disease, remained high. Many attempts were made to reduce the incidence of the disease in the city. In conjunction with the School Medical Officers, in 1913 Hay forbade the sharing of pencils by pupils and arranged for the School Board to provide each pupil with a small box or case for their own set of writing materials. Bubble fountains were introduced to replace communal drinking mugs. Hay also wondered whether the rapid growth of cinematograph houses, which were crowded, hot and stuffy, might be promoting the spread of the disease. Brushings of the throat and nose for bacteriological examination were also taken from persons in infected households to try and discover diphtheria carriers.[60]

Hospital admissions and the introduction of immunisation: Figure 15 shows the number of cases of the 'minor infections'– diphtheria, scarlet fever and measles – admitted to the City Hospital during the period 1887–1923. These were consistently responsible for a far greater number of admissions than the major infections. Scarlet fever was initially by far the commoner disorder but from 1914 was overtaken by diphtheria. As already mentioned, immunisation against scarlet fever was not introduced until 1925, several years after that for diphtheria.

Figure 15 Minor infections
Cases admitted to City Hospital 1887–1923

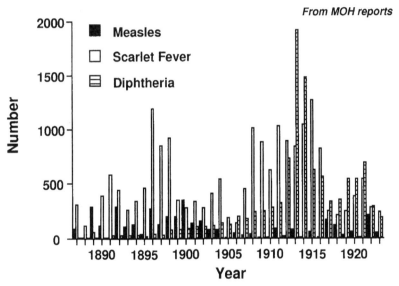

Active immunisation against diphtheria by the use of toxin/antitoxin mixture was first suggested around 1900 but there was a long time lag in its introduction because of doubts as to its efficacy. It became popular in America from 1913 but was adopted more slowly in this country. The intradermal test devised by Bela Schick (1877–1967) aided the immunisation programme in two ways. Firstly, it limited the need for immunisation to those who showed susceptibility to diphtheria. Secondly, if used before and after immunisation, it provided evidence of the success or failure of the procedure. The Schick test involves injecting 0.2 ml of diphtheria toxin of known strength into the skin of the forearm. If there is no antitoxin (or very little) in the patient's blood, a slight infiltration of the skin surrounded by a bright red areola develops in 24–48 hours at the injection site. This indicates susceptibility to the disease. As a control a similar volume of the diluted diphtheria toxin, heated to destroy its action, is injected into the other arm.[61]

Schick testing and active immunisation of the staff at the City Hospital was inaugurated in January 1922.[62] The full effects of the introduction of diphtheria immunisation in Aberdeen will be dealt with in a later chapter.

References for Chapter Six

[1]   Aberdeen City Archives, Public Health Minute Book no. 1 (hereafter PHMB/1), 20 January 1868.

[2]   PHMB/1, 16 March 1868.

[3]   W. J. Simpson, *Health History of Aberdeen During the Past Quarter of a Century*, Aberdeen, 1883.

[4]   Aberdeen City Archives, Public Health Minute Book no. 2 (hereafter PHMB/2), 19 August 1878.

[5]   Report of the Medical Officer of Health for March 1891, p. 5.

[6]   Aberdeen Central Library, Town Council Minutes (hereafter TCM), 16 February 1891.

[7]   Report of the Medical Officer of Health for February 1903, p. 5.

[8]   Annual Reports of the Medical Officer of Health, 1908–1921.

[9]   Annual Report of the Medical Officer of Health for 1910, pp. 59–60.

[10]   Annual Report of the Medical Officer of Health for 1892, Appendix, pp. 1–4.

[11]   Annual Report of the Medical Officer of Health for 1897, p. 5.

[12]   M. Hay, 'The City Hospital' in J. Scott Riddell (ed.), *BMA Aberdeen 1914. Handbook and Guide to Aberdeen*, Cheltenham, Burrow, 1914, pp. 52–7.

[13]   PHMB/2, 19 February 1877.

[14]   Annual Reports of the Medical Officer of Health, 1888–1908.

[15]   Annual Report of the Medical Officer of Health for 1908, pp. 20–4.

[16]   Annual Report of the Medical Office of Health for 1914, pp. 37–41.

[17]   Report of the Medical Officer of Health for the years 1922 and 1923, pp. 50–2.

[18]   PHMB/2, 18 February 1878.

[19]   E. S. Murphy, 'Rickettsial Disease – The Typhus Group' in P. B. Beeson and W. McDermott (eds), *Textbook of Medicine*, London, Saunders, 1975, pp. 248–50.

[20]   Annual Report of the Medical Officer of Health for 1905, pp. 23–9.

[21]   W. W. C. Topley and G. S. Wilson, *The Principles of Bacteriology and Immunity*, vol. II, London, Arnold, 1929, pp. 980–1012.

[22]   A. B. Christie, *Infectious Diseases: Epidemiology and Clinical Practice*, Edinburgh, Livingstone, 1969, p. 54.

23   Topley and Wilson, op. cit., pp. 980–1012.

24   P. Pringle, *The Romance of Medical Science*, London, Harrap, 1948, p. 130.

25   A. S. Benenson, 'Typhoid Fever' in Beeson and McDermott, op. cit., pp. 361–2.

26   Report of the Medical Officer of Health for January 1884.

27   Report of the Medical Office of Health for October 1898, pp. 6–8.

28   Ibid., p. 7.

29   Ibid., p. 8.

30   L. A. Wilson, 'Matthew Hay (1855–1932)' in G. P. Milne (ed.). *Aberdeen Medico-Chirurgical Society. A Bicentennial History 1789–1989*, Aberdeen, Aberdeen University Press, 1989, p. 195.

31   Report by the Medical Office of Health for the years 1916–1921, pp. 57–8.

32   Simpson, op. cit., p. 7.

33   Report of the Medical Officer of Health for December 1884.

34   Annual Report of the Medical Officer of Health for 1910, p. 53.

35   Report of the Medical Officer of Health for the years 1916–21, p. 43.

36   Topley and Wilson, op. cit., pp. 980–1012.

37   Annual Report of the Medical Officer of Health for 1902, Appendix pp. 1–12.

38   Annual Report of the Medical Officer of Health for 1910, pp. 52–3.

39   Ibid., p. 52.

40   Pringle, op. cit., p. 130.

41   G. H. Stollerman, 'Group A Streptococcal Infection' in Beeson and McDermott, op. cit., pp. 290–4.

42   Simpson, op. cit., pp. 5–6.

43   PHMB/2, 15 July 1878.

44   Report of the Medical Officer of Health for June 1890, p. 6.

45   Report of the Medical Officer of Health for April 1898, pp. 5–7.

46   Report of the Medical Officer of Health for September 1898, pp. 6–7.

47   Annual Reports of the Medical Officer of Health, 1913–22.

48   Alexander Gordon, *A Treatise on the Epidemic Puerperal Fever of Aberdeen*, London, Robinson, 1795.

49   Pringle, op. cit., p. 130.

50   Report of the Medical Officer of Health for November 1893, p. 7.

51   TCM, 5 September 1898.

52   Annual Report of the Medical Officer of Health for 1913, p. 37.

53   F. Plum, 'Acute Anterior Poliomyelitis' in Beeson and McDermott, op. cit., pp. 696–700.

54   Report of the Medical Officer of Health for the years 1916–1921, pp. 53–5.

55   Topley and Wilson, op. cit., p. 1668.

56   Simpson, op. cit., p. 10.

[57] Report of the Medical Officer of Health for March 1898, p. 7.

[58] Annual Report of the Medical Officer of Health for 1900, pp. 11–12.

[59] Annual Report of the Medical Officer of Health for 1906, pp. 16–18.

[60] Annual Report of the Medical Officer of Health for 1913, pp. 27–32.

[61] Topley and Wilson, op. cit., pp. 135–6.

[62] Report of the Medical Officer of Health for the years 1922 and 1923, pp. 35–6.

Chapter Seven

Tuberculosis and Venereal Disease in Aberdeen and the City Hospital 1856–1923

TUBERCULOSIS

History

Although there is palaentological evidence that tuberculosis (TB) infected man in neolithic times, and evidence of spinal caries has certainly been identified in Egyptian mummies,[1] it was only following the industrial revolution with the resultant overcrowding and atmospheric pollution favouring its spread, that the disease became a major scourge.

In the mid-nineteenth century it is said to have accounted for one quarter of adult deaths in Europe, fully justifying its title as 'captain of the men of death'.[2] The lives of innumerable famous artists, composers, poets, writers and even royalty were brought to a premature end by this dread affliction. Earlier referred to as consumption, the term tuberculosis came into use around 1839. Although the spitting of blood was long realised to be a major sign of the common pulmonary form, referred to as phthisis, diagnosis was initially crude and indirect. Improvement followed the introduction of percussion as an examination technique, first described by the Austrian Leopold Auenbrugger (1722–1809) in 1761, and by the method of auscultation using the stethoscope popularised by the French doctor René Laennec (1781–1826).[3] Laennec was also the first to establish by careful necropsy study that the many different forms of the condition in the lungs and elsewhere were in fact manifestations of the same disease. The infective nature of the condition was first shown in 1865 by Jean Antoine Villemin (1827–92) when he transmitted the disease to animals from tissue of patients who had died from the disease. The causative organism, the tubercle bacillus, was identified in 1882 by the German, Robert Koch, who also enumerated the different methods of spread.[4]

Greater diagnostic precision in the common pulmonary form followed the discovery of x-rays by Wilhelm Röntgen (1845–1923) in 1895, and this new technique came to be used for this purpose more than any other.[5]

Tuberculosis in Aberdeen – Historical Aspects

As elsewhere in the country, tuberculosis, especially the pulmonary form, became a major scourge in Aberdeen, and in the nineteenth century was responsible for one-eighth of all deaths.[6] The mortality per 100,000 population for all forms of tuberculosis and for the most common pulmonary form in quinquennial periods from 1856–1920 is shown in Figure 16.

Figure 16 Tuberculosis 1856–1920
Mortality / 100,000 population, quinquennial periods

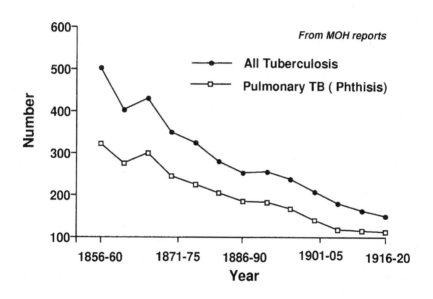

It can be noted that the mortality rate was steadily falling during the period covered by the Figure. The fall was particularly marked in the 1860s, having been initially high, because it was believed many of the sufferers will have succumbed readily to the other then prevalent epidemics because of their debilitated state. Dr Simpson, the MOH, believed the decrease was due to the improved sanitary condition of the city.[7] The drainage had been improved in 1867 and, following the Public Health (Scotland) Act of 1867, there had been a Sanitary Department regulating and improving such matters. A local Corporation Act passed in 1881 restricted overcrowding, regulated the width of the streets, and resulted in efficient ventilation being installed in all schools. The water supply and state of registered milk shops (dairies) were also now under regular inspection.

Tuberculosis was known to be related to poor socio-economic circumstances, the mortality rate being highest in the poor and unemployed and those living in unhygienic crowded surroundings. School children, adolescents and young adults were especially severely affected. It was, however, a point of pride to the public health authorities in Aberdeen that in the 1880s the mortality rate was lower in the city than in any of the other large towns in Scotland.[8]

Prevention and Treatment

Following the recognition of the infective nature of the disease and its mode of spread, public health measures aimed at reducing overcrowding and banning spitting in public places were introduced, but had little effect on mortality.[9]

The occurrence of the disease in animals, especially cattle, was recognised by Villemin who also made the important observation that material from bovine tuberculosis, when injected into rabbits, set up a more rapid and more generalised disease than material from human tuberculosis.[10] Tuberculin testing for the identification of infected animals and their eradication was not introduced until after the classic work of Clemens von Pirquet (1874–1929) in 1907 and Charles Mantoux (1877–1947) in 1910 which showed that the injection into or under the skin of a minute amount of tuberculin – a protein material obtained from tubercle bacilli – could be used as a diagnostic test for TB and was also positive in persons or animals who had been exposed to tuberculous infection in the past.[11] It was some time, however, before the pasteurisation or boiling of all milk except that from tubercle-free herds was widely practised. Great hopes were raised with the development of a vaccine against tuberculosis from a bovine bacillus in 1921 by the French bacteriologist Camille Guérin (1872–1961) and the veterinarian Albert Calmette (1863–1933).[12] While not providing complete protection, use of the BCG (Bacille-Calmette-Guérin) vaccine markedly reduced the incidence of the severe acute forms of the disease, such as miliary tuberculosis or tuberculous meningitis, in protected individuals.

The only treatment measures initially available were rest, nutritious diet and fresh air. Pasteur was the first to show that germs were less frequent in the air of country uplands, and very rare in the air of the high alps.[13] Sanatoria were developed on the continent to provide rest in optimal surrounds, with exposure to sunlight and clean healthy air, usually in medium altitude mountains, in pine forests or by the sea.

The first special accommodation designated for the treatment of tuberculosis in the North-East of Scotland was at the private Nordrach-on-Dee Sanatorium at Banchory. This sanatorium, later Glen O'Dee Hospital, was the brainchild of Dr David Lawson (1868–1952). A graduate of St Andrews and Edinburgh, he had become interested in the treatment of pulmonary tuberculosis and was struck by the lack of special sanatoria facilities in this country compared with the continent. In collaboration with others, he built and in 1900 opened the facility at Banchory which was modelled on the famous Nordrach Sanatorium at Baden in Germany.[14] The Banchory sanatorium was set in its own 25-acre grounds and situated on a southern pine-clad slope, well sheltered from the north, east and west. All the rooms were south-facing, spacious and airy, and x-ray and other up-to-date facilities were available, including ultra-violet light installations which often formed part of the treatment. The sanatorium initially had accommodation for 36 patients but was later enlarged.[15] This was a private institution admitting patients from all over the country and probably had relatively few patients from Aberdeen and the surrounding area. There was no specific facility for the treatment of local tuberculous patients until 1902, when special accommodation was built at Newhills Convalescent Home. Situated at Bucksburn, just outside Aberdeen, the home had been started in a small house at Dykeside which first opened to convalescent cases in 1874. This was replaced in 1881 by a larger house, situated on the slopes of the Brimmond Hill, some 400 feet above sea level. There was accommodation in the new home for 22 patients, but extensions were added, and cases with tuberculosis were taken, although there were initially no special treatment facilities. In 1900, of a total of 161 admissions, 22 were tuberculous cases. A special extension, designed specifically for tuberculosis treatment, started in 1902, largely at the instigation of Matthew Hay. There was accommodation for sixteen men and sixteen women, and the ward had a wide south-facing veranda. There were also special examination rooms and ultra-violet treatment facilities. Various other amenities were later provided by generous benefactors and it was to continue in use for over 50 years, having been known since 1902 as Newhills Convalescent Home and Sanatorium.[16]

The City Hospital and TB in Aberdeen

Voluntary notification of pulmonary tuberculosis was introduced in Aberdeen in 1911 and that year, at Matthew Hay's instigation, one pavilion at the City Hospital, specially reconstructed for the purpose, was set aside for the admission of patients with pulmonary tuberculosis. The pavilion, which accommodated 48 cases, was connected with two shelters, built to a lean-to-model designed by Hay and providing accommodation for an additional 22 cases. These shelters, designed by Hay himself on a lean-to model, exhibited a number of novel features such as folding and removable screens enclosing the front of the shelters. Including cost of shower baths (hot and cold), sanitary conveniences, dressing rooms and electric lighting, but exclusive of beds and bedding, the shelters were erected at the small cost of about £24 per bed. They proved very useful and comfortable, and were preferred by the patients to the pavilion beds.[17] Two years later, as described in Chapter 5, the TB dispensary or Institute, was opened at the edge of the hospital grounds for the management of out-patients from the city, and an extra medical officer was appointed to supervise this work. Dr George S. Banks was made assistant medical officer and tuberculosis medical officer.[18]

In 1914 the Town Council had also come to an agreement with the Parish Council to provide 40–50 beds for the consumptive poor in specially adapted accommodation in one of the hospital blocks at Oldmill (now part of Woodend Hospital). When these beds were commandeered with the rest of Oldmill by the military authorities in 1915, all 46 tuberculous patients there had to be transferred to the City Hospital. A second pavilion at the City Hospital then had to be taken over for tuberculous cases, raising the total number of such beds to 103. Later the same year an additional nineteen beds were approved and created by erecting a balcony on one pavilion, and the next year, a further small extension raised the total number of beds assigned to tuberculous cases in the City Hospital to 125.[19]

The new accommodation opened at the City Hospital in 1911 for tuberculous patients was practically full within a month of its opening. Patients at all stages of the disease were admitted. It was hoped that the condition of those in the early and middle stages could be improved and progress of the disease arrested, while the more advanced cases were admitted chiefly to prevent the spread of infection. The number of cases of TB admitted to the City Hospital from 1911–23 is shown in Figure 17 and also the number of deaths there from this disease. Based on the known infectious nature of the condition, the objective of admission was to train sufferers in such precautions and modes of treatment which would, if pursued after they had returned home, not only assist in improving their own health but lessen the risk of spread of the disease in their homes and work-places.[20] The value of fresh air and good ventilation was emphasised and breathing exercises taught.

A trial of tuberculin treatment was also started. This had been introduced by Robert Koch using a preparation from tubercle bacilli. The technique had, however, quickly fallen into disrepute when it failed to fulfil expectations. Later study showed that the poor early results were due to inadequate knowledge of dosage and administration. The procedure had been reintroduced and encouraging results reported by some physicians, and it was on these grounds that Matthew Hay started his trial in 1911. The results, however, were disappointing and the treatment was largely abandoned in 1915.[21] Following the introduction of notification, all notified cases from 1913 were visited at home by an officer of the Public Health Department and for those not admitted to hospital or a sanatorium, arrangements were made for their isolation and care at home. A special health visitor was appointed and visited the patients fortnightly, and any contacts with suspicious symptoms were examined at the TB dispensary at the City Hospital, where out-patients were also seen.[22]

Figure 17 Tuberculosis
Cases admitted to City Hospital and deaths 1911–23

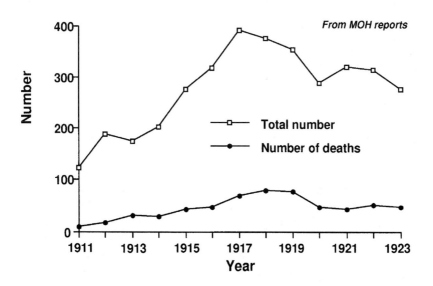

As shown in Figure 17, the number of annual admissions of TB cases rose to over 300 per year from 1916 as extra beds for such cases were made available. Of the 275 cases admitted in 1923, all but 46 had respiratory tuberculosis. From 1920, the number of deaths remained fairly steady at just under 50 cases a year.[23]

During and after World War I, there was an urgent demand for beds for officers invalided from the services due to tuberculosis. Dr David Lawson, the founder of Nordrach-on-Dee, was approached by the British Red Cross Society, and decided to open a new facility for this purpose at Tor-na-Dee Sanatorium. This had originally been built as the Murtle Hydropathic in 1899 and was popular and successful until World War I when it became under-utilised and was put on the market. Dr Lawson and a number of influential men with knowledge of the technical and economic aspects of sanatorium administration formed a private company and purchased the site and building. After extensive alterations, the institution, renamed the Tor-na-Dee Sanatorium, opened in 1918 with Dr Struthers Stewart as first medical superintendent. There were initially 56 beds and the British Red Cross Society had first call on them for the treatment of officers, but civilian patients were admitted as vacancies occurred. Because of demand, an additional wing containing sixteen beds and other extra facilities was built and opened in 1920. After the war, the Ministry of Pensions assumed responsibility for the treatment of officers invalided from the services for tuberculosis, but after a number of years the proportion of these declined, and it became a purely private institution for the treatment of both sexes suffering from pulmonary and other forms of the disease.[24]

VENEREAL DISEASES

Historical

Venereal diseases had been recognised since ancient times but progress and separation of the different conditions awaited the invention of the microscope. Gonorrhoea was described in Biblical times, while epidemics of syphilis swept Europe in the sixteenth century, probably following its introduction from the New World by Columbus's sailors. It was workers in Paris in the late nineteenth century who, on the basis of microbiological discoveries, first made the distinction between the different venereal diseases of the period. Augosto Ducrey (1860–1940) in Rome identified the micro-organism responsible for chancroid, and in Breslau, Albert Neisser (1855–1916) discovered the gonococcus responsible for gonorrhoea. Finally, in Hamburg, Fritz Schaudinn (1871–1946) discovered the spirochaete, *Treponema pallidum*, which causes syphilis.[25]

Venereology was slow to develop as an independent specialty, probably because of the lack of effective treatments, and the venereal diseases were initially regarded as the province of the dermatologist. This was probably related to the frequency of cutaneous manifestations of syphilis in both the early and late stages, and the fact that mercury, already widely used in dermatological practice, was found to be of some value. Indeed for many years this was the only treatment available.

VD Services in Aberdeen

Although British dermatology developed in the late eighteenth century, it was not until the beginning of the twentieth century that a special department was formed in Aberdeen. In January 1901, Dr John F. Christie (1870–1931), who had graduated in Aberdeen in medicine in 1895, was appointed lecturer in skin diseases at the Royal Infirmary. In March of that year, a special department for diseases of the skin was formed. In 1903 Dr Christie was re-styled assistant physician in charge of diseases of the skin, and also became responsible for cases of erysipelas in the Infirmary wards. He was also early involved in the care of patients with syphilis. In 1910 he was given the status of physician in charge of the department for diseases of the skin.[26]

The Venereal Diseases Regulations (Scotland) were introduced in 1916. These made it the duty of local authorities to formulate a scheme for the early diagnosis and treatment of venereal infections, and the government agreed to meet three-quarters of any expenditure involved. Following a report from Matthew Hay in June 1916, Aberdeen Town Council's Public Health Committee agreed in principle to initiate such a scheme,[27] but the service provided was to remain fragmented for many years.

After discussion, the work was largely contracted-out by the Council to the Royal Infirmary, and the service started in 1917. Dr Christie was appointed clinical officer in the scheme and in 1918 was made lecturer in venereal diseases. In 1920 he was made part-time chief officer of the VD department, with a whole-time junior officer assistant.[28] (See Appendix 6 for a full list of junior medical officers in the VD department.) Dr Christie initially used two rooms in the out-patient department of the Royal Infirmary at Woolmanhill but in 1921, new improved and larger accommodation in the same building was provided. Meanwhile the laboratory area at the City Hospital had, since 1917, been used as a treatment centre for cases of VD from Aberdeen which did not 'take advantage of the general clinic'.[29]

In the early years, syphilis does not seem to have been very prevalent in Aberdeen. According to Simpson, in the ten-year period 1871–80 there were only 95 cases, 45 of which occurred in 1880.[30] No record of the number of cases was then kept until after the diseases were made notifiable in 1916. Table 1 shows the total number of new cases dealt with and the numbers of cases of syphilis and gonorrhoea at the two treatment centres in Aberdeen for the years 1919–23.

TABLE 1: New cases of VD dealt with at Treatment Centres in Aberdeen 1919–23

Year	Total	Syphilis	Gonorrhoea
1919	621	354	267
1920	737	439	298
1921	572	309	263
1922	491	285	206
1923	469	256	213

The number of cases per 1,000 population was about half those being seen in Glasgow, Edinburgh or Dundee. The MOH felt this was due to the inadequacy of the premises available for this service and considered there was an urgent need for new institutional accommodation for venereal diseases for both in-patients and out-patients.[31] During the same period a total of 458 new cases, which was about a sixth of the total number, were seen at the City Hospital Sub-Centre and 95 cases admitted. The impression is created that less interest was taken in these diseases than in the other zymotics, and this may account in part for the fragmented service then available. It was to be several years before this was rationalised and centralised.

References to Chapter Seven
[1]   J. C. Sourma, *The Illustrated History of Medicine*, London, Starke, 1992, p. 15.
[2]   John Bunyan, *Life and Death of Mr Badman*, Oxford, Clarendon, 1988.

3   P. Pringle, *The Romance of Medical Science*, London, Harrap, 1948, pp. 92–6.

4   W. W. C. Topley and G. S Wilson, *The Principles of Bacteriology and Immunity*, London, Arnold, 1929, pp. 822–9.

5   Pringle, op. cit., pp. 186–9.

6   W. J. Simpson, *Health History of Aberdeen During the Past Quarter of a Century*, Aberdeen, 1883, p. 10.

7   Ibid., pp. 15–17.

8   Report by the Medical Officer of Health for the quarter year ending 31 March 1889, p. 6.

9   'Tubercular Disease: Suggestions for its Prevention and Control', bound with the Annual Report of the Medical Officer of Health for 1899, p. 13.

10 Topley and Wilson, op. cit., pp. 822–9.

11 Thomas Dormandy, *The White Death – The History of Tuberculosis*, London and Rio Grande, Hambledon, 1999, pp. 206–7.

12 Sourma, op. cit., p. 426.

13 Topley and Wilson, op. cit., pp. 822–9.

14 Obituary, David Lawson, *British Medical Journal*, 1952, vol 2, pp. 1423–4.

15 G. Lucas, 'Nordrach-on-Dee Sanatorium, Banchory' in J. Scott Riddell (ed.), *BMA Aberdeen 1914. Handbook and Guide to Aberdeen*, Cheltenham, Burrow, 1914, pp. 75–8.

16 E. Oliphant, 'Newhills Convalescent Home and Sanatorium' in D. Rorie (ed.), *The Book of Aberdeen*, Aberdeen, Lindsay, 1939, pp. 94–8.

17 M. Hay, 'The City Hospital' in Riddell, op. cit., pp. 52–7.

18 Annual Report of the Medical Officer of Health for 1913, pp. 44–5, 51.

19 Report of the Medical Office of Health for the years 1916–21, p. 138.

20 Annual Report of the Medical Officer of Health for 1910, pp. 64–9.

21 Annual Report of the Medical Officer of Health for 1914, pp. 101–5.

22 Annual Report of the Medical Officer of Health for 1913, p. 45.

23 Annual Reports of the Medical Officer of Health, 1911–23.

24 J. M. Johnston, 'Tor-na-Dee Sanatorium' in Rorie, op. cit., pp. 92–3.

25 Sourma, op. cit., p. 411.

26 T. E. Anderson, 'The Development of Dermatology in Aberdeen', *Aberdeen Postgraduate Medical Bulletin*, September 1973, pp. 38–42.

27 Town Council minutes, 19 June 1916.

28 Anderson, op. cit., p. 39.

29 Report of the Medical Officer of Health for the years 1916–21, p. 155.

30 Aberdeen Local Authority Public Health, *Report and Tables by the Medical Officer of Health*, Aberdeen, Cornwall, 1881.

---

[31]   Aberdeen Medico-Chirurgical Society: 'City of Aberdeen. Health Services Report by the Medical Officer of Health', 6 October 1924, in J. Parlane Kinloch, *Research Papers and Reports*, 1914–28.

Chapter Eight

Dr J. Parlane Kinloch's Tenure as MOH 1923–29: Years of Advance and Strife

John Parlane Kinloch, who had been deputy MOH since 1914, became acting MOH during Matthew Hay's leave of absence over the winter of 1922–3, and after Hay's retirement in May 1923 he was appointed MOH.[1]

Parlane Kinloch has been described as a man of ideas, foresight, great organising ability, energy and determination and also a brilliant and exciting lecturer.[2] He was, however, obsessed with the need to reorganise and extend the local authority health services. During his term of office he achieved major extensions to the City Hospital and radical re-organisation of the municipal hospitals, but in the process he had to oppose the supporters of the voluntary hospital system, and by his actions, Matthew Hay's dream of a Joint Hospital Scheme nearly foundered.[3]

Born near Dumbarton in 1886, Parlane Kinloch was educated at Glasgow High School and qualified in medicine at Glasgow University in 1909. After house officer posts at the Victoria Infirmary, Glasgow, he decided to devote himself to public health, and in 1910 obtained the Cambridge DPH with distinction. He was then, for a short period, a pupil-assistant in the Glasgow Public Health Department until in 1911 he became resident medical officer at Ruchill Fever Hospital where he gained extensive clinical experience in infectious diseases. He obtained his MD with commendation in 1913.[4]

In 1914 he was appointed deputy MOH in Aberdeen and lecturer in public health at Aberdeen University. On his arrival in Aberdeen he joined the RAMC Territorial Forces as a captain, and commanded the Aberdeen University Training Corps. As mentioned in a previous chapter, because of staff shortages at the City Hospital during the war, he had in 1915 to take on the posts of senior resident physician and tuberculosis officer until 1918, when he himself was sent to France in command of a mobile hygiene laboratory. On return from the war, he resumed his public health duties and had to act for a period as visiting physician at the City Hospital. In 1920, with the opening of extended laboratory facilities there, he was initially put in supervisory charge, although this arrangement was terminated in December 1921 when Dr John Smith was placed in charge of the laboratory services. Several months after Kinloch's appointment as MOH he was also confirmed as physician superintendent at the City Hospital. His salary was £850 per annum. Soon after his taking office, new larger improved x-ray apparatus was purchased for £623. Other minor alterations took place and further ground to the south of the hospital was purchased to allow of future expansion.[5]

In early 1924, the Scottish Board of Health withdrew restrictions on grant-aided public health services and the Town Council asked the MOH to prepare a report on all 'the special health services of the city with respect to the urgency of their varying needs and the necessity for their development'.[6] He submitted his report, which was dated 6 October and covered fourteen pages.

Development Plans

Dr Kinloch noted that at that time the Town Council's health institutions were concentrated on the site at the City Hospital in Urquhart Road and formed an ideal nucleus for future development. There were then the fever wards with accommodation for 150 beds, the tuberculosis wards with 125 beds, the children's ward for wasting infants with twenty beds and the skin and cleansing department with twelve beds. There were also the TB dispensary and x-ray department, the VD sub-centre for out-patients, and the bacteriological and chemical laboratories. The nurses' home had accommodation for 50 nurses and fifteen maids, with four temporary annexes throughout the grounds providing supplementary accommodation. The site then embraced ten acres, of which two were available for building extensions. He also noted that there was a considerable acreage of ground on the other side of Urquhart Road which could be acquired by the Town Council and made available for a comprehensive scheme of City Hospital extensions. In this section dealing with the present state of the municipal services, he also recorded that the venereal diseases service of the Town Council was provided mainly at the Royal Infirmary, the work having been contracted out to the Infirmary.

His next section dealt with requirements and possible future developments. As an introduction he noted that in the previous twelve years various statutory enactments and regulations had extended the responsibility of the Council from general conditions of health and 'fevers' to the provision of comprehensive health services in relation to tuberculosis, venereal diseases, maternity and child welfare and welfare of blind persons. Because of restrictions in building during the war and the immediate post-war years, no additional institutional accommodation could be provided, and space for these new services had had to be found in the City Hospital in the buildings originally provided for the isolation and treatment of fever cases. Thus the 125 beds there then devoted to TB cases had been made available by taking over and extending two wards originally intended for infective diseases. Similarly the twenty beds used for marasmic infants was in accommodation originally provided for fevers. This concentration of additional diseases had led to a considerable augmentation of the nursing and domestic staff for whom the accommodation was inadequate and unsatisfactory.

Dr Kinloch felt that extensive and costly additions were essential to maintain the required standard. In order of urgency, he set these forth as follows.

1. *Nurses' Home Extension*: An extension of the nurses' home to the extent of 120 beds was, he felt, required to provide accommodation for those staff at present inadequately housed and to meet the demands of the additional staff who would be required for additional wards. New kitchens and teaching accommodation for nurses were also needed.

2. *Resident Medical Staff*: A new residence was required.

3. *Venereal Diseases*: He said the Town Council were aware that accommodation provided for the treatment of VD at the Infirmary was inadequate and the amount of work done there compared unfavourably with that in Glasgow, Edinburgh and Dundee. In none of these other centres had the work been contracted out to anything like the same degree to which it had been done in Aberdeen. He did not blame the staff working in this field in Aberdeen for the disappointing results, but firmly believed that the atmosphere and environment of a general hospital out-patient department was inimical to successful results by failing to attract cases. He believed the best results would be achieved by new buildings for both in-patient and out-patient treatment of cases 'homogenous with the institutional provision of the health services of the city' (presumably this rather obtuse phrasing meant at the City Hospital). He stated the need for 30 beds and an out-patient department.

4. *Tuberculosis*: He noted that the Town Council had never made any claim for capital expenditure for provision of facilities for TB, having utilised two of the wards at the City Hospital originally designed for fevers. It was Dr Kinloch's view that these wards should, come time, revert to their original fever use, and he felt it was necessary to provide a total of 200 beds

for tuberculosis cases. If regarded as a new provision these would qualify for full capital and maintenance grants.

5. *Fevers*: The encroachment on the fever beds by the requirements of beds for tuberculosis and marasmic infants had made the number of fever beds quite inadequate. Furthermore, new instructions from the Scottish Board of Health required the Town Council to provide accommodation for cases of measles and whooping cough. The two wards freed by the provision of new accommodation for tuberculosis would make adequate provision for these cases. He also noted that additional infectious diseases, including poliomyelitis, epidemic encephalitis, the dysenteries, primary and influenzal pneumonias and ophthalmia neonatorum, had been made compulsorily notifiable so that it was now the responsibility of the local authority to make provision for the isolation and treatment of such cases. There was currently no adequate accommodation for cases of 'mixed infection'. A new cubicle isolation ward of 30 beds was, he felt, needed.

Sections 6 and 7 dealt with maternity and child welfare and welfare of blind persons and as neither of these directly impinged on the City Hospital they are not further considered here.

8. *Municipal Laboratories*: The laboratories were then situated on the upper floor of the Tuberculosis Institute, and space was quite inadequate and was required there for other purposes. The laboratory was now responsible for all the bacteriological work of the City and North-Eastern region and in 1923, a whole-time chemist and city analyst had been appointed and had had to be accommodated within the existing laboratories. A new greatly-extended municipal laboratory should be built.

9. A new administrative headquarters for the Public Health Department was also needed.

The estimated capital expenditure to provide the suggested requests and developments was £227,000 in total, of which £140,000 was required for the proposed developments and new buildings on the City Hospital site.

Dr Kinloch then described other local authorities exercising health functions, and of future relevance noted that the Aberdeen Parish Council was responsible for medical relief of the poor. The Parish Council provided their service at Oldmill, which had opened on 15 May 1907. It consisted of two main parts – the poorhouse and the hospital section for the treatment of the sick, comprising a 'general' hospital block and a detached 'special' hospital. There was a total of 900 beds. During World War I, the whole complex was evacuated and used entirely as a military hospital.[7] The Parish

Council had resumed occupation in 1919 but the 'special' hospital with some 180 beds lay empty. Dr Kinloch noted that the Town Council might become responsible for the poor law medical services, in which case they would be left with more than 400 unoccupied beds. At this time he suggested these might be occupied by chronic or convalescent cases.

His report then briefly discussed the voluntary medical institutions and the university medical school. He recorded that the Sick Children's Hospital was wholly inadequate and that the directors had funds available to move immediately. The Royal Infirmary also required considerable extension but money was meantime not available. A new maternity hospital was also urgently required. He then proceeded to give detailed consideration to the Joint Hospital Scheme as promulgated by Professors Matthew Hay and Ashley Mackintosh. Dr Kinloch agreed that a concentration of the hospitals on a common site would be 'incalculable in the interest of patients, as well as in the training of medical students and nurses'. Transfer of the clinical departments of the university from Marischal College to the site would also be 'of inestimable advantage to the clinical work of the hospital, to medical education and to the scientific investigation of disease'. The authorities involved in the scheme were the directors of the Sick Children's Hospital, the directors of the Royal Infirmary, the University Court, and the Town Council. All had approved generally of the scheme. The Foresterhill site had been approved and the Town Council was in a position to dispose of the land to the various participating bodies. Dr Kinloch noted that one of the original proposals was for the Town Council to erect a tuberculosis hospital and sanatorium of 200 beds on this site, thus liberating the TB wards of the City Hospital for ordinary fever cases. With further consideration, however, he felt that there were fatal objections to this proposed disruption of the medical institutions of the Town Council, and believed that their concentration at the City Hospital was the more ideal arrangement. He also mentioned an alternative proposition whereby the Town Council might decide to transfer all of Aberdeen's municipal health institutions to the Joint Hospital site, but estimated this would involve capital expenditure of about half a million pounds and so seemed impractical.

There then followed a lengthy section discussing the inter-relationship of the participating bodies in the scheme and he recommended that no quick decision be reached. Detailed discussions were required with all the other participating bodies before the practicalities and financial commitments involved could be determined.[8]

The preparation of this detailed report for the Town Council must have taken much time and effort and doubtless had been through many drafts before reaching its final form. It has been cited here at considerable length because it so clearly reveals Dr Kinloch's views at this time. It records the many proposed changes at the City Hospital and reveals his dominant concerns with the municipal services, he taking a much narrower view of matters than his predecessor. Many of his statements, however, reveal his foresight. Thus, when discussing the Joint Hospital Scheme, he said he was not greatly impressed with some of the arguments in favour of the scheme, such as the advantages of having common services and equipment, common staff accommodation and common departments of special medical requirements such as x-rays and clinical laboratories. He believed that there were strict limitations in size within which any hospital unit could function efficiently and stated this as being within the range of 400–800 beds. Within this limit, hospital management, he said, 'can be vital and can adequately measure and supply hospital requirements. Beyond these limits of size, the hospital unit is uneconomical and uncoordinated in function, or economy being imposed, it becomes a dull unwieldy machine'. Many who have worked at Foresterhill during the past 40 years of steady further expansion would agree!

In the section on the university medical school and its relation to the laboratory services he said it was his opinion that:

> … it would be prejudicial to the best interests of both the medical school and the hospitals for the university laboratories to absorb the work of the municipal laboratories. Any such arrangement would interfere with the essential teaching and research work of the academic staff and would subject the laboratory requirements of the health services to the influence of professional needs or caprice.[9]

Prophetic words indeed!

Years of lengthy discussion were to take place before final agreement on the different proposals was reached and in the process, there were to be major clashes of personality and much ill-will generated. Kinloch's views about the Joint Hospital Scheme hardened over the next few years because of several developments.

Following a series of discussions between the Parish and Town Councils, it was agreed that the Town Council would take over the running of the hospital blocks at Oldmill. This was approved by the Scottish Board of Health and arrangements were completed in May 1927. The hospital was formally opened by the Secretary of State for Scotland on 14 November

1927, the Town Council having earlier agreed to change its name from Oldmill Hospital to Woodend Hospital.[10]

Dr Kinloch was made physician superintendent. The Town Council also retained the services of the previous physician at Oldmill, Dr George Williamson, and in addition appointed him visiting physician at the City Hospital. Dr Harry Rae, who was then MOH for Aberdeen county, was also made a visiting physician to both hospitals. There were three resident medical officers of different grades and it was stipulated that only males should be resident medical officers. Dr Elizabeth Innes, who was then in post, had her contract summarily terminated and compensation was paid![11] The opening of Woodend Hospital also led to a number of changes affecting the senior nursing staff, both there and at the City Hospital. Miss Shirras, who had been nurse superintendent at Oldmill Hospital, was made matron of Woodend Hospital.[12] The following year, Miss Margaret Frater, who had been matron at the City Hospital since 1896, became supervising matron of both the City and Woodend Hospitals, and Miss Margaret D. Frater, assistant matron at the City, was made matron of that hospital.[13] (See Appendix 2 for a list of City Hospital matrons.)

Dr Kinloch stated that 'this unification of the statutory hospital services in Aberdeen was an exhibition of statesmanship which would serve as an inspiration and example to the rest of the country and would pass into the historical record'. He gave a detailed report on the reform of the hospital services in Aberdeen in his annual report for 1927.[14] He felt there was a need for increasing co-operation between the statutory hospitals and voluntary hospitals and believed that in future, to have an efficient hospital organisation in Scotland, it should be based on a regional basis grouped around the four medical schools of Scotland. These ideals were not to be achieved until the introduction of the National Health Service in 1948.

Because of new regulations which had come into being, Dr Kinloch intended providing considerable facilities in Woodend for non-pulmonary tuberculosis which were not previously available. He also indicated his intention to admit all cases of pneumonia, poliomyelitis, venereal diseases and some other diseases needing hospital treatment. He was in effect proposing the creation at Woodend of a municipal general hospital working in competition with the Royal Infirmary. This proposal caused outrage to both the managers of the Royal Infirmary and the university authorities who foresaw the removal of a large wedge of clinical practice and some of the best teaching material. Legal counsel was sought and the Scottish Board of Health intervened saying there must be collaboration between the different bodies before final agreement to these plans could be given.[15] As an initial token gesture, John Marnoch, the professor of surgery, was made consulting surgeon to the hospital,[16] but it was to be 1935 before the charge of beds was given over to the three senior physicians at the Infirmary – Professor Stanley Davidson, Dr A. G. Anderson and Dr John A. Innes, working in a consultative capacity, while the day-to-day work would be done by their assistants – Dr Ian Hill (later Sir Ian Hill, professor of medicine at Dundee), Dr T. N. Morgan and Dr R. J. Duthie.[17]

City Hospital Extensions

During the mid 1920s, the accommodation at the City Hospital was under great pressure. Because of the expansion of the service for tuberculosis as described in Chapter 7, only three wards remained available for the treatment of zymotic diseases, apart from the reception block, the main ward of which was allocated to the treatment of marasmic children, under the mother and child welfare scheme. The fluctuating prevalence of the common zymotics led to repeated overcrowding of these fever wards and over the years, the number of different diseases requiring treatment there had been greatly augmented. In 1922 the Scottish Board of Health had instructed that additional accommodation had to be made for measles and whooping cough. If new accommodation could be provided for tuberculous cases, the wards freed would meet this need. There was also a great requirement for a cubicle isolation ward for the segregation of cases of mixed infection. Dr Kinloch repeatedly stressed the need for this extra accommodation, but it was not until 1926 that the Town Council reached a final decision. Even then, because of financial constraints, the extensions approved were less than those originally asked for in 1924. It was agreed that a new nurses' home, a new kitchen, one 60-bed and two 40-bed wards plus a ward and centre for treatment of venereal diseases would go ahead, although this last proposal was later to drop out. The original design for one of the 40-bed wards had also been changed from a pavilion type to a cubicle isolation ward with twenty compartments each containing two beds. It was to be 1928 before the relevant tenders were agreed and on 28 June of that year, the Lady Provost cut the first turf on the site of the proposed extensions. The new nurses' home was formally opened in 1931.[18]

During the intervening years there were a number of additional less costly developments. New balconies were constructed for some of the fever wards and the ward for marasmic infants in 1925, a teacher was engaged for the education of children in the tuberculosis wards, and ultra-violet light apparatus was installed in 1926,[19] ultra-violet light therapy often being used then as an adjunct in the treatment of tuberculosis.

The Joint Hospital Scheme

The years 1923–7 have been described as the years of threat, strife and confrontation for this far-reaching scheme.[20] The taking over of Oldmill Hospital by the municipal authorities and its opening as Woodend Hospital had, as mentioned, led to considerable conflict between the MOH and the directors of the Royal Infirmary and the university authorities. Kinloch's policies and methods aroused bitter hostility and posed a considerable threat to the voluntary hospitals and medical teaching and to the future of the scheme. Medicine at this time was in an era of great change. Major advances had been made. Insulin had been discovered, liver extract treatment for pernicious anaemia introduced and radiological, bacteriological and biochemical investigations had become more elaborate and important. These activities all created the need for more equipment, more accommodation and more staff. This all needed money. At this time, most of the senior doctors working in the voluntary hospitals received no remuneration for their services. They were dependent on private practice for their livelihood, and it was feared that there would not be enough of this to support more honorary staff. Furthermore, the Infirmary directors were at this time unwilling to spend money on extensions to the Infirmary until a final decision on the proposed move to Foresterhill had been reached. Kinloch's actions and his constant statements in reports in subsequent years that there were not enough funds available to support all the medical projects desirable, led the Town Council to delay taking any action or agreeing to provide financial support to the Infirmary for the proposed move. The stalemate was broken by two separate developments.

The Turn of the Tide – 1926–7 [21]

The directors of the Sick Children's Hospital, who already had money available to fund a move, became impatient at the constant delay, and in 1925 decided to go ahead on their own. They purchased the land at Foresterhill which had been allocated for them and began building their new hospital on the pavilion system, as originally planned pre-war. They had the foresight, when building the laundry, steam and other services, to allow of expansion 'if and when' the Joint Hospital Scheme materialised.[22]

The second relevant factor was the election in 1925 of Andrew Lewis as Lord Provost and *ex officio* Chairman of the Corporation of the Aberdeen Royal Infirmary and Asylum. In 1926, at the request of the Infirmary Board, he convened a meeting of all interested bodies – representatives of the University Court, the voluntary hospitals, the City Hospital, the Medico-Chirurgical Society, and the Health Insurance Societies who contributed annually to the Infirmary – to discuss the hospital policy of the Town Council and the overall problem of hospital accommodation. Several previous similar meetings had either not materialised or had failed, but this meeting was productive. Compromise and agreements were reached, and a consultative committee was set up to consider the whole question. It was then decided that a new maternity hospital should be included in the scheme, and when in 1927, Lord Provost Lewis announced that he had personally obtained pledges of financial support to the scheme of close on £130,000 from a number of generous local donors, 'the scheme was set alight', and progress thereafter rapid.[23] The first sod was cut on 19 June 1930, and the Infirmary buildings were completed in 1936. There were several changes made in the final planning phases. It was decided to leave the casualty and out-patient departments at Woolmanhill. The nurses' home, which had earlier been dropped from the scheme because of financial constraints, was brought back in when it was decided, as will be discussed later, not to build the proposed tuberculosis hospital. The medical school buildings were opened by Lord Dawson of Penn in 1938.[24] Contrary to Dr Kinloch's earlier advice, the university took over the laboratory services previously run by the Infirmary, but in the interim, the local authority had expanded the laboratory services at the City Hospital, under the direction of Dr John Smith and they now provided a comprehensive service including pathology, haematology and bacteriology. They operated an 'open door' service not only to the doctors of the city but to the whole North-East, including Orkney and Shetland.

The building of a tuberculosis hospital of 150–200 beds had been an important part of the original Joint Hospital Scheme and remained a theoretical concept for several years. As mentioned earlier, Dr Kinloch in 1924 proposed an alternative scheme whereby a large number of additional beds for this purpose would be built on new ground at the City Hospital, on the other side of Urquhart Road. The subsequent development of Woodend Hospital, following its acquisition by the Town Council, with the availability of large numbers of additional beds, rendered both the earlier proposals obsolete and both plans were dropped.

The exact siting of a new adequate service for the diagnosis and treatment of venereal diseases was a further source of conflict between the Town Council, represented by the MOH, and the directors of the Infirmary, and it was to be many years before a final agreement was reached. In his 1924 report Dr Kinloch had recommended building a centre and ward at the City Hospital. Later, following the opening of Woodend, he proposed admitting VD patients requiring hospital treatment to that institution. This move caused dismay to the Royal Infirmary, but after lengthy discussion was eventually agreed to, and approved by the Department of Health for Scotland in 1929.[25] Earlier, when the extensive but reduced alterations at the City Hospital were approved, the proposal to build a new VD centre and ward there had been dropped because of financial constraints. Later, when the Joint Hospital Scheme was finally underway, it was alternatively suggested that a new centre should be built at Foresterhill. This plan was, however, rejected by the Department of Health for Scotland, who would not approve major capital expenditure in this field. They also requested that the facility be located centrally in the city. About half the patients attending at this time came from outwith the city and access for those travelling in by bus or train would be much easier. It was finally agreed in 1930 to make alterations in the out-patient block at Woolmanhill for this service to be accommodated.[26]

Parlane Kinloch's Other Contributions

Dr Kinloch is probably unfortunately best remembered locally because of his bitter, continued, unfettered opposition to the Joint Hospital Scheme. What his predecessor had conceived, the successor almost destroyed.[27] It must be remembered, however, that as Medical Officer of Health, he was employed by the Town Council and so his prime responsibilities were to the medical projects and services provided by the local authority. As has been recorded, he made major contributions in this regard, but the manner in which he pursued these ends made him intensely unpopular with many in the Royal Infirmary and the University.

He made other notable contributions in the field of public health in Aberdeen[28] and published work on the best methods of destroying lice and other body vermin and on the 1919 Aberdeen epidemic of milk-borne bacillary dysentery.[29] He collaborated with others in articles on epidemic enteritis in Aberdeen due to food infections,[30] paratyphoid fever[31] and Sonne dysentery[32] and also did original work in the field of immunity and diphtheria, measles and scarlet fever. It was on his initiative that there was an active campaign in 1925 to increase the utilisation of methods then

available using injections of diphtheria toxin/antitoxin combined with
scarlatinal streptococcus toxin to protect against these diseases.[33] With his
assistant, J. A. Stephen, and his bacteriological colleague, John Smith, he
also published an important paper on maternal mortality in Aberdeen in
1918–27, with special reference to puerperal sepsis. Major advances in this
field were to be made in Aberdeen by John Smith.[34]

In 1928 Dr Parlane Kinloch was appointed Chief Medical Officer
to the Department of Health in Edinburgh and resigned from his post as
MOH on 12 November 1928. He demitted office on 18 April 1929.[35] He
died suddenly at his father's residence at Dumbarton on 31 January 1932.[36]

Dr Banks, deputy MOH and tuberculosis medical officer, was made
interim MOH on Dr Kinloch's departure until the appointment of Dr Harry
Rae as MOH on 17 June 1929. He accepted the post later that month and in
September was also appointed lecturer and head of the department of public
health at the university.[37]

References to Chapter Eight

[1] Aberdeen Central Library, Town Council Minutes (hereafter TCM), 7 January
1924.

[2] N. J. Logie, 'History of the Aberdeen Joint Hospital Scheme and Site' in G. P.
Milne (ed.), *Aberdeen Medico-Chirurgical Society – A Bicentennial History
1789–1989*, Aberdeen, Aberdeen University Press, 1989, pp. 155–78.

[3] Ibid.

[4] Obituary, John Parlane Kinloch, *British Medical Journal*, 1932, vol. 2, pp. 311–3.

[5] TCM, 7 January 1924.

[6] Aberdeen Medico-Chirurgical Society: 'City of Aberdeen. Health Services
Report by the Medical Officer of Health', 6 October 1924, in J. Parlane Kinloch,
Research Papers and Reports, 1914–28.

[7] Ibid., p. 8.

[8] Ibid., pp. 10–14.

[9] Ibid., p. 10.

[10] TCM, 16 May 1927.

[11] Ibid.

[12] Ibid.

[13] TCM, 15 October 1928.

[14] Annual Report of the Medical Officer of Health for 1927, pp. 1–26.

[15] Logie, op. cit., p. 168.

[16] TCM, 16 May 1927.

17   TCM, 15 May 1935.
18   TCM, 15 June 1931.
19   TCM, 1 March 1926.
20   Logie, op. cit., pp. 166–70.
21   Ibid., pp. 170–1.
22   Ibid., p. 172.
23   Ibid., p. 173.
24   Ibid., p. 176.
25   TCM, 16 December 1929.
26   TCM, 18 May 1930.
27   Logie, op. cit., p. 167.
28   Kinloch, *Research Papers and Reports*, op. cit.
29   J. Parlane Kinloch, 'An Investigation of the Best Methods of Discharging Lice and Other Body Vermin', *British Medical Journal*, 1915, vol. 2, pp. 1–11; J. Parlane Kinloch, 'The Aberdeen Epidemic of Milk Borne Bacillary Dysentery, March to May 1919', *Journal of Hygiene*, 1923, vol. 21, pp. 451–57.
30   J. S. Anderson, J. Parlane Kinloch, J. Smith, 'Epidemic Enteritis in Aberdeen Due to Food Infections', *Journal of Hygiene*, 1923, vol. 22, pp. 89–99.
31   F. J. T. Bowie, J. Parlane Kinloch, J. Smith, 'Paratyphoid Fever and *Aertrycke* Enteritis in Aberdeen – A Contrast', *Journal of Hygiene*, 1926, vol. 25, pp. 444–52.
32   A. M. Fraser, J. Parlane Kinloch, J. Smith, 'Sonne Dysentery in Aberdeen', *Journal of Hygiene*, 1926, vol. 25, pp. 453–60.
33   TCM, 19 October 1925.
34   G. P. Milne, 'The History of Midwifery in Aberdeen' in Milne op. cit., pp. 222–40.
35   TCM, 18 March 1929.
36   Obituary, John Parlane Kinloch, op. cit., p. 311.
37   TCM, 16 September 1929.

Chapter Nine

The City Hospital 1929–48: Years of Administrative Change

This period was to be dominated by the effects of new legislation. Firstly, the Local Government (Scotland) Act of 1929 led to major alterations in local health administration, and then the National Health Service (Scotland) Act of 1947 was to alter radically both the administration and the staffing of the hospital. The successful transition which these changes involved was in large part due to the untiring efforts of Aberdeen's next MOH, Dr Harry J. Rae.

Harry James Rae (1886–1955) MOH 1929–52

He was born in Aberdeen on 30 January 1886 and received both his scholastic and university education locally. He obtained his MA in 1907 and graduated in medicine with honours in 1911. After holding various hospital appointments, he took the DPH in 1914 and was appointed to a vacancy in the recently-established school medical service of the County of Aberdeen.[1] The public health services for the town and county were then quite separate. In 1915 he became chief tuberculosis officer for the county, but soon afterwards joined the RAMC and served with a field ambulance unit in the Middle East. He was awarded the MC during his war service. On demobilisation, he returned to his duties of tuberculosis officer until, in 1925, he became Medical Officer of Health for the county. He established good friendly relations with Parlane Kinloch in the city and, in advance of legislation, a partnership was formed with the object of avoiding redundancy and reduplication in all health service projects.[2] When Woodend Hospital opened in 1927, facilities there were made available to patients from both town and county and, as mentioned in the previous chapter, Dr Rae was appointed a visiting physician both there and at the City Hospital.

The Local Government (Scotland) Act 1929[3]

This Act transferred certain of the functions of existing local authorities to town and county councils. Matters relating to poor relief, lunacy, mental deficiency and public health were affected, and it was recommended that MOH posts of town and county be amalgamated as vacancies arose. Harry Rae was appointed MOH to the city in 1929, following J. Parlane Kinloch's resignation the previous year. He was at the same time made head of the public health department of Aberdeen University.

In 1930, after considerable negotiation, the Town Council of Aberdeen and Aberdeen County Council decided to form a Regional Medical Services Scheme on a partnership basis[4] and Rae was maintained in office to serve both organisations. Shortly afterwards, when the MOH for Kincardine retired, the County Council of Kincardine was also admitted to the combination. All the officials concerned in the discussions had supported the amalgamation, feeling it would be mutually advantageous to the combining authorities. The counties would benefit in that patients from their somewhat scattered areas would receive the most expert advice and treatment, the whole hospital and clinical resources of the Town Council being made available for their use. The city would benefit from the fact that the council's hospital beds would be kept full by the complement of county patients, and thus their institutional costs lessened. The unification of the public health service under one medical head would ensure uniformity of treatment and advice in the numerous statutory diseases for which local authorities were now responsible. The amalgamation would also, it was felt, be beneficial for the control of infectious diseases. With improved public transport, and for other reasons, people had become more mobile. More and more of the business of the agricultural area was now being transacted in the town for instance. The area embraced by the new regional medical unit had a population of approximately 300,000. This enlargement of the catchment area for the hospital was also to be of great advantage to the university medical school.[5] Dr Rae became the Chief Regional Medical Officer and although this produced a large workload, he having to write reports for and attend meetings of no less than three local authorities, due to his untiring efforts, the project proved successful. This pattern of arrangement was in fact to be followed by many health authorities in other parts of Scotland.[6]

New Developments at the City Hospital

Dr Rae became physician superintendent for the City Hospital just as the major extensions and expansion planned by his predecessor were coming into operation. It was to be June 1931 before the new nurses' home was formally opened.[7] This provided up-to-date accommodation capable of housing 100 nurses. Each nurse had a separate bedroom and there were spacious dining and recreation halls. The building also included accommodation for the resident medical staff.[8]

In the time that elapsed between planning and completion of the earlier extensions, it was acknowledged that further developments were required. More cubicle ward accommodation was needed and more laboratory space was also urgent.[9] It was also proposed that after the nursing accommodation in the administration block was freed by the opening of the new nurses' home, the block should be reconstructed. The out-patient services for tuberculosis and the radiological department moved there, and a new x-ray apparatus was purchased at a cost of £500.[10]

Aberdeen's Iron Lung

As mentioned in Chapter 6 and as will be recounted further in the next chapter, cases of poliomyelitis were regularly admitted. Some of these ended fatally, usually due to respiratory failure. This could be due to either paralysis of the intercostal muscles and diaphragm or damage to the respiratory centre in the brain stem in bulbar poliomyelitis. The latter form was particularly lethal. The first widely-used mechanical device capable of artificial respiration was the cabinet respirator invented by Philip Drinker of Harvard University in 1929.[11] It consisted of a metal tank, sealed at one end, in which the patient was placed with the head protruding from the other end and supported on a platform. An air-tight rubber diaphragm encircled the neck, and electrically-driven pumps controlled the pressure in the tank. When pressure was increased, the chest was compressed forcing air out of the lungs. Later, negative pressure was applied inducing inspiration. The speed of pressure changes could be varied, and by this means artificial ventilation could be performed for prolonged periods. Known as the Drinker Respirator in America, or more popularly as the 'iron lung', this apparatus quickly proved its worth and saved many lives.[12] Dr Robert Henderson (1902–99), senior resident medical officer in the City Hospital, saw this machine in use when on a visit to the USA in 1932 and took full details of its construction and function. On his return he collaborated with Mr John Mitchell (1876–1954), who was the City Hospital engineer, to construct one of their own. They made this in secret in the hospital workshop, using materials purchased from local engineering firms, with portholes and special plated screws obtained from a ship chandlers, and the cabinet constructed was mounted on the base of a hospital children's cot.[13] Four weeks after its completion, it proved its worth. A ten-year-old boy from New Deer was admitted to the City Hospital with acute poliomyelitis on 1 August 1933. He was febrile, though not unduly toxic, and had flaccid weakness of both legs and both upper arms and shoulders. Little movement of the chest wall was visible, although his abdominal muscles were moving well. By the next day, however, he had deteriorated and was paralysed from the neck down. Breathing had become difficult and ineffective, and at 2pm on 2 August he was placed in the artificial respirator, with immediate dramatic effect. He was kept alive for 28 days by this intervention and, although he had to spend nearly a year in hospital, he went on to make a good recovery although left with considerable muscle wasting and weakness.

Inevitably the local press heard of this case and on Saturday, 12 August the Aberdeen *Press and Journal* published a lead story under the heading 'Remarkable Feat at Aberdeen: Boy Kept Alive for Eleven Days: New Artificial Respirator'. Full details of the patient were given and tribute paid to Dr Henderson's and Mr Mitchell's work in constructing the apparatus, together with a description of the design and method of use and a photograph of it with the patient and a nurse. Dr Rae was apparently much annoyed at this unsolicited publicity and reprimanded Dr Henderson and Mr Mitchell for having secretly made the machine and making unauthorised use of hospital materials and facilities! He also forbade the provision of further details or photographs to the press. Dr Henderson had been anxious to publish details of the case but felt inhibited from doing so by Dr Rae's response. Dr Rae's actions in this case seem to have been uncharacteristically harsh and churlish. Sixty-four years later, however, an account of Henderson's innovative work was published.[14]

This iron lung, the first such in Scotland, gave sterling service for several years until 1938 when, through a munificent gift from Lord Nuffield, new machines were provided to all hospitals in Great Britain that wished one.

Medical Staffing at the City Hospital

Although Dr Rae, as MOH, was in nominal charge of the beds at the City Hospital, his increasing administrative and public health duties permitted only the occasional token visit. In practice, the day-to-day care of the patients was the responsibility of the senior resident medical officer, while tuberculous patients were under the charge of Dr Banks, the tuberculosis medical officer. Holders of the senior resident post from 1925–48 are shown in Appendix 5. The number of junior resident posts had been steadily increased to five in the 1930s. Holders of this post between 1925–45 are shown in Appendix 7.

Dr Robert Fraser, later to be senior chest physician, has given an interesting account of his days as junior resident at the City Hospital in 1935.[15] He and his fellow residents lived on the ground floor of the west wing of the new nurses' home where each bedroom had its own wash basin. There were two bathrooms and a sitting room with comfortable chairs and a coal fire. Newspapers were provided, shoes were cleaned and clothes were laundered and repaired as required free! A garage was provided for doctors' cars. For recreation there was table-tennis in an adjoining library, a piano and radio in the sitting room, a croquet set for use on the lawn, and outside a hard tennis court for use by both medical and nursing staff. Doubtless several romances started in these sporting arenas. Catering facilities were also good. Lunch was a formal occasion. Several members of the public health staff usually attended and all, with the residents, would gather in the sitting room just before one o'clock to await the arrival of Dr John Smith from the laboratory. He would often bring distinguished visitors, he by this time being a bacteriologist of international repute. On his arrival in the sitting room, the bell would be rung and, after a few minutes, the maid, having brought the soup to the table, would open the door to the dining room, and the gathering would troop in, in strict order of seniority, with Dr Smith in the van. The most junior resident would serve the soup unless there were visitors when Dr Bell, who was then senior resident medical officer, would do the honours. After coffee, on Dr Smith's command 'let's adjourn', all repaired to the sitting room until two o'clock before returning to work. All gathered at four o'clock for tea. Dr Smith again appeared but on this occasion rarely engaged in small talk and often read the newspaper. Dinner was served to the residents on their own around half past six and in these distant relaxed days, scrambled eggs on toast was usually produced by the night maid for the residents in night sister's office, after final checks on patients before going to bed.

Dr Fraser confirms that the senior resident medical officer was really in clinical charge of all patients in the hospital and virtually had the authority of a present-day consultant. Although Dr Banks, the tuberculosis medical officer, was responsible for the care of cases of tuberculosis, he was not greatly interested in treatment and left patient-care to Dr Bell. Dr Bell had the authority to seek help if required from any of the Royal Infirmary physicians or surgeons whose specialist fees would then be paid by the local authority. Dr George Williamson, an elderly physician who, as mentioned in Chapter 8, had been appointed visiting physician to both Woodend Hospital and the City Hospital, visited once a week. There were at this time 285 beds in the hospital and cases were distributed in the wards as follows:

Ward 1	Diphtheria
Ward 2	Clean cases of scarlet fever
Ward 3	Complicated cases of scarlet fever requiring surgical intervention, there being an operating theatre attached to this ward
Ward 4	Pulmonary tuberculosis
Ward 5	VD
Ward 6	Half cases of puerperal fever; half children with broncho-pneumonia
Ward 7	Ailing babies unit
Ward 8	This ward was a complex of small rooms with some 'out wards' for cases of dysentery. The ward area housed cases of erysipelas and other infections.

The beds were, however, used flexibly according to changing demands. Thus in early 1929 when there was a serious outbreak of diphtheria, one of the scarlet fever wards was used for diphtheria cases. In September 1930, an epidemic of measles occurred and a ward usually occupied by tuberculous patients was set aside for cases of measles accompanied by broncho-pneumonia or other complications requiring admission.[16]

The resident medical staff were not then assigned to any particular ward but were informed by Dr Bell, morning and afternoon, which wards he wished them to visit that day. All patients were examined in the ambulance before admission, to prevent cases of measles being admitted to the scarlet fever ward or vice versa to prevent cross infection. Dr Fraser recollects how one day Dr Bell had come into lunch rather late and in an aggrieved tone had asked 'which BF let that case of measles into Ward 2?' (the scarlet fever ward). It transpired that the ambulance driver had asked the first doctor who appeared to see the case and that it had been Dr John Smith!

The resident medical staff had no fixed off-duty time and the workload varied, being hectic at the time of epidemics. Dr Fraser remembers that at one time there were no fewer than 84 cases of diphtheria in the hospital. In addition to seeing all patients on admission and supervising their day-to-day care, residents would also be responsible for giving anaesthetics to patients requiring surgical treatment and for seeing out-patients with syphilis and gonorrhoea at the VD Centre. Residents also had to deputise for the MOH and visit ships in the harbour that had come directly to Aberdeen from foreign ports. This was not, however, a frequent occurrence and Dr Fraser only recollects having made three such trips in his eighteen months' tenure of the post, although it was a pleasant social interlude. The doctor involved was allowed to use his own car and draw petrol from the hospital petrol pump for the trip, and the captain of the ship visited would usually invite the caller for a drink!

Life for the residents then was not, however, all work and no play. Dr Bell would regularly take his junior residents out for meals and there were regular nursing staff functions which all attended. The medical and nursing staff of Woodend and the City Hospital also combined to hold an annual dance in the Beach Ballroom, and all male staff of the public health departments of Aberdeen and the counties held an annual dinner to which the resident doctors from Woodend and the City Hospital were also invited. These social events were also enlivened by John Smith who brought along a private roulette wheel![17]

Further Developments at the City Hospital

Although agreement in principle to the construction of a new cubicle block had been obtained from the Department of Health in 1931, it was 1938 before plans were submitted and discussed, and another year before the Department accepted these, with some alterations. It was to be early December 1940 before this new block was formally opened. It was a two-storey building, situated to the east of the nurses' home and close to the tennis courts. It provided 30 beds and included a small operating theatre which was to be put to diverse uses in the future. There were also other less major alterations. A wooden building, used as a schoolroom for children with tuberculosis, was no longer required and was demolished in 1936. The venereal diseases unit was reconstructed in 1938 and later, in 1941, a small brick pavilion was built adjacent to Ward 5 for the treatment of scabies and verminous children, the previously available area having become unsuitable.[18]

Yet another new development was the establishment of a preliminary training school for nurses at the City Hospital. This was first suggested in May 1937 by Dr Rae in a long memorandum submitted to the Public Health Committee. He thought this would aid recruitment of nurses for both the City Hospital and Woodend and suggested they could accept fifteen applicants every four months, which, allowing for wastage for various reasons, should provide them with about 30 nurses annually to fill vacancies. He felt this scheme would lead to an improvement in the type of nurse involved and during preliminary training they could be given intensive instruction in methods of protecting themselves against infection and in minimising the risk of conveyance of infection to others. There were no accommodation problems, as there was vacant accommodation in the administration block and space also for classrooms. They would require to appoint a sister tutor and provide her with board and lodgings, and also uniforms for her, and the pupil nurses. The estimated annual outlay required was £885.[19]

The scheme was approved and was soon underway. There were no problems attracting suitable entrants from the town and county, and later, applicants from Inverness were also admitted. The innovation proved successful and in 1939 the MOH was able to record that the shortage of nurses which had been complained of practically all over the country, had not become acute in Aberdeen's local authority hospitals.[20]

Rheumatic Diseases I

The provision of facilities for rheumatic diseases was to be a late development at the City Hospital and discussion on the subject was intermittent and prolonged.

Stanley Davidson (later Sir Stanley Davidson), who had been appointed regius professor of medicine in 1930, had an early interest in rheumatic diseases. He had appointed Dr J. J. R. Duthie, an Aberdeen graduate and native of Portsoy, as clinical assistant in his department in 1937, to have a special interest in this subject. The same year, Professor Davidson wrote to the local authority asking if the time was not now opportune for the council to consider the provision of special facilities for the diagnosis and treatment of rheumatic diseases. The new Justice Mill Lane baths were at this time under construction. It had already been decided to have facilities for thermal baths and some other measures there, and he wondered whether some area for rheumatic diseases could not be efficiently and economically included. His letter was considered at a meeting of the Public Health Committee on 19 April 1937 and a sub-committee, including the MOH, was set up to look further into the matter.[21]

The MOH reported in September the same year that he and some members of the sub-committee had visited London for discussions. At the British Red Cross Clinic they had seen Lord Horder and Dr W. S. C. Copeman, chairman and secretary respectively of the British Empire Executive Committee for Rheumatic Diseases. At the Royal Devonshire Hospital they had also seen Dr Buckley. Dr Copeman and Dr Buckley were two of the doyens of British rheumatology. The visiting group was told there was a great need to inaugurate clinics for rheumatic diseases throughout the country and, as the voluntary hospitals were not in a financial position to provide these, it was felt that the responsibility would devolve on the local authorities. It was confirmed that these diseases were devastating to health and working capacity, and ignorance as to the significance of initial symptoms often led to delay in seeking advice, with resultant permanent disability.[22] Dr Rae had obtained some data on the local incidence of these disorders among the insured population, this being the only group for which such information could be obtained. The figure varied between town and county patients, ranging from 1.6 per cent to 4 per cent of the population.

The sub-committee appeared to favour the establishment of a clinic for rheumatic disorders and had given some thought to its possible location. They believed such a facility would work most effectively if the clinic for out-patients and beds were contiguous, and near laboratory facilities. This did not, however, appear attainable in Aberdeen. The City Hospital was considered but deemed impractical, there being no space available. The new Royal Infirmary at Foresterhill was also deemed inappropriate. The Justice Mill Lane Baths could be used to provide clinics and some specialised treatment facilities, but could have no beds and no laboratory facilities. The sub-committee thought Woolmanhill would be the best location. They wondered if space would be available there when the Royal Infirmary beds moved to Foresterhill, and if so, and if the Infirmary managers were agreeable, then the reconstruction, equipment and running costs could be met by the local authority.

Formal decision rested with the Public Health Committee and they recommended investigation to discover what income the local authority might expect to obtain for such a project from bodies such as the Red Cross and the Department of Health for Scotland.[23] Probably because of the war and the fact that the Royal Infirmary managers did not show great interest in the scheme at this juncture, nothing came of these discussions.

The War Years

In the years preceding the outbreak of war the workload and size of the City Hospital had further increased. There was then accommodation for 285 patients which was to increase with the opening of the new cubicle block to 325.

In the pre-war period the beds were allocated as follows:

Diphtheria	93 beds
Scarlet fever	60 beds
Ailing babies department	22 beds
Tuberculosis – male	26 beds
Tuberculosis – female	50 beds
Puerperal fever	16 beds
Erysipelas	6 beds
Miscellaneous, including VD	12 beds
Total	285 beds[24]

In 1941 Miss Margaret Frater, who had been matron of the City Hospital for 13½ years and in the nursing service for 36½ years, had to retire through ill health and was replaced by Miss Helen Paterson (See Appendix 2).

The war caused considerable disruption to the City Hospital, as elsewhere in the city and country. Windows in the wards and other accommodation were all blacked out and taped, and the iron railings from the front wall bordering Urquhart Road removed for salvage.[25] New water hydrants were installed, with fire-hose equipment and couplings to comply with the equipment used by the National Fire Service. Emergency water tanks were installed, and in 1941, an air-raid shelter to accommodate 60 persons was constructed.[26] It is not clear what was to happen to the many more patients and staff on the site daily!

Many of the younger medical staff left on war duties and a number of retired doctors were temporarily re-employed to fill gaps. There was an embargo on major new building, although as mentioned, the new cubicle block was completed in late 1940 and the new accommodation for scabies treatment and disinfection built the next year. Some extensions were also made to the mortuary and chapel, and Ward 6 was reconstructed, being changed from a large pavilion into four smaller ward units.[27]

The end of war in Europe in 1945 was celebrated at the hospital in appropriate fashion. The Town Council decreed that on 'cease fire' day there should be a short service of thanksgiving in the morning followed by a special lunch for patients, and a concert in the evening. There was also additional entertainment, as in the later evening, a bonfire was lit on the nearby Broad Hill where there was also a firework display.[28]

Immediately after the war, there were further structural changes when Ward 3 was converted into additional cubicle accommodation, Ward

8 and the administration block were reconditioned, and additional recreation accommodation provided at the nurses' home.[29]

Further Developments in Venereology

As mentioned in the previous chapter and discussed further in Chapter 11, the siting of services for the diagnosis and treatment of venereal diseases had been a source of constant discussion. The local authority had initially decided to largely contract out this work to the Royal Infirmary although there was also the out-patient clinic at the City Hospital. After the at times acrimonious discussions between Dr Parlane Kinloch and the directors of the Royal Infirmary in the 1920s, it had finally in 1930 been decided to have the main out-patient facility at Woolmanhill, where there were also a small number of beds available, while the facility at the City Hospital continued, and in-patient accommodation was also available at Woodend.

As mentioned in Chapter 7, Dr J. F. Christie had been put in charge of all the VD services in Aberdeen and from 1920 had a series of junior medical assistants. He remained in charge of this service until his retirement in April 1931, when Dr F. (Fred) J. T. Bowie became chief medical officer of the VD Department. Bowie, who since 1926 had been a junior medical officer in the department, had later been put in charge of the municipal hospitals VD service. Dr Thomas (Tom) Anderson, who was training in dermatology, became his assistant.[30] The increasing workload for the years 1918–42 is shown in Table 2.

TABLE 2: Average new registrations and sources of cases of VD
at the Infirmary and City Hospital treatment centres

| | | Source | |
Years	Total No	City	Elsewhere
1918–22	727	573	154
1923–27	735	544	191
1928–32	1,003	753	250
1933–37	1,085	764	321
1938–42	1,280	714	566

Apart from a true increase in those suffering from these diseases, there was also a greater readiness for the public to seek medical advice when in doubt, so that there were also increasing numbers seen who were found on examination not to be suffering from the condition.[31]

In 1937 congestion in the dermatology and VD departments, which shared accommodation at Woolmanhill, became a major problem, and it was agreed to reallocate accommodation, with out-patient facilities and beds there exclusively for use by the VD clinic.[32] As mentioned earlier, the VD clinic at the City Hospital was also reconstructed the next year. The war years led to a further considerable increase in workload, and additional temporary medical and technical help was required. This help was provided first provided by Colonel A. Dawson and later by Dr Schwartz.[33] During this time, fever therapy had been introduced in the treatment of late syphilis with nervous system involvement causing general paralysis of the insane (GPI). The necessary equipment for this had been purchased, firstly for Woodend in 1938 and then in 1947 also for the City Hospital.[34]

Ear, Nose and Throat (ENT) Work

A consultant otologist for the City Hospital was first appointed in 1925, with arrangements for twice-weekly visits. Mr H. Ross Souper (1887–1936) was the first appointee and held the post until his death in 1936 when he was replaced by Mr Jack Otty (1904–1974). The bulk of the work then probably consisted of cases of peritonsillar abscess (quinsy), ear infection and problems in children with measles, and patients with tuberculous laryngitis which was then a common complication of open pulmonary TB. In 1937 the ENT work at the City Hospital was taken over by John Gerrie (1908–49), assisted later by E. Godfrey Collins (1902–76).[35]

In 1939 a very long waiting list for tonsillectomy and adenoidectomy (T&As) had accumulated at the Royal Infirmary, and the managers asked if it would be possible to use vacant beds at the City Hospital for some extra lists to help clear the problem. This was agreed, and in May 1939, a time of year when bed demand at the City Hospital was reduced, a ward was set aside for this purpose to allow two batches of 30 cases per week to be operated on there. A similar request the following year had to be denied, as there were no free beds then available, but was acceded to again in 1943.[36]

Tuberculosis

There were no new structural changes in the wards for TB patients during this period but, as mentioned, the out-patient clinics had been moved from the TB dispensary into the administration block along with the x-ray department, and the facilities there were to further extend. There were also a number of staff changes. Dr Banks, the tuberculosis medical officer, retired in late October 1944. Dr Austin C. Clay, later to be a distinguished city general practitioner, was then senior resident medical officer, while his wife was a junior resident medical officer, but resigned her post in December of that year. Dr Clay was then given permission to live outwith the hospital and was asked to conduct all the TB clinics pending a new senior appointment. Supervision of the service was provided by Dr Robert J. Duthie (1901–71)[37] who was then an assistant physician at the Royal Infirmary and part-time assistant and deputy medical superintendent at Torna-Dee Sanatorium.[38] He was to become full physician to the Aberdeen Royal Infirmary in 1948 and started the cardiology department. He was assisted in his supervisory work at the City Hospital by Dr Anna Mason, then senior assistant medical officer in the TB wards at Woodend.[39] These arrangements continued until the appointment of Dr Douglas Bell in 1945 as tuberculosis officer for the city of Aberdeen.[40]

Dr Douglas Bell (1902–1975)

He was born at Lockerbie, Dumfriesshire, son of the local general practitioner. He received his medical training in Edinburgh, graduating in 1924. After a resident hospital appointment in Doncaster, he took a short service commission in the Royal Navy, serving in the China Station. He then had a spell in his father's practice before coming to Aberdeen in 1934 when, as mentioned earlier, he was appointed senior resident physician at the City Hospital. He took the DPH the same year. He gained considerable experience in infectious diseases and then had a period at the Bridge of Weir Sanatorium obtaining further experience in the management of TB. He returned to Aberdeen in 1937 when he was appointed tuberculosis officer to the county. He took his MD with commendation in 1938. From 1940 to 1945 he served in the RAMC in Palestine, Egypt and Italy, attaining the rank of major. He came back to Aberdeen on demobilisation and soon afterwards was appointed TB officer to the city. He was to become senior consultant chest physician, a post he held until his retirement in 1967, and was awarded the OBE for his services in 1968.[41]

Major changes in the management of TB were to follow the discovery of streptomycin in the United States in 1944 by Dr S. A. Waksman (1888–1973). Supplies were initially very restricted but in 1948 five treatment centres for its use in Scotland were set up by the Department of Health. The City Hospital was the designated centre in Aberdeen, and five beds were set aside for the treatment of suitable cases from the whole North of Scotland. Because of the shortage of supplies, treatment was initially restricted to cases of miliary tuberculosis and TB meningitis, which were previously almost universally fatal.[42] The supply position improved slightly the following year, when manufacture of the drug started in this country, and the number of allocated beds in Scotland was then increased from 27 to 37, and those in Aberdeen from five to seven.[43]

Rheumatic Diseases II

Nothing had come of the discussions initiated by Professor Stanley Davidson in 1937 regarding the provision of special facilities for rheumatic diseases. He left Aberdeen in 1938 when appointed professor of medicine in Edinburgh, where he was to establish an international reputation, particularly in the field of medical teaching. Davidson was replaced as professor of medicine in Aberdeen by Robert S. Aitken who was to hold the chair until 1948, when he became vice-chancellor of the University of Birmingham. Aitken started a department of rheumatic diseases based at Stracathro Hospital in 1945, largely under the supervision of Dr Logie Bain who was then his assistant and in 1946 a rheumatic out-patient clinic was set up in relation to the orthopaedic out-patient clinic at Foresterhill.[44] The same year, the MOH reported to the Public Health Committee that he had been approached by the professor, requesting re-opening of the question of providing facilities for the treatment of rheumatic diseases in the city.[45] The Town Council were stimulated to look into the matter by a munificent bequest of £12,000 from the estate of a Miss Margaret Cran of Aberdeen for the treatment of rheumatism in Aberdeen, but with the stipulation, that if no clinic was available within five years, the bequest would go elsewhere. It was 1948 before it was finally agreed to establish, equip and maintain a rheumatism treatment centre at the municipal baths in Justice Mill Lane, and the necessary structural alterations were made, and equipment obtained.[46] Dr Logie Bain was to take charge of this facility, when, somewhat to his surprise, he was made consultant in charge of rheumatology. It was, however, to be 1960 before accommodation for this specialty was provided at the City Hospital.[47]

Dr Logie Samuel Bain (1914–1988)

He was the fourth son and fifth member of an illustrious family, two of his brothers also working with distinction in the medical profession, one, John, as an anaesthetist and Sandy as a radiologist. Logie was educated at Aberdeen Grammar School and graduated in medicine at Aberdeen University. His main contribution to the university was in the sporting arena, he being awarded a 'Blue' for both rugby and golf. After graduation he worked for a period at Tor-na-Dee Sanatorium before filling a surgical post at Aberdeen Royal Infirmary. He joined the RAMC on the outbreak of war and served in the Middle East, East Africa and Italy. He returned to Aberdeen on demobilisation in 1945 as assistant to Professor Aitken, where, as mentioned earlier, he was somewhat reluctantly diverted into the field of rheumatology.[48] Some of his many contributions in this field will be recorded later.

Introduction of Antibiotics

The first use of streptomycin in Aberdeen in 1948 has already been mentioned. Earlier, at the time of the Second World War, penicillin, the first of the new 'wonder drugs', had been produced in Oxford by Howard Florey (1898–1968) and Ernest Chain (1906–79), following up earlier observations by Alexander Fleming (1881–1955) at St Mary's Hospital in London around 1928.[49] Supplies were initially very limited and were largely confined to war usage. In 1945, however, the City Hospital was designated as the centre in Aberdeen for its use in treatment, and a special refrigerator for its storage was purchased.[50] The antibiotic era had arrived. Subsequent years were to see many other important advances in this field, and the treatment of many of the common infectious diseases managed at the City Hospital was to be revolutionised. This will be discussed later.

The National Health Service (Scotland) Act 1947[51]

This was introduced in Scotland on 5 July 1948 and followed on the Beveridge Report which had been produced and circulated during the war and had first been discussed by the Public Health Committee in early 1943.[52] The main thrust of the National Health Service Act was the provision of a free comprehensive health service for all persons. It was hoped as a result to secure improvement in the physical and mental health of the people of Scotland. Almost all hospital accommodation in both voluntary and local authority hospitals was to be taken over by the government, as were the majority of medical and nursing staff and numerous other services. The Act required each of the five designated areas to set up a Regional Hospital Board and to constitute Boards of Management for the control and management of individual hospitals or groups of hospitals. The North-Eastern Regional Hospital Board was then started, and the City Hospital became the responsibility of the Aberdeen Special Hospitals Board of Management. The Town Council's Public Health Committee was then disbanded and became the Health and Welfare Committee.[53]

Consequent on these changes, Dr Rae's duties altered somewhat, he ceasing to have any administrative responsibilities towards the City Hospital, but in 1948 he was made honorary consultant to the Board's Infection Fever Hospitals.[54] In appreciation of his many years of service, he was allowed to continue in post for a year after he was due to retire. He was appointed an honorary physician to King George VI in 1950, and an honorary physician to the Queen in 1952–3. He died in 1955.[55]

Many of the hospitals throughout the country inherited by the National Health Service were old and crumbling, but this was not the case in Aberdeen. The foresight of many in the inter-war years, aided by local generosity, had secured both the Foresterhill site and all its main buildings which remain standing. The City Hospital was also in a healthy vigorous state, ready to face the many changes which were to occur in the ensuing decades.

References to Chapter Nine

[1]   Obituary, Harry J. Rae, *British Medical Journal*, 1955, vol. 1, pp. 1285–6.

[2]   Ibid.

[3]   *Local Government (Scotland) Act, 1929, The Public General Acts 1928–9*, Eyre and Spottiswoode, London, 1929, pp. 589–686.

[4]   H. J. Rae, 'Public Health Administration in Aberdeen' in D. Rorie (ed.), *The Book of Aberdeen*, Aberdeen, Lindsay, 1939, pp. 66–81.

[5]   Annual Report of the Medical Officer of Health for 1929, pp. 32–4.

[6]   Obituary, Rae, op. cit.

[7]   Aberdeen Central Library, Town Council Minutes (hereafter TCM), 15 June 1931.

[8]   Rae, op. cit.

[9]   TCM, 21 December 1931.

[10] TCM, 17 October 1932.

[11] P. Drinker and L. A. Shaw, 'An apparatus for the prolonged administration of artificial respiration I – Design for adults and children', *Journal of Clinical Investigation*, 1929, vol. 7, pp. 229–47; L. A. Shaw and P. Drinker, 'An

apparatus for the prolonged administration of artificial respiration II – A design for small children and adults with an appliance for the administration of oxygen and carbon dioxide', *Journal of Clinical Investigation*, 1929, vol. 8, pp. 33–46.

[12] P. Drinker and C. F. McKhann, 'The use of a new apparatus for the prolonged administration of artificial respiration', *Journal of the American Medical Association*, 1929, vol. 92, pp. 1658–60; P. Drinker, T. J. Shaughnessy and D. P. Murphy, 'The Drinker Respirator. Analysis of case reports of patients with respiratory failure treated from October 1928 to June 1930', *Journal of the American Medical Association*, 1930, vol. 95, pp. 1249–53.

[13] R. G. Henderson, personal communication.

[14] I. A. Porter and M. J. Williams, 'Scotland's first iron lung', *Scottish Medical Journal*, 1997, vol. 42, pp. 122–4.

[15] R. Fraser, 'Memories of Aberdeen City Hospital', unpublished manuscript, n.d., currently in the possession of Professor J. Friend.

[16] Annual Report of the Medical Office of Health for 1930, p. 58.

[17] Fraser, op. cit.

[18] TCM, 1 December 1941.

[19] TCM, 17 May 1937.

[20] Rae, op. cit., p. 71.

[21] TCM, 19 April 1937.

[22] TCM, 20 September 1937.

[23] TCM, 20 September 1937.

[24] Rae, op. cit., p. 71.

[25] TCM, 5 August 1940.

[26] TCM, 15 September 1941.

[27] TCM, 7 February 1944.

[28] TCM, 2 April 1945.

[29] TCM, 8 May 1946.

[30] T. E. Anderson, 'The Development of Dermatology in Aberdeen', *Aberdeen Postgraduate Medical Bulletin*, September 1973, pp. 38–42.

[31] H. Mackenzie, *Third Statistical Account of Scotland. The City of Aberdeen*, Edinburgh and London, Oliver and Boyd, 1953, p. 392.

[32] TCM, 20 December 1937.

[33] TCM, 19 April 1943.

[34] TCM, 20 October 1947.

[35] TCM, 21 June 1937.

[36] TCM, 18 October 1943.

[37] TCM, 18 September 1944.

[38] J. M. Johnston, 'Tor-na-Dee Sanatorium' in D. Rorie, op. cit., pp. 92–3.

[39] TCM, 18 September 1944.

40 'Retiral of Dr Douglas Bell', *Aberdeen Postgraduate Medical Bulletin*, April 1967, p. 19.

41 Obituary, Douglas Bell, *British Medical Journal*, 1975, vol. 3, p. 598.

42 TCM, 17 May 1948.

43 TCM, 21 June 1949.

44 I. D. Levack and H. A. F. Dudley (eds), *Aberdeen Royal Infirmary*, London, Baillière Tindall, 1992, p. 166.

45 TCM, 15 September 1946.

46 TCM, 18 June 1945.

47 Levack and Dudley, op. cit., p. 166.

48 J. S. R. Innes, 'Logie Samuel Bain' (Obituary), *Aberdeen Postgraduate Medical Bulletin*, 1988, vol. 22, no. 2, pp. 39–40.

49 P. Pringle, *The Romance of Medical Science*, London, Harrap, 1948, pp. 222–35.

50 TCM, 11 May 1945.

51 *The National Health Service (Scotland) Act 1947, The Public General Acts of 1947*, HMSO, 1947, I, pp. 144–231.

52 TCM, 18 June 1943.

53 TCM, 20 September 1948.

54 TCM, 5 September 1948.

55 Obituary, Rae, op. cit.

Chapter Ten

Infections in Aberdeen and the City Hospital 1923–48

Cholera, plague, typhus and smallpox – the dread epidemic scourges of the past – were no longer a significant problem. The first three had disappeared completely from Britain and only occasional cases of smallpox occurred in Aberdeen in persons infected abroad or elsewhere in the country where the disease still occurred.

The other common zymotics – diphtheria, scarlet fever, measles and whooping cough – however, remained prevalent and continued to take their toll in sickness and death, the first two, with tuberculosis, being the most frequent reason for admission to the City Hospital in this period. Some new problems, however, emerged which were of particular interest to workers at the City Hospital, and Dr John Smith, consultant-in-charge of the City Hospital Laboratory, was to make notable contributions in many different fields. Advances in understanding of immunology also led to the introduction of new preventative measures, and diphtheria and scarlet fever were the first to be involved.

Dr Parlane Kinloch prepared a detailed memorandum on this subject for the Town Council in November 1925.[1] He pointed out that in the previous ten years there had been a total of 4,563 cases of diphtheria with 254 deaths. In the same period there had been 5,526 cases of scarlet fever with 215 deaths. Treatment of these two diseases in that time at the City Hospital had incurred a total expenditure of £150,000. The main brunt of these diseases and deaths fell on children, especially young children. Thus 29 per cent of the diphtheria cases and 65 per cent of the diphtheria deaths occurred in children under five years of age, and 73 per cent of the cases and 95 per cent of the deaths were in children under fifteen years of age. The picture for scarlet fever was very similar.

It had been established that children were unsusceptible to diphtheria and scarlet fever during the first six months of life, this 'passive immunity', as it is now known, being transmitted to the unborn child by the mother's blood, and to the infant by the mother's milk. This passive immunity, however, quickly decays, and by the age of six months, children become very susceptible to both diseases, and remain so until they slowly develop natural immunity as they grow older. This is active immunity, now known to be due to exposure to the relevant infecting organisms in quantities not sufficient to cause manifest disease.

It had been quickly found that diphtheria antitoxin, introduced around 1890 for the treatment of cases of diphtheria, would produce passive immunity lasting about three weeks. Subsequently, active immunisation against this disease was introduced, using first toxin/antitoxin mixtures and then toxoid/antitoxin mixtures which were much safer. Toxoid is toxin so modified that it no longer possesses its toxic properties. This had been shown to be both safe and efficacious. As mentioned in Chapter 6, it was also possible to test individual susceptibility to diphtheria by the Schick test, involving the intradermal injection of a minute amount of diluted diphtheria toxin. These procedures had been used in Aberdeen since 1922. Active immunisation against scarlet fever using scarlatinal streptococcus toxin was introduced later, with a comparable skin test for susceptibility known as the Dick test. An anti-streptococcus serum for specific treatment of cases of scarlet fever had also been produced. A combined diphtheria and scarlatina prophylactic (toxoid/antitoxin and streptococcus toxin mixture) for producing concurrently active immunity to diphtheria and scarlet fever had also become available and all these different biological products could be obtained from the City Hospital.[2] Dr Kinloch advised the Town Council to conduct a campaign to encourage the use of these agents but it was to take many years of encouragement and endeavour before they were widely used and fully effective.

The Advent of Chemotherapy

Chemotherapy literally means 'treatment by chemicals'. The Egyptians and Babylonians had used compounds of mineral origin in medical treatment but early chemotherapy was based on the more scientific principles discovered by Louis Pasteur and his followers. It was a new phase in the war against germs, and the campaign was designed to discover an internal antiseptic that would kill micro-organisms already in the body, just as Lister had killed them by the external application of carbolic acid. Indeed this very agent was given by injection to 'disinfect the blood' but of course failed, having a similarly destructive effect in the tissues in which the bacteria were lodged.[3]

Paul Ehrlich (1854–1915), a German–Jewish pupil of Robert Koch is rightly regarded as the father of the new science, searching as he did for 'magic bullets' which strike only those objects for whose destruction they had been prepared. It took years of patient endeavour, but working with aniline dyes, he eventually in 1910, with the 606th compound he tried, discovered the organic arsenical arsphenamine – known simply as 606 – which was found to be effective in the treatment of syphilis and some other less common diseases. It was not to be until 1932 that the work of the German chemist Gerhard Domagk (1895–1964) led to the introduction of prontosil rubrum, the forerunner of the sulphonamide group of drugs, and not until the time of the Second World War that penicillin, the first of the new 'wonder drugs' was produced in Oxford by Florey and Chain. Many other important discoveries were to follow, including in 1944 streptomycin, the first drug to be effective in tuberculosis. The introduction of these and later antibiotics was to revolutionise the management of many of the common infectious diseases.[4]

The sulphonamides were first used at the City Hospital in 1938 and the MOH commented in a report on the dramatic effect they had in various streptococcal diseases such as scarlet fever, puerperal sepsis and erysipelas. They were also effective in many cases of gonorrhoea.[5] Penicillin was first available for use in selected cases at the City Hospital in early 1945 and streptomycin for use in selected cases of acute tuberculosis in early 1948.[6]

The dramatic effect of these new discoveries will be discussed further when dealing with the individual infections.

MAJOR INFECTIONS

Smallpox

This remained an occasional problem but significant outbreaks were prevented by widespread vaccination. The number of unvaccinated children had steadily fallen and by 1924 was the lowest ever at 7.7 per cent.[7] There were single cases of smallpox in 1924, 1925 and 1929, all of whom were admitted to the City Hospital. All had contracted their infection elsewhere. The 1924 case was a ship's engineer who contracted the infection in Yorkshire, and the 1925 case was a man working in Aberdeen who had returned to his home in Middlesborough for Christmas, and became ill after his return to Aberdeen in January. In both cases, all known contacts were vaccinated or re-vaccinated and no secondary cases occurred. The 1929 case was a male adult, aged 28, who, returning by ship from abroad, had been in contact with a sick seaman. The seaman had been put ashore at Marseilles where he died from smallpox. Of 457 passengers who went ashore at Marseilles and proceeded home overland, four including the patient came to Aberdeen. The patient had not been vaccinated since infancy but the three others, who had been recently re-vaccinated, remained free of the disease and no secondary cases occurred in the city. Another sixteen persons from Scotland, who had been either passengers or crew in the ship, also contracted the disease.

A larger outbreak occurred in Aberdeen in 1930 and saw the last admission for this disease to the City Hospital. The initial case was a female mill worker, aged 30 years, who was admitted to the City Hospital on 4 June with suspected measles. Severe smallpox was immediately diagnosed and the patient forthwith transferred to the county's infectious diseases hospital at Summerfield, it having been just earlier agreed that all cases of smallpox in the city and county would henceforth be admitted there. There were a total of ten cases in this outbreak, with one fatality. Vaccination had been performed on all other patients at the City Hospital at the time of admission of the original case. Three patients, however, had refused vaccination and were immediately discharged home. One of these, a woman with puerperal fever complicated by venous thrombosis, who had been in a ward adjacent to the initial case, went to stay with an unmarried sister in Kincardineshire. The patient later developed some spots on her forehead and was seen by the family practitioner but no diagnosis of infectious disease was made. The unmarried sister later took ill and was admitted to Summerfield Hospital with smallpox and this was the case which ended fatally. The original source of the infection was never established, there having been no other cases of smallpox in Scotland that year.[8]

This was to be the last outbreak of this disease in Aberdeen.

THE OTHER COMMON ZYMOTICS

Diphtheria

This remained initially prevalent and was a frequent reason for admission to the City Hospital. The number of cases admitted during the period 1924–47 is shown in Figure 18A. Virtually all cases from the town were admitted and also a number from the county. There were major epidemics in 1934–5 and in 1938 and 1940. The mortality rate was lower than before but this disease still caused a total of 346 deaths between 1924–45. Although effective immunisation against the disease had been available since 1922 little advantage was initially taken of this procedure and by 1939 only 50 per cent consent for immunisation of pre-school children was being obtained, well below the 80 per cent rate required for effective control in a community. In the war years, however, the Town Council agreed to an active campaign of immunisation of children on school entry and this was

Figure 18A Diphtheria
Cases admitted to City Hospital 1924–47

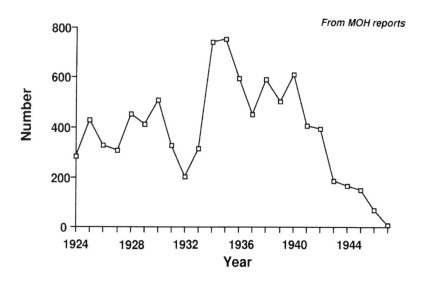

From MOH reports

Figure 18B Scarlet Fever
Cases admitted to City Hospital 1924–47

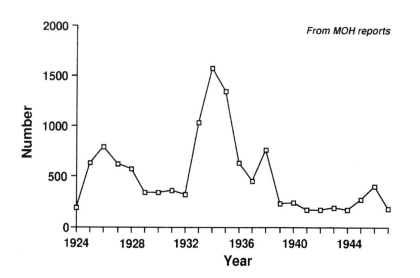

From MOH reports

quickly effective. From 1943 there was a dramatic fall in the incidence of the disease and there were no deaths from this cause in 1946 and 1947.[9]

Scarlet Fever

This disease also remained prevalent with major epidemics in 1925–8, 1933–9 and a lesser outbreak in 1946. As shown in Figure 18B this was also a major source of admission to the City Hospital.

In 1923–4 the husband and wife team George F. Dick (1881–1967) and Gladys H. Dick (1881–1963) had conclusively established that scarlet fever was the result of infection with a haemolytic streptococcus and that the rash was due to the effect of an exotoxin produced by the organism. John Smith confirmed these findings at the City Hospital, obtaining haemolytic streptococci from throat cultures of 92 per cent of cases of scarlet fever in the first two days of the disease.[10] A specific anti-streptococcus serum was later produced and found to be of great benefit in treatment, particularly in severely toxic cases, if given early.[11]

The intradermal injection of a small amount of toxin – the Dick test – was also widely used to test susceptibility to the disease, and active immunisation of the staff at the City Hospital, using scarlatinal streptococcus toxin injections, was used from June 1925. From that date, no nursing or domestic staff working in the scarlet fever ward contracted the disease whereas previously this had been a common occurrence. Immunisation of family contacts was also started and from 1926 it was in general use in the community. In 1927 the MOH reported that of a total of 7,931 children aged 1–15 years who had been immunised, 0.5 per cent contracted scarlet fever, compared with an incidence of 4.1 per cent in 33,521 unprotected children in the same age range.[12]

During the whole period scarlet fever seemed less virulent than in earlier years, with a lower mortality rate. Between 1924–38 there were a total of 88 deaths from this disease. The sulphonamides introduced in 1938 were quickly found to be highly effective and the later discovery of penicillin was to virtually eradicate the disease. Between 1939–48 there were only four deaths from this disease.[13]

Typhoid and Paratyphoid Fevers

These had declined in incidence due to improvement in the water supplies and improved domestic sanitation. They had largely become food-borne diseases due to infection of milk or other food by carriers. Bacteriological advances had shown that the clinical entity of enteric fever could result from infection with several distinct though related bacterial species, and various paratyphoid bacilli had been identified. Paratyphoid fever tended generally to be milder than classical typhoid but was now included in the official returns. The majority of cases of these infections were now admitted to the City Hospital and the annual number of admissions in the period 1924–47 is shown in Figure 19.

Figure 19 Typhoid and Paratyphoid Fevers Admissions to City Hospital 1924–47

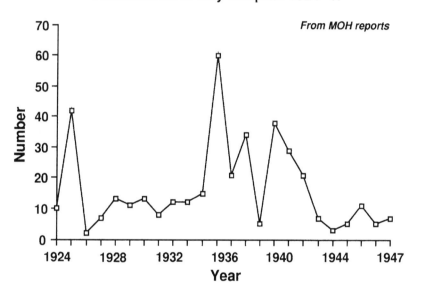

The outbreak in 1925 involved five cases of typhoid and 35 of paratyphoid. Twenty-one of these latter cases occurred in the Woodside area and were due to *B. paratyphosus B* and were traced to infected ice-cream.[14] There was a larger outbreak of typhoid fever in the same area in 1935, involving 35 individuals. The source of infection was traced to a cooked-meat shop where the owner's mother, who often served in the shop, had previously been unwell with an undiagnosed illness and was found to be a typhoid carrier. Cooked meats were to feature in a more dramatic outbreak nearly 30 years later. The mortality rate from this disease in the years 1924–47 was relatively low, there being only seventeen deaths from this cause during this period, seven of which occurred in the 1935 outbreak.

Measles

This remained common, with significant outbreaks in 1924–5, 1928, 1930, 1932, 1935, 1938 and 1940 as shown in Figure 20A which shows the notifications in the period 1924–48. As before, only relatively small numbers were admitted to the City Hospital, with a peak of 254 cases in 1940, as shown in Figure 20B, although for that year the listing of admissions for measles included cases of German measles (rubella). The mortality rate in the earlier years was still relatively high, 294 cases dying from this disease in the City Hospital between 1924–35 but the mortality thereafter fell following the introduction of the sulphonamides, as most of the deaths were due to infective complications. There were only 51 deaths from this disease from 1936–48.

In the period 1918–25, an American bacteriologist Ruth Tunnicliff, working in Chicago, claimed that she was able to isolate a gram positive diplococcus from the blood of measles cases, if cultured under anaerobic conditions. Because this organism produced a green pigment it was known as the 'green-producing diplococcus'. Tunnicliff had later reported that if the culture medium from this organism, killed by phenol, was used as a skin test, it produced an inflammatory reaction in those who had not had measles and no reaction in 96 per cent of persons who gave a history of having had the disease. Later work suggested that the skin reaction was due to an extracellular toxin produced by the green-producing coccus which was considered to be the causative organism of measles. Other workers initially produced support for these findings, but others obtained conflicting results.[15] John Smith investigated this matter at the City Hospital. He first studied skin tests with toxin obtained from the relevant organism on normal individuals and in cases prior to and after an attack of measles and found no evidence that the organism had an aetiological relationship to measles.[16] In a later study, although he himself was able to culture strains of green-producing cocci from the pharyngeal secretions of acute and convalescent cases of measles, he also found it in non-measles cases and believed it was part of the normal bacterial flora of the upper respiratory tract and of no aetiological relevance to the disease.[17] It was to be many years before the viral nature of measles was demonstrated.

Whooping Cough

This was overall less prevalent than before, the number of notifications from 1924–48 being shown in Figure 21A. There was a major epidemic in 1924 continuing into 1925, with a total of 2,645 cases in these

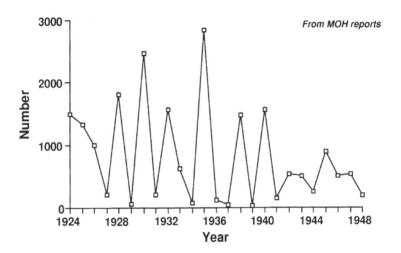

Figure 20A Measles
Notifications 1924–48

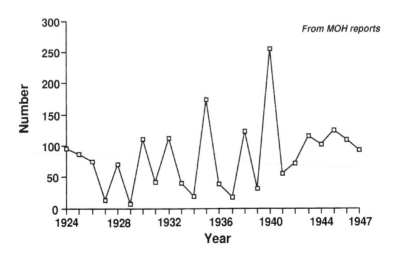

Figure 20B Measles, including German Measles from 1940
Annual admissions to City Hospital 1924–47

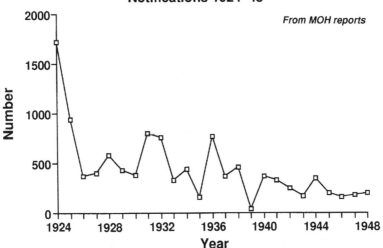

Figure 21A Whooping Cough
Notifications 1924–48

From MOH reports

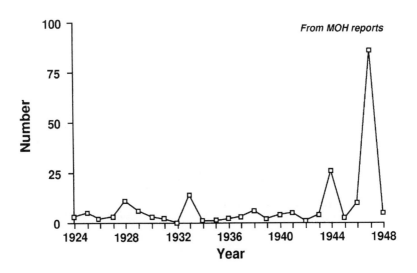

Figure 21B Poliomyelitis
Cases admitted to City Hospital 1924–48

From MOH reports

two years, but the annual incidence was thereafter much lower and remained low after 1937. As before, only a small number of cases were admitted to the City Hospital, usually around 20–50 a year. A total of 139 cases were admitted in the large epidemic of 1924–5. Immunisation against the disease was introduced on an experimental basis in 1948 and the effect of this will be considered in a later chapter.

Poliomyelitis

As shown in Figure 21B, this was relatively uncommon during the period under consideration apart from two outbreaks, one involving 20 cases in 1944 and a larger outbreak of 86 cases in 1947. Nearly all cases of this disease were admitted to the City Hospital and there were a total of twelve deaths, all related to respiratory paralysis.[18] The 1947 outbreak coincided with a major epidemic in Scotland causing a total of 1,698 cases. Thirty-eight of the 86 cases admitted to the City Hospital came from outwith the city, and all but sixteen of the total manifested paralysis of some degree. Six of the twelve deaths during the whole period occurred in this outbreak.[19]

Puerperal Fever

This was to remain a common problem. The majority of cases were admitted to the City Hospital and the mortality rate initially remained high. The incidence of the disease and the number of deaths from 1924–48 is shown in Figure 22A. In October 1929 'puerperal pyrexia' was also made compulsorily notifiable. Although this heading included all cases of true puerperal fever and other types of puerperal infection, it also embraced other causes of rise in temperature in the puerperium such as urinary infections, mastitis or unrelated conditions such as pneumonia and meningitis. Only those cases established as true puerperal fever are shown in the Figure.[20]

There were several notable contributions to the understanding and control of the condition by workers in Aberdeen. In 1928 the Scottish Board of Health published a report by Drs J. Parlane Kinloch, J. Smith and J. A. Stephen entitled 'Maternal Mortality in Aberdeen 1918–1927 with Special Reference to Puerperal Sepsis'.[21] They concluded that in puerperal fever, as in other streptococcal diseases, the essential mode of infection was by contagion, this term being used to embrace all the channels by which any droplet or spray infection was spread, and that an important factor in this

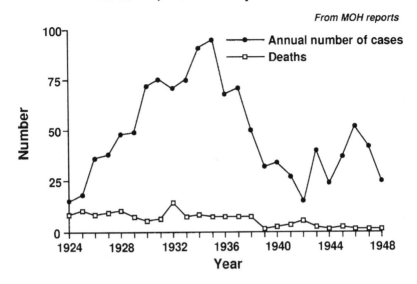

Figure 22A Puerperal Fever
Incidence, with mortality rate 1924–48

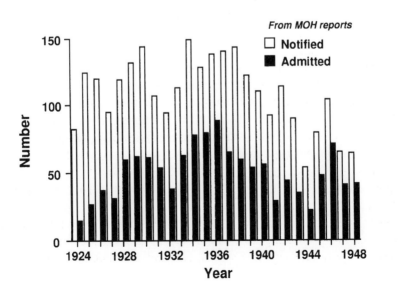

Figure 22B Erysipelas
Cases notified, and admissions to City Hospital 1924–48

spread was streptococcal carriage by physicians, nurses or the patients themselves.

John Smith expanded this work by routine bacteriological investigation of 221 cases of puerperal fever, with a detailed study into the source of infection in eighteen cases. He confirmed the important role of the *S. haemolyticus*, this organism being cultured from swabs of the uterus in 76 per cent of cases, while 22.9 per cent showed it in the blood, and of those with secondary suppurative processes, 93.4 per cent showed it in the pus. It was especially common in those cases with a fatal outcome. In nearly all cases the source of infection could be traced to the attending physician or midwife, and methods of prevention were detailed.[22] In a small number of cases the infection was due to a different organism, the *B. coli* derived from an infected urinary tract or introduced from the intestine of the patient. Dr Smith confirmed all these findings in later studies.[23] These studies received universal acclaim and the introduction of the prophylactic measures suggested led to a steady fall in incidence from 1935 onwards. Related to the introduction of the sulphonamide drugs which were effective in treatment, the mortality rate also fell from around 20 per cent to 8 per cent.[24]

Erysipelas

This remained prevalent with around 100–150 cases notified a year but, as shown in Figure 22B, only a proportion of cases were admitted to the City Hospital. However, a relatively larger proportion were admitted in the later years when there was less demand on the beds from cases of diphtheria and scarlet fever. The mortality rate for erysipelas was relatively low, with usually around 5–10 deaths each year.[25]

The situation dramatically changed following the introduction of the sulphonamides into clinical practice in the late 1930s.[26] Erysipelas responded dramatically, the condition usually being controlled within 48 hours, and there was a steady fall in the mortality. There were only ten deaths from this cause in the ten-year period from 1939–48. Penicillin was to prove even more strikingly effective.

References to Chapter Ten

[1]   Aberdeen Medico-Chirurgical Society: 'Prevention of Diptheria and Scarlet Fever. Memorandum by Medical Officer of Health' in J. Parlane Kinloch, *Research Papers and Reports*, 1914–28.

[2]   Kinloch, ibid.

3   P. Pringle, *The Romance of Medical Science*, London, Harrap, 1948, pp. 222–43.
4   Ibid.
5   Annual Report of the Medical Officer of Health for 1938, p. II.
6   Aberdeen Central Library, Town Council Minutes (hereafter TCM), 17 May 1948.
7   Annual Report of the Medical Officer of Health for 1925, p. 107.
8   Annual Report of the Medical Officer of Health for 1930, pp. 32–4.
9   Annual reports of the Medical Office of Health for the years 1924–48.
10 J. Smith, 'The serological classification of haemolytic streptococci obtained from cases of scarlet fever', *Journal of Hygiene*, 1926, vol. 25, pp. 165–75.
11 J. Parlane Kinloch, J. Smith and J. S. Taylor, 'The newer knowledge of diphtheria and scarlet fever and its application to hospital practice and in community immunisation', *Journal of Hygiene*, 1927, vol. 26, pp. 327–56.
12 Annual Report of the Medical Office of Health for 1927, p. 40.
13 Annual reports of the Medical Officer of Health for the years 1924–48.
14 F. J. T. Bowie, J. Parlane Kinloch and J. Smith, 'Paratyphoid fever and *Aertrycke* enteritis in Aberdeen – a contrast', *Journal of Hygiene*, 1926, vol. 25, pp. 444–52.
15 Annual Report of the Medical Office of Health for 1927, p. 41.
16 J. Smith and A. M. Fraser, 'Skin tests for susceptibility to measles', *Journal of Hygiene*, 1928, vol. 28, pp. 83–8.
17 J. Smith, 'Green-producing cocci in measles', *Journal of Hygiene*, 1929, vol. 28, pp. 363–75.
18 Annual reports of the Medical Officer of Health for the years 1924–48.
19 Annual Report of the Medical Officer of Health for 1947, pp. 4–6.
20 Annual reports of the Medical Officer of Health for the years 1924–48.
21 J. Parlane Kinloch, J. Smith and J. A. Stephen, *Report on maternal mortality in Aberdeen with special reference to puerperal sepsis*, Edinburgh, HMSO, 1928.
22 J. Smith, *Causation and source of infection in puerperal fever*, Edinburgh, HMSO 1931.
23 J. Smith, 'A further investigation into the source of infection in puerperal fever', *Journal of Obstetrics and Gynaecology of the British Empire*, 1933, vol. 40, pp. 991–1023.
24 Annual reports of the Medical Officer of Health for the years 1935–48.
25 Annual reports of the Medical Office of Health for the years 1924–48.
26 Pringle, op. cit., pp. 225–8.

Chapter Eleven

Tuberculosis, Venereal Disease and Some New Diseases 1923–48

Tuberculosis

This remained prevalent with around 150–250 new cases a year notified, although over the period 1923–48 the proportion due to pulmonary tuberculosis rose and that due to non-respiratory TB fell. As shown in Figure 23A, the mortality rate steadily fell from 1924–34 and then remained reasonably stable, although there was a slight rise during and after the war years. The number of cases admitted each year to the City Hospital and the number of deaths there from this cause are shown in Figure 23B. It was mostly cases of pulmonary tuberculosis which were admitted and the number fell steadily from 1924–34 (after 1927, some patients were admitted to Woodend Hospital). Thereafter, the number of admissions increased, especially from 1943, probably related to the increased prevalence of pulmonary TB at this time.

The basis of institutional treatment remained as before but exposure to sunlight (heliotherapy), which had been shown by others to be beneficial, was first used at the City Hospital in the summer months of 1925 and 1926.[1] It was particularly beneficial in cases of surgical tuberculosis but was also found helpful in chronic cases of pulmonary TB. It was not used in acutely ill patients. Artificial sunlight, using ultra-violet light from various sources, was also started and the relevant equipment installed the same year.[2]

It was also around this time that it was appreciated that there were two distinct forms of tuberculous infection – human and bovine. The human type was responsible for most cases of pulmonary and generalised tuberculosis, whereas a large proportion of cases of tuberculous neck glands, abdominal tuberculosis and tuberculosis involving bones and joints – so-called surgical tuberculosis – was of bovine type. The eradication of this latter disease by the introduction of safe milk was not, however, to be achieved until the 1950s.[3]

The idea of resting an affected lung by compressing it with air introduced into the pleural cavity was introduced almost simultaneously around 1890 in Italy by Carlo Forlanini (1847–1918) and in the USA by John Murphy (1850–1916).[4] This pneumothoracic technique, supplemented later by surgical methods such as thoracoplasty and other procedures, was widely practised. The first reference to the use of artificial pneumothorax in Aberdeen was in the MOH's report for 1928 when it was recorded that five

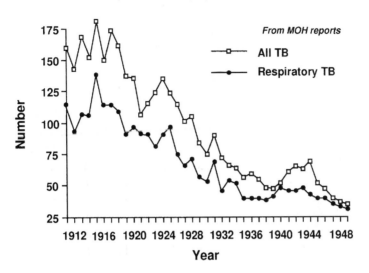

Figure 23A Tuberculosis
Deaths per 100,000 population 1911–48

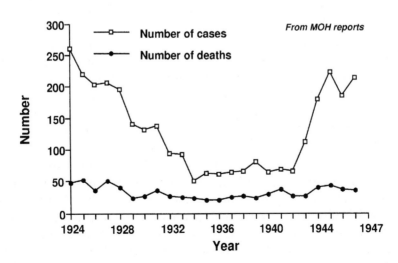

Figure 23B Tuberculosis
Cases admitted to City Hospital and deaths 1924–47

cases were so treated, and thoracoplasty was also performed on three cases.[5] Although not stated, the latter will almost certainly have been performed by the general surgeon William Anderson (1886–1949) who had had extensive experience of chest injuries and their management in the First World War. With increasing use of this procedure, however, he was unable to cope with the growing number of patients and many in consequence had to be sent to London or elsewhere for their surgery.[6] It was not until 1946 that F. J. Sambrook Gowar was appointed as the first thoracic surgeon in Aberdeen, he initially holding a joint appointment to the British Red Cross Society at Tor-na-Dee Sanatorium and at Woodend Hospital. The bulk of the initial surgery was to be done in rather primitive facilities at Tor-na-Dee until a modern theatre there was opened in 1950. Later, a proper thoracic surgery unit with 36 beds was established in the Emergency Medical Service annexe at Woodend.[7]

The use of artificial pneumothorax and later pneumoperitoneum treatment was well-established in the 1930s. In 1938 it was recorded that over 50 per cent of pulmonary cases were being so treated and a formal artificial pneumothorax (AP) clinic had been established at the City Hospital where patients were seen every two to four weeks for 'refills'. Seventy patients were attending this clinic in 1938 and the numbers were to increase steadily, with 156 patients attending by 1948.[8] As mentioned in Chapter 9, streptomycin was first available in 1948 but, because of shortage of supplies, its usage was initially restricted to cases of generalised tuberculosis or TB meningitis. Further advances in chemotherapy were soon, however, to revolutionise the management of this disease.

Venereal Diseases

The incidence of this group of diseases steadily increased during the period 1924–48, as shown in Figure 24A, and there was a particularly marked rise during the war years when very large numbers of service personnel based in the North of Scotland were also being seen. The steady growth in numbers was of concern to the health authorities, and in 1935 a series of public lectures to increase health awareness in this topic was arranged.[9] These were, in the main, given by Dr F. J. T. Bowie, chief medical officer to the VD department at the Infirmary since 1931.

The number of new cases being seen at the City Hospital treatment centre and the number of cases admitted in the period 1924–47 are shown in Figure 24B (no annual figures are available for cases seen 1940–45). Although attendances fell steadily from 1931, when more patients were seen

PLATE 1: Aerial photograph of the City Hospital, c. 1950.

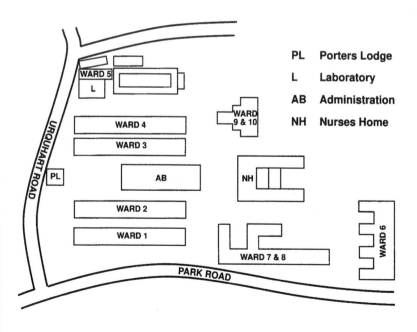

PL   Porters Lodge

L   Laboratory

AB Administration

NH Nurses Home

WARD 5
L
WARD 4
WARD 3
WARD 9 & 10
AB
NH
PL
WARD 2
WARD 1
WARD 7 & 8
WARD 6
URQUHART ROAD
PARK ROAD

PLATE 2A: Entrance to the City Hospital on Urquhart Road and the administration block with clock tower, c. 1925.

PLATE 2B: The laboratory, later the Regional Laboratory, opened in 1920. Previously the Tuberculosis Institute.

PLATE 3A: Tuberculosis pavilion with 'shelter' on right, designed by Professor Matthew Hay. Opened in 1911.

PLATE 3B: Wards 9 and 10. The adult and paediatric infection units. Opened in December 1940.

PLATE 4A: Outside view of Ward 4 with veranda, c. 1925.

PLATE 4B: Inside one of the wards with sister, nurses and patients.

PLATES 5A and 5B: Open-air treatment of tuberculosis, c. 1925.

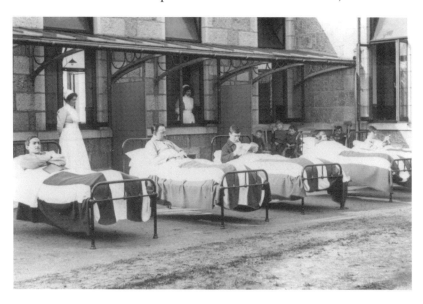

PLATE 6: The City Hospital ambulance, 1895.

(The ambulance arrived in February 1888 and cost £40 - 6s. The driver, George Paterson, held post from 1893 until his death on 19 January 1905, from typhus contracted in course of his duties. The ambulance was replaced by motorised vehicle in 1916.

PLATE 7: The staff of the City Hospital, 1929.
From the left, back row: J. S. Harper (RMO), A. B. Weir (City Analyst), J. R. W. Hay (RMO), J. W. Lobban (RMO), J. L. Gammie (RMO), W. E. Morrison (RMO). Front row: A. M. Fraser (Senior RMO), J. Smith (Director, City Lab), G. S. Banks (TB MO, J. A. Stephen (Assistant MO, Public Health Dept.), F. J. T. Bowie (Junior MO, VD Dept.), D. W. Berry (Lecturer in Public Health).

PLATE 8: Aberdeen's Medical Officers of Health.

Francis Ogston
1868–80*

W. J. R. Simpson
1881–86

Theodore Thomson
1886–7

Professor Matthew Hay
1888-1923

J. Parlane Kinloch
1923–28

Harry J. Rae
1929–52

Ian A. G. MacQueen
1952–73

*NB: Ogston
performed many
of the functions
of a Medical
Officer of
Health, although
the title was not
employed until
1881.

PLATE 9 Senior medical staff at the City Hospital.
(Dates are period worked at city hospital; * = now working on the Foresterhill site.)

Adult Infection and General Medicine

W. Chambers
1952–63

W. Walker
1964–73

C. C. Smith
1973 - 1995

Paediatric Infection

W. H. Galloway
1949–80

P. Smail*
1980–90

Adult Infection and Chest Medicine

General Medicine

J. M. Stowers
1961–80

M. J. Williams
1968–80

J. G. Douglas*
1986–97

PLATE 9 (Continued)

TB/Chest Medicine

G. S. Banks
1913–44
TB Medical Officer

D. Bell
1945–67

R. Fraser
1948–76

E. G. Barnes
1949–73

J. Friend*
1973–97

J. Legge*
1977–97

Venereal Diseases

J. Christie
1917–31

F. J. T. Bowie
1931–58

H. W. Rutherford
1968–80

PLATE 9 (Continued)

Physical Medicine - Rheumatology

L. S. Bain
1948–79

H. Balch
1960–79

J. A. N. Rennie*
1979–94

C. Eastmond*
1979–94

D. Reid*
1986–94

PLATE 10:

Consultants-in-charge of the City Hospital Laboratory.

John Smith
1923–58

James Brodie
1958–78

Ian A. Porter
1978-83

Thomas M. S. Reid
1983–91*

Figure 24A Venereal Diseases 1924–48
Total new cases seen at Aberdeen Treatment Centres

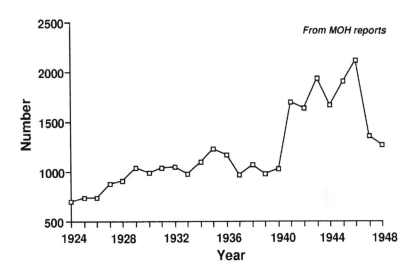

Figure 24B Venereal Diseases 1924–47
New cases seen at City Hospital and number admitted

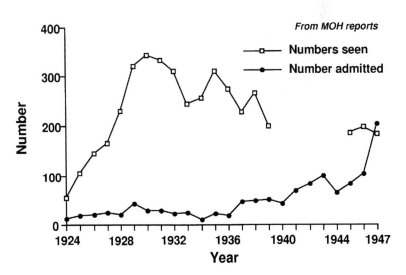

at the Aberdeen Royal Infirmary centre, the number of admissions in contrast increased. This occurred because in 1937 the Infirmary managers became unable to provide accommodation for in-patients with VD in the previous ward in the out-patient block of the old Infirmary and, for a trial period, all male VD patients were admitted to Woodend and all female patients to the City Hospital. As this arrangement proved successful it was continued until 1946, when the male VD ward at Woodend was shut, and thereafter all cases of VD requiring hospital treatment were admitted to the City Hospital. This resulted in a peak of 205 admissions in 1947.[10]

The introduction of the sulphonamides in the late 1930s had a striking effect on the management of gonorrhoea. Penicillin was even more strikingly effective but because of shortage of supplies, its use in this condition until 1945 was restricted to service personnel. It was also found to be highly effective in syphilis and was to radically alter the management of this disease.

SOME NEW DISEASES

Infective Jaundice – Weil's Disease (Leptospirosis)

Adolf Weil (1848–1916) in 1886 gave an account of five cases of infective jaundice with a symptom-complex of fever, jaundice, enlargement of the liver and spleen and the occurrence of haemorrhages, and the term Weil's disease was applied. A Japanese bacteriologist, Inada, in 1915 showed that the disease was due to a spirochaete named the *Leptospira icterohaemorrhagiae*, and the alternative name spirochaetosis icterohaemorrhagica was suggested for the condition. It was later found, however, that in some cases jaundice did not occur and haemorrhagic manifestations were not overall frequent, and so the original term Weil's disease was preferred. Later it became recognised that other types of leptospira occurred, tending on the whole to cause less serious disease than the *L. icterohaemorrhagiae* and the inclusive term leptospirosis is now used.

In 1916 it was found that the rat was the main vector for Weil's disease. Infected animals passed large numbers of organisms in their urine, and the disease was found to be common in Holland, infection being acquired by bathing or accidental immersion in the canals. A higher occupational incidence was reported among bargemen and workers in abattoirs and other rat-infested premises.

The MOH for Aberdeen, in his annual report of 1923, drew attention to a report from East Lothian on an outbreak of infective jaundice among miners, where the doctor involved had drawn attention to the frequency of infection in rats and suggested a study of this problem in other areas of the United Kingdom. In accordance with this recommendation, Dr John Smith examined 100 rats caught in various parts of Aberdeen and found typical leptospira in 24, either by direct examination of the rat's tissue or as a result of animal inoculation.[11]

The condition was not, however, recognised as a clinical problem for several years. Infective jaundice was made compulsorily notifiable in December 1924 but no cases were reported in Aberdeen until 1934. In June that year, two fish workers suffering from an acute febrile disease associated with jaundice and nephritis were admitted to the wards of the Aberdeen Royal Infirmary under the charge of L. S. P. Davidson, the professor of medicine. A diagnosis of Weil's disease was made on clinical grounds. Inoculation of blood and urine into guinea-pigs gave negative results, but serum, obtained later in the illness and sent to an expert in Amsterdam, gave positive results with the classical Weil strain. Enquiries showed that other fish workers had had a similar disease, and Professor Davidson arranged for the MOH to circularise medical practitioners in Aberdeen and the regional area for information on any cases of infective jaundice which they had or had had under their care in the past. Following this enquiry, Professor Davidson and his colleagues were able, later that year, to report on nineteen cases, detailing the clinical and bacteriological findings.[12] Thirteen of the patients were employed in the handling or cleaning of fish, and Davidson and his co-authors believed fish workers should be included in the occupational groups especially liable to Weil's disease. The illness they described was usually sudden in onset, with fever, severe headache, muscle pains, weakness and prostration and non-specific gastro-intestinal symptoms. Of fifteen cases confirmed bacteriologically, jaundice was detected in eleven. Conjunctival injection – 'red eyes', which had been stressed as a feature by authors in Holland – was not noted in any patient. Haemorrhage from some situation was found in nine cases. Nose-bleeding was the most common and was usually slight. They stressed urinary features. Albumin and casts were found in the urine in nine cases, and one fatal case died of anuria. They considered the association of jaundice and nephritis to be of great diagnostic value. Raised blood urea levels were found in the small number of cases where this was measured. They failed to recover the causative organism by intra-peritoneal injection of blood or urine into guinea-pigs, as it had been established by workers in Holland that the organism was only found in the blood of the sufferers in the early stages of the disease and only occurred in the urine in the period from 10–21 days after the onset. The diagnosis was, however, confirmed in all cases by specific serological tests. Dr John Smith had gone to Amsterdam to learn the technique from the expert there who had introduced the test, and quickly mastered the procedure. In characteristic fashion he also generously shared his expertise with others. Sir James Howie recounts how, as a junior worker in the university bacteriology department, he had been asked to set up reliable diagnostic methods for leptospires, but ran into many technical problems and so sought John Smith's help. This was unstintingly given, despite Howie working for what was then considered 'a rival establishment'.[13]

In 1936 John Smith and Professor Davidson published what was to be a seminal paper on the disease, by which time their experience had increased to 40 cases. They gave a detailed account of the clinical and bacteriological findings, giving proof of the occupational nature of the disease and establishing the connection between infected rats, which were the carriers of the disease, and the sufferers, through contaminated water and slime in the fish-houses.[14] In a separate study, they also showed that latent or inapparent infection in fish workers was common, as of 210 blood samples from workers in the fish trade, 51 or 24.2 per cent gave positive serological reactions. By contrast, no sero-positive reactions were found in 406 blood samples from individuals not employed in the fish trade. The authors believed the disease should be scheduled under the Workmen's Compensation Act as an occupational disease.[15] Various preventative measures were also detailed. When they published a final joint report on the disease in 1939 their experience had increased to 104 cases.[16] By 1949, John Smith's own experience had extended to 214 cases, no fewer than 184 or 86 per cent of which occurred among fish workers.[17]

Cerebrospinal Fever (Meningococcal Meningitis)

The first clinical description of this disease was given by Gaspard Vieusseaux (1740–1818) in Switzerland in 1805 and the causative organism was discovered by Anton Weichselbaum (1845–1920) in Vienna in 1887. He named it the *Diplococcus intracellularis meningitidis*, now known better as the meningococcus. The spread of the disease is favoured by overcrowding and whilst the disease is generally endemic, huge epidemics have occurred, involving armies and cities.[18]

Figure 25 shows the number of cases with this disease admitted to the City Hospital from 1924–47. Initially uncommon, there was a large epidemic from 1940–43, with a peak of 149 cases admitted in 1940. The mortality was initially high, the great majority of cases ending fatally. The introduction of the sulphonamides in the late 1930s dramatically affected the outcome, and of the 401 cases admitted from 1940–45 there were only 33 deaths, and even fewer following the introduction of penicillin.

Figure 25 Cerebrospinal Fever (Meningitis) Cases admitted to City Hospital 1924–47

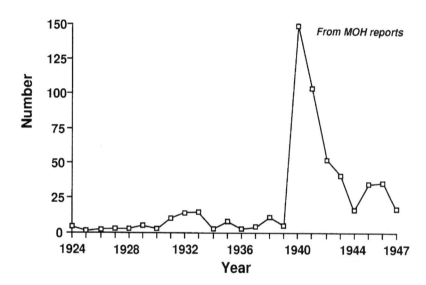

Undulant Fever

An infectious disease with non-specific features and fever, which was either remittent or intermittent explaining the name, this was another condition of considerable interest to John Smith.

A febrile condition related to drinking raw goat's milk was first identified in Malta and became known as Malta Fever. Bruce (later Sir David Bruce, 1855–1931) subsequently demonstrated coccobacilli in the spleen of soldiers dying in Malta from this disease in 1887. Later, Bernhard L. F. Bang (1848–1932) in Denmark isolated a similar organism from cattle with infectious abortion. Alice Evans (1881–1975) in the United States in 1918 showed that these organisms were morphologically, culturely and serologically similar. The generic name brucella was applied and the term

Brucella abortus given to the organism found in cattle, *Br. melitensis* to that found in sheep and goats and *Br. suis* to a strain found in pigs. These organisms were also found to be the cause of human disease and serological tests were introduced for diagnosis. The condition is now more usually referred to as brucellosis. In 1932 John Smith reported the clinical, bacteriological and serological findings in ten cases of undulant fever in North-East Scotland and believed the disease was mostly acquired by drinking infected milk. He had also examined 373 specimens of serum submitted for examination from cases of 'fever' and found eleven with positive serological tests to *Br. abortus*. He also tested 1,446 serum samples which had been submitted for Wassermann reaction tests and found 66 positive tests, although in only eight of these were the results significant. Two of these individuals were farm servants and one a butcher.[19] In a separate study, Dr Smith found *Br. abortus* in 28.3 per cent of 279 different specimens of raw milk examined, while it was reduced to 9.4 per cent of treated samples from eight separate pasteurising plants.[20]

In another study, he found that locally-prepared butter and cheese were free of this infection but found serological evidence of latent infection among slaughtermen who had contact with infected animals and carcasses, although no serious illnesses were encountered.[21] With colleagues from Edinburgh and St Andrews, he was later able to report on 97 cases of undulant fever occurring in Scotland between 1929 and 1934. Of those, fourteen were in persons having contact with animals or meat, and in the remainder, the consumption of infected milk appeared to have been the cause.[22] By 1951, Dr Smith's own experience of this disease had extended to 285 cases.[23]

The eradication of this disease in the cattle of North-East Scotland was to be a challenge for the county medical officers for some years until brought to a successful conclusion.

References to Chapter Eleven

[1]   Annual Report of the Medical Officer of Health for 1925, p. 57.

[2]   Ibid., pp. 58–9.

[3]   J. Smith, 'Reviews of Progress of Dairy Science, Section F. Milk-Borne Diseases', *Journal of Dairy Research*, 1950, vol. 17, pp. 91–105.

[4]   J. C. Sourma, *The Illustrated History of Medicine*, London, Starke, 1992, p. 447.

[5]   Annual Report of the Medical Officer of Health for 1928, p. 23.

[6]   I. D. Levack and H. A. F. Dudley (eds), *Aberdeen Royal Infirmary*, London, Baillière Tindall, 1992, pp. 144–5.

[7]   Ibid.

[8]   Annual Report of the Medical Officer of Health for 1938, p. 16; Annual Report of the Medical Officer of Health for 1948, p. 24.

[9]   Annual Report of the Medical Officer of Health for 1935, pp. 51–2.

[10]   Annual Report of the Medical Officer of Health for 1947, p. 48.

[11]   Report of the Medical Officer of Health for the years 1922 and 1923, pp. 56–7.

[12]   L. S. P. Davidson, R. M. Campbell, H. J. Rae and J. Smith, 'Weil's Disease (Leptospirosis) A Clinical and Bacteriological Study of 19 Cases Occurring Chiefly Among Fish Workers', *British Medical Journal*, 1934, vol. 2, pp. 1137–42.

[13]   J. Howie, 'Dr John Smith' in *Portraits from Memory*, (The Memoir Club), Cambridge, The University Press, 1988, pp. 95–9.

[14]   L. S. P. Davidson and J. Smith, 'Weil's Disease in Fish Workers: A Clinical, Chemical and Bacteriological Study of 40 Cases', *Quarterly Journal of Medicine* 1936, vol. 5 (NS), pp. 263–86.

[15]   J. Smith, and L. S. P. Davidson, 'The Incidence of Weil's Disease in Fish Workers in Aberdeen', *Journal of Hygiene,* 1936, vol. 36, pp. 438–45.

[16]   L. S. P. Davidson and J. Smith, 'Weil's Disease in the North-East of Scotland – an Account of 104 Cases', *British Medical Journal*, 1939, vol. 2, pp. 753–7.

[17]   J. Smith, 'Weil's Disease in the North-East of Scotland', *British Journal of Industrial Medicine*, 1949, vol. 6, pp. 213–20.

[18]   Sourma, op. cit.

[19]   J. Smith, 'Undulant Fever in the North-East of Scotland', *Quarterly Journal of Medicine*, 1932, (NS1), pp. 303–17.

[20]   J. Smith, '*Brucella abortus* in milk', *Journal of Hygiene*, 1932, vol. 32, pp. 354–66.

[21]   J. Smith, 'Sources of Infection in Undulant Fever', *Journal of Hygiene*, 1934, vol. 34, pp. 242–9.

[22]   C. P. Beattie, J. Smith and W. J. Tulloch, 'Undulant Fever in Scotland', *The Lancet*, 1935, vol. 2, pp. 1427–43.

[23]   J. Smith, 'The Epidemiology of Undulant Fever in the North–East of Scotland 1929–50', *Health Bulletin*, 1951, vol. 9, pp. 57–61.

Chapter Twelve

The City Hospital in the National Health Service 1948–71: Years of Change

Introduction

Under the terms of the National Health Service (Scotland) Act, almost all the local authority and voluntary hospitals became the property and responsibility of the Secretary of State for Scotland, and he in turn vested control and responsibility for the running of these and the provision of all hospital-based medical services in five Regional Hospital Boards. As much administrative re-organisation was required, the North-Eastern Regional Hospital Board was set up some months in advance of the planned date for change, which was 5 July 1948. The Board early constituted separate Boards of Management to supervise the running of individual hospital groups. These included the Board for the Aberdeen General Hospitals, the Board for the Aberdeen Special Hospitals and the Board for the Kincardine Hospitals. The City Hospital, along with the Maternity Hospital, the Sick Children's Hospital, Summerfield Hospital, Queen's Cross Maternity Home, Fonthill Maternity Hospital and Newhills Sanatorium and Convalescent Home, became the responsibility of the Aberdeen Special Hospitals Board.[1]

The needs of the region for infectious diseases were discussed at one of the early preliminary meetings of the Regional Board. In addition to the beds at the City Hospital there were then also designated infectious diseases beds in county hospitals at Peterhead, Inverurie, Aboyne, Strichen, Portsoy, Dufftown and Elgin, with beds also in Kirkwall and Lerwick in the Orkney and Shetland Islands. The beds available were much in excess of demand and many in the peripheral hospitals were then being used for other purposes. It was soon decided to reduce the designated infectious disease beds to two sites – the City Hospital in Aberdeen and the Joint County Infectious Diseases Hospital in Elgin. It was agreed that there would be 118 beds designated for infection at the City Hospital and 30 in Elgin.[2]

The Regional Board also decided early to base the main hospital centre for the management of tuberculosis at the City Hospital and to move TB clinics, which were then being held twice weekly at the public health offices in Albyn Place, to the City Hospital.[3]

Staffing Re-organisation

At the time of implementation of the National Health Service (NHS), all the beds in the City Hospital were nominally under the charge of Dr Rae, the MOH, and Dr John Smith. Dr Rae, however, was fully occupied with his public health and administrative duties, and Dr Smith with the laboratory. In practice, the patients were under the charge of the senior medical resident, assisted by three junior residents. Patients of all age groups, irrespective of the nature of their disease were supervised by these staff. The TB patients were under the care of the TB officer.

The Regional Board became responsible for all hospital medical appointments other than those of residents, which were delegated to the respective Boards of Management. Over the next two decades, the complement of resident house officers at the City Hospital was steadily increased as other services were developed so that by 1970 there were six accredited posts. A rotational scheme was devised, each house officer spending two months in different units, with each resident having at least one period in general medicine. These posts were immensely popular and there was never any shortage of high-class applicants. Living accommodation was reasonable and there was the small hospital friendly atmosphere lacking in the anonymity of large complexes. When, however, a married couple were appointed there was some difficulty finding a double bed! The formal luncheon for medical staff described in Chapter 9 ceased in the early 1970s when all staff used a communal dining area.

With regard to the senior staffing, the Regional Board, at an early meeting, recommended appointing a consultant physician to take charge of infectious diseases, and also to visit Elgin fortnightly.[4] It was considered that a vacant senior lectureship in the department of medicine might be filled by advertising for someone with a special interest in infectious diseases, thus using a university appointment.[5] Nothing, however, came of this. In the meantime, Professor John Craig (1898–1977), who had been appointed professor of child health in Aberdeen University in 1948, suggested that it would be more appropriate for all children under the age of twelve years, other than those under treatment for TB or VD, to be under the supervision of a visiting consultant paediatrician. He indicated that his department was in a position to provide this staffing.

This was eventually agreed in 1950, and it was decided that the consultant in chest diseases (Dr Bell) would be responsible for the treatment of all cases of TB over the age of twelve, and the consultant in VD (Dr Bowie) responsible for all cases of VD. It was also later decided that cases of puerperal fever or septic abortion should be supervised by a visiting obstetrician.[6] There was delay in deciding on the future management of the bulk of the beds, which continued under the nominal charge of Dr William Chambers, then senior resident medical officer, and it was 1952 before he was finally appointed consultant.

Dr William Chambers (1912–63): Bill Chambers was born at Motherwell on 19 August 1912. He was educated at Hamilton Academy, and then, for family reasons, spent several years in his father's business before entering Glasgow University in 1936. He had been a victim of poliomyelitis in childhood, which left him permanently lame, and this probably influenced his choice of career. He graduated in 1941 and after resident posts at Cleland Hospital and Bridge of Weir Sanatorium he was appointed senior resident physician at the City Hospital in 1945. He took his MD in 1947, the subject of his thesis being poliomyelitis, a condition in which, because of his own experiences, he took a particular interest.[7] When appointed consultant in 1952, he also became lecturer in infectious diseases. One of us (MJW) remembers his lectures as being clear and lucid and he had an excellent collection of coloured photographs and slides to demonstrate the rashes of the different exanthemata.

Other staff changes will be discussed later under the separate specialties.

Administrative Changes

The Board of Management for the Aberdeen Special Hospitals first met on 31 May 1948.[8] The City Hospital they inherited was running smoothly and efficiently, and the structure was generally sound. The next several years were, however, to see many changes in bed utilisation, consequent on the control of many of the earlier common infectious diseases and the later improved control of tuberculosis. The day-to-day supervision of the various hospitals in the group was put in the care of a Group Medical Superintendent. Dr John Morrison was the first appointee to this post, which he held until he retired in June 1959. Dr Alexander H. Duncan was then the incumbent until September 1967, when he resigned on being appointed principal medical adviser to Livingston area, and was replaced by Dr J. P. Sexton. There was a delay of several months between Dr Duncan's departure and Dr Sexton being able to take up duties, and that period was covered by Dr Elizabeth Russell (now professor of public health at Aberdeen University), who was appointed Acting Group Medical Superintendent.[9]

Structural Changes

Various structural changes were early made in the central block at the City Hospital to accommodate the enlarged chest clinic and additional staff. Some rooms were sub-divided and others, currently unused, were refurbished.

The demands on the infectious beds were initially heavy, there still then being many cases of scarlet fever and poliomyelitis. Cases of diphtheria, which had previously been admitted to Ward 1, were now rare and so it was decided to cubicilise this ward. This, however, was to cost £9,000 and although given priority, had to be deferred. This was fortunate, as by the time monies became available in 1957, polio had virtually disappeared as a result of widespread immunisation and scarlet fever had also become uncommon.

Numerous other minor adjustments and alterations were regularly carried out. A wall, which remained between Wards 3 and 4 from the old days when each pavilion was walled off from the others, was demolished. Staff needs were also considered. The dining-room was enlarged and a tennis court built, the earlier one having been lost when Wards 9 and 10 (the new cubicle block) were constructed. A croquet set for relaxation on the lawn was also purchased.

In 1959 piped oxygen was provided for several of the wards, and in 1963 this arrangement was extended when a liquid oxygen plant was installed. It is noteworthy that the City Hospital was the first hospital in the region to have this facility.[10]

Infectious Diseases

At the time of NHS take-over, 118 of the then total of 254 beds in the City Hospital were designated for infection, 106 being for tuberculosis and 30 for marasmic infants.[11] The hospital was well-equipped for the management of infections, with cabinet respirators (iron lungs) for poliomyelitis patients with respiratory paralysis, and a motorised oxygen tent was purchased in 1952.[12] Dr Chambers was also given leave of absence for a period the following year to visit Copenhagen to study a new method of treatment which had been introduced there following a huge polio epidemic.[13]

Demand soon required extra beds to be given over to tuberculosis, and there was for a period considerable pressure on the infectious diseases beds but from 1955 onwards this steadily declined. By 1961 the infection beds had been reduced and only Wards 3, 8, 9 and 10 and occasionally

Ward 7 were now being used for this purpose. Half of Ward 3 and all of Ward 10 were under the care of the paediatricians and Ward 4, which was initially used for tuberculous patients, was reallocated for general medicine cases in 1959.[14] The hospital by this time had become more a general hospital containing some infectious disease beds, but it was constantly reiterated that the whole hospital might have to be given back to infectious diseases if some major epidemic were to strike. These were to prove prophetic statements.

Dr Chambers remained in charge of the infectious diseases beds and the general medical beds in Ward 4, sharing the latter from 1961 with Dr John Stowers who will be mentioned later. In the late autumn of 1962, Bill Chambers took ill with what was to prove a fatal illness. Dr Fraser, who had been appointed consultant chest physician in 1953, but had had previous experience of infectious diseases, was asked to cover Bill Chambers' ward, with a reduction in his commitment to TB. John Stowers agreed to cover all the general medical beds in Ward 4.[15] Many patients admitted to the infectious disease beds then turned out to have acute medical problems and medical cover was provided for Dr Fraser by Drs Kenneth Palmer and Malcolm MacLeod, readers in the department of medicine. They in fact visited on alternate weeks. Dr Fraser recollects that Dr Palmer could produce a diagnostic label for all cases, while Dr MacLeod was prepared to admit that some cases were too difficult for precise diagnostic labelling.[16]

Bill Chambers died on 19 August 1963. He was only aged 51 years. For reasons now unclear, the resultant vacancy was not filled until the following year but in May 1964 Dr William Walker was appointed. He was then senior lecturer in the department of therapeutics in Dundee.

Dr William Walker (1920–84)

Bill was born and raised in Dundee and was proud of his Scottish roots. He was educated at Harris Academy and gained a scholarship to the arts faculty at St Andrews University where he read history, French, Latin, German and philosophy. He gained several medals and prizes and was also captain of the university boxing team. His destiny then probably lay in the diplomatic service but the outbreak of war changed all. He joined the army at nineteen years of age and became an officer in the Royal Scots, but his army service ceased in 1940 when he sustained a bullet wound in the right ear, which left him deaf and with a functionless labyrinth on that side. Many disabilities carry some vicarious benefit. So it was with Bill's functionless labyrinth. He was immune to sea sickness, and when in later years he had to travel by sea monthly to Lerwick to do the Shetland medical clinic, he always enjoyed the on-board catering when crossing the stormy Pentland Firth, while many fellow travellers were confined to their cabins with the dreaded *mal de mer*. He was invalided from the army in 1941 and resumed his university studies, graduating MA in 1942. Against professional advice, he had also commenced the study of medicine. He had a distinguished undergraduate career being awarded medals in several subjects and graduated with commendation in 1946. After a period as house physician to Professor Adam Patrick in Dundee, he worked for eighteen months in pathology with Professor A. C. Lendrum, before moving to Newcastle as medical registrar with Dr C. C. Ungley. He there obtained special experience in haematology. In 1950 he returned to Dundee as senior medical registrar and then in 1952 became lecturer and later senior lecturer and consultant physician in the department of therapeutics. He also spent a year in Boston, USA, in 1954–5, again working in haematology.[17]

He was appointed to the Aberdeen post of consultant physician with special interest in infection in May 1964. Although not due to take up his appointment until the end of the academic term, he was released from his post in Dundee early because of the large typhoid epidemic in Aberdeen, which will be described fully in the next chapter, and he arrived on 1 June.[18] His early months in his new post were hectic. After the typhoid patients were all discharged there was a brief lull as all wards had to be thoroughly cleaned and repainted. When the hospital returned to normal activity, Bill had charge of 62 beds, 42 in Wards 8 and 9 classed as infectious diseases beds, sixteen general medical beds in Ward 4, and four unclassified beds in Ward 8. He initially also had some unclassified beds in Ward 7.[19]

Patients with suspected gastro-intestinal infections, usually presenting with diarrhoea, were admitted to an outlying section of Ward 8 where there was isolation accommodation with special toilet facilities. Known as 'the outhouses', these were connected to Ward 8 by a covered veranda and the accommodation provided was rather old-fashioned. Periodically, very sick patients with fulminant colitis or other abdominal problems would be admitted under the suspicion of infection, and their management in these facilities was not easy. Diverse infections were mostly admitted to the cubicle accommodation in Ward 9. The common problems then were hepatitis, glandular fever and suspected meningitis, with occasional cases of adult chickenpox, herpes zoster ophthalmicus (shingles involving the eye) and quinsies (tonsillar abscesses following throat infection). A wide variety of acute medical problems turned up under the guise of 'fever', and the supervising staff had always to be on their toes. Dr Walker also admitted many general medical cases, including many diverse haematological disorders referred from the haematology laboratory after blood counts on samples referred by general practitioners had shown some abnormality. An excellent service was provided. Patients with acute leukaemia were admitted to the cubicles in Ward 9, as the chemotherapy they were given rendered them prone to infection. Other cases were admitted to Ward 8.

Bill Walker continued in charge until his appointment to the regius chair of therapeutics in Aberdeen University in 1973. He was an erudite scholar besides being a first class physician and loyal colleague. His mastery of the English language was shown in all his writings, speeches and addresses. He died after an unpleasant illness on 18 December 1984.[20]

Paediatric Infections

As recorded earlier, from 1950 the paediatricians took charge of all children under the age of twelve years with infections in the City Hospital. They had twelve beds in half of Ward 3 which was cubicilised, fifteen cubicilised beds in Ward 10 for infants with diarrhoeal illnesses, and also all of Ward 7, which took children with tuberculous meningitis and chest problems such as primary tuberculosis, or infective problems often following measles or whooping cough. These beds were initially supervised by Professor John Craig and Dr Norman S. Clark who had been appointed lecturer and later became senior lecturer in the department of child health. Later this paediatric work was largely taken over by Dr W. Hugh Galloway who came from Liverpool, but had graduated in medicine in Edinburgh. He had returned to Liverpool to train in paediatrics at the famous Alder Hey Children's Hospital in that city. He was appointed assistant paediatric specialist and consultant paediatrician in Aberdeen in 1949 and caused quite a stir when he arrived driving a Rolls Royce, which remained in his possession for five years before being replaced by a less conspicuous vehicle. Dr Clark continued to look after Ward 7 but the workload there soon reduced when sixteen beds in Newhills Sanatorium became available for cases of primary TB in children. Later, when tuberculous meningitis and complications of measles and whooping cough became rare, Ward 7 was used for other purposes, although in 1969 it had to be taken over temporarily when there was a large outbreak of dysentery in a children's home.[21] Dr Galloway remained in charge of the infectious disease beds at the City Hospital until his retirement in late 1980.

Tuberculosis

In 1948 tuberculosis was still a common disease. Those detected with the condition still required prolonged rest and in-patient treatment to try to arrest the disease and encourage healing, and subsequent prolonged follow-up, as later recrudescence or recurrence was still frequent. Under the National Health Service Act, the responsibility for the diagnosis and treatment of tuberculosis transferred from local authorities to Regional Hospital Boards. There was no shortage of hospital beds for this purpose but a lack of medical staff. There were then around 100 beds designated for tuberculosis at the City Hospital, although this was to be reduced later to 84, as well as beds at Woodend Hospital and Newhills Sanatorium in the city and beds for this purpose at other North-East hospitals at Strichen, Inverurie, Aboyne and Stonehaven. There were also the Red Cross sanatoria on Deeside at Tor-na-Dee and Glen O'Dee. The Regional Board quickly decided that the main hospital centre should be in Aberdeen, at the City Hospital. Dr Bell, who was then TB officer for the city, and Dr Fraser, who was TB officer for the county, were transferred to full-time NHS service, Dr Bell as senior physician to co-ordinate the service and Dr Fraser as a senior hospital medical officer (SHMO).

Dr Robert Fraser (1911–98): The son of a company director, he was born in Aberdeen on 28 December 1911. He was educated at the Aberdeen Grammar School, his schooling being interrupted by a period of several weeks spent in the City Hospital as a patient with scarlet fever. He spent much of the time in isolation and only learnt many years later, when he looked at his own case notes, that this was because his throat swab had also cultured diphtheria bacilli.[22] He graduated in medicine in 1935 and then, as mentioned in Chapter 9, spent a period as junior house physician at the City Hospital before doing other house officer posts at Woodend and in Newcastle. His initial thoughts had been of a future in general practice but then in 1938, when working as a locum general practitioner, he developed TB pleurisy and had to spend a few months in the City Hospital. He had already taken his DPH in 1937 and so decided to make his future in public health. He was appointed assistant medical officer to Aberdeen County Council in 1939. He took over the duties of Dr Bell, then the county TB officer, when the latter left for the war, and kept in touch with the staff at the City Hospital by periodic visits there.[23] In 1946 he obtained his MD, the subject of his thesis being the follow-up of nearly 1,300 patients with pulmonary tuberculosis who had attended the clinic between 1934–43. When Dr Bell was appointed tuberculosis officer to the City in 1946, Dr

Fraser resumed work as acting TB officer for Aberdeenshire and his appointment was made permanent in 1947. As mentioned, he became SHMO in the NHS in 1948. Dr Anna Mason, who was in charge of the TB patients at Woodend, was also made SHMO. An additional vacancy was advertised and Dr Eric Barnes was appointed.[24]

Dr Eric G. Barnes (1908–96): He was born in Tunbridge Wells and graduated in Edinburgh in 1935. He contracted tuberculosis during war service with the RAMC in the Mediterranean. He later required a laminectomy in 1947 for a disc prolapse which left him with a permanent limp. Not long after taking up his appointment he was off ill with recurrence of his tuberculosis and required a pneumonectomy. He continued in full-time service thereafter until 1973 and died of cor pulmonale in 1996.[25]

About the same time as Dr Barnes was appointed, Dr Maurice Waters was appointed to work in tuberculosis in Banffshire and Moray.[26] He left in 1957 to take up a chest physician post in Australia.[27]

The TB clinics which had been held at the public health offices in Albyn Place were transferred to the City Hospital after alterations were made there to accommodate the additional staff. Clinics were held daily and there were also many peripheral clinics. In 1951 Dr John Young was appointed tuberculosis medical officer and junior hospital medical officer (JHMO). He was to be mainly engaged in running the Mass Miniature Radiography Service but also did some clinics. Dr Hugh Rutherford was appointed assistant TB officer and JHMO in 1953.[28]

Hubert W. Rutherford (1915–88): He was born in Grantown-on-Spey but spent his youth in Northumberland. He studied medicine at Aberdeen, graduating in 1942, and after working as a resident at Woodend, joined the RAMC. He served in north-west Europe and India, and gained experience in venereal diseases. On demobilisation in 1947 he took the DPH and was appointed District Medical Officer of Health in Lancashire, prior to returning to Aberdeen in 1953.[29]

The workload at the City Hospital clinic was initially heavy, with around 200–300 new cases a year and between 1,200–2,000 new out-patient visits annually.[30] The large refill clinics continued on Sunday mornings, where patients under treatment by artificial pneumothorax or pneumoperitoneum had air put into their chests or abdomens. Around 80–100 patients attended these clinics.[31] Medical students could also attend and one of us (MJW) remembers that after watching a few of the procedures and being shown what to do, students were allowed to do some themselves on the long-suffering but always cheerful and tolerant patients. Following the introduction of the anti-tuberculous drugs, the demand on in-patient beds for TB fell as the duration of required hospital stay shortened, and later indeed, many patients were able to be treated as out-patients.

Considerable redeployment of beds occurred in 1955 when the Red Cross Society, unable to afford to maintain the Deeside sanatoria, gifted both Tor-na-Dee and Glen O'Dee to the NHS. Dr Keers, who had been the medical superintendent in these institutions, and his staff left shortly afterwards, and the Regional Board decided to move all TB patients from Woodend, Inverurie, Strichen, Arduthie (Stonehaven) and Aboyne Hospitals to these institutions.[32] Dr Douglas Kay was then appointed senior hospital medical officer and physician superintendent at Tor-na-Dee.

Douglas T. Kay: He qualified in Edinburgh in 1944, then served in the RAF in India before returning to Edinburgh to train in respiratory diseases with Professor John Crofton. He was involved there as co-ordinator in some of the earliest controlled clinical trials of drug therapy in pulmonary tuberculosis. In Aberdeen, in addition to his responsibilities at Tor-na-Dee, he also saw out-patients at the chest clinic.

During the 1960s, the bed requirements for TB at the City Hospital declined and several of the wards were redeployed for other uses, as will be discussed. It was also soon realised that with effective anti-tuberculous drug treatment TB could be cured. Long-term follow-up was not now needed and so the staff requirements for the management of this disease decreased. Dr Anna Mason took early retirement on health grounds in 1965,[33] Dr Bell retired in 1967, and neither was replaced in this field. Shortly after Dr Bell's retirement, Hugh Rutherford, the assistant TB officer, who had for some time been working part-time in the venereal diseases department, moved to whole-time work there and became consultant in charge, a position he was to hold until his retirement in 1980.

Dr Fraser had been left for a period then as sole consultant chest physician and it was only after an inquiry that an additional consultant post was agreed to.[34] The Board would not automatically upgrade Dr Barnes, who had to apply in competition for the post, but was appointed and continued in this role until his retirement in 1973.[35]

Around 1968, the Aberdeen Royal Infirmary radiology department took charge of the Mass Miniature Radiography Centre and x-ray facilities in King Street, and Dr John Young left to join a newly-opened course for the Diploma in Medical Radiology in Aberdeen. He later came into conflict with the examiners in London in the second part of his examination and decided to abandon continuance, returning to work in the chest clinic until he retired early on health grounds in 1976.[36]

Dr Douglas Kay, after Tor-na-Dee ceased to be needed for tuberculous patients, moved for a period to geriatric medicine but did not enjoy that and returned to work in the chest clinic until his retirement in 1986. He was one of many specialists in the field of tuberculosis who suffered when their expertise in the management of chronic tuberculosis became largely redundant because of the now effective treatment. In the latter part of the period under consideration, increasing numbers of non-tuberculous chest diseases were being seen at the clinic which since the 1950s had been known as the chest clinic rather than the TB department. From 1966 there were no designated beds for tuberculosis at the City Hospital although the chest physicians could, by arrangement, admit some patients under their care to the medical wards.

Tuberculosis, the dread affliction of the past, was now largely controlled although not fully conquered.

Radiology Department

It is appropriate to discuss developments in this field next as x-ray facilities at the City Hospital had initially been established linked to the TB dispensary. An x-ray apparatus was first installed in the TB Institute opened in 1914 (see Chapter 5) and had moved with the latter to the central administration block (see Chapter 9). Gradual extensions had occurred but the x-ray service remained under the control of the chest physicians. In 1951 the Regional Board set up a Mass Miniature Radiography (MMR) Unit based at King Street and, as mentioned earlier, Dr John Young, who had been appointed to supervise this, was also a tuberculosis medical officer working in the chest clinic. There was also a mobile MMR unit for touring the region. In 1952, however, it was decided that a radiologist should be put in charge of the x-ray department at the City Hospital, and Dr Milligan, radiologist at the Sick Children's Hospital was given this task and visited regularly. Facilities were further increased, with a new entrance, more suitable for patients on stretchers, and the chest physicians were displaced from some of their rooms to other accommodation in the building.[37] In 1964 Dr L. A. Gillanders became consultant in charge of radiology and, as the general radiological workload at the City Hospital had increased with the increasing development of general medical beds, Dr J. H. Palmer was appointed consultant radiologist at the City Hospital that year. He died tragically in 1967 and was replaced by Dr W. M. C. Allen.

Venereal Diseases

At the time of implementation of the NHS Act there were still the two treatment centres for VD in the city, one at the Aberdeen Royal Infirmary out-patient block at Woolmanhill and the other at the City Hospital. These were both under the control of Dr Fred Bowie who was later made consultant in charge. There had been structural changes made in the facilities in Woolmanhill and, consequent on these, the number of patients being seen at the treatment centre at the City Hospital fell. Because of this, in October 1950, Dr Bowie proposed that the centre there should be closed. This was agreed and from 1 January 1951 no further new cases were seen at the City Hospital, although follow-up cases continued to attend for a few months.[38] In-patients were still admitted to Ward 5 but with the advent of penicillin there were now fewer such cases. Ward 5, which had also admitted infective skin disorders, was shortly closed and incorporated into the laboratory. However, the venereologists could arrange admission for the few such cases requiring it to either Ward 8 or 9.

Dr Bowie was also university lecturer in venereal diseases. His lectures were comprehensive. One of us (MJW) remembers filling one whole foolscap page of notes on all the possible stigma of congenital syphilis. His lectures were also enlivened by racy anecdotes. 'The time between exposure and the onset of symptoms in the more virulent forms of gonorrhoea could be very short – even within the timespan of a Number 1 tram journey!' (The Number 1 tramway route was the longest in Aberdeen, plying between the Bridge of Dee and the Bridge of Don) 'Use of a condom was not guaranteed protection against the transmission of gonorrhoea – the most virulent strains could penetrate a Wellington boot!'. 'Prostitutes were not an important source of venereal infection – the problem was the enthusiastic amateur!'. One notorious prostitute of the time was 'Sandpit Mary' who plied her trade in a bunker on Balnagask Golf Course! Not the most comfortable of boudoirs!

Dr Bowie also gave excellent out-patient demonstrations. Large numbers of patients, all of whom he knew well, were brought up to demonstrate the various skin manifestations of syphilis, and also patients with aneurysms, tabes dorsalis and the various features of congenital syphilis. All were rewarded after attendance with a silver coin, presumably a half-crown (2s 6d or 12.5p), from a leather bag. He was handicapped by indifferent health and retired in 1959. Dr Bowie died on 14 November 1973.[39] Following Dr Bowie's retirement, the venereal diseases service was covered by the dermatologists, helped from 1967 by Hugh Rutherford who had previously been an assistant physician in the chest clinic. In 1968 he was appointed consultant in charge of the VD service.

Rheumatic Diseases (Rheumatology)

Developments in this field were slow. Professor R. S. Aitken (professor of medicine 1939–48), who had succeeded L. S. P. Davidson on the latter's departure to the chair of medicine in Edinburgh, had established a department of rheumatic diseases in 1945.[40] This consisted of twenty beds at Stracathro Hospital and six beds in the professorial medical unit at Woodend Hospital. A rheumatic out-patient clinic was also set up in relation to the orthopaedic out-patient clinic and Dr Logie S. Bain was put in charge of this development (see Chapter 9). There were also some out-patient facilities at the Justice Mill Lane Baths but after the departure of Professor Aitken, activity there had temporarily declined. In 1948, however, after discussion with the Town Council the clinic facilities at the Baths were reactivated and extended. At this time Dr Hubert Balch, who was a registrar in rheumatology in Dundee working in the clinic at Stracathro, was made JHMO to the Regional Board in Aberdeen to assist Logie Bain in his work.[41]

Hubert W. Balch (1914–96): Born in Geneva on 23 June 1914, he graduated in medicine in Aberdeen in 1937 and then entered the tuberculosis service before joining the RAMC in 1940. He served in India for five years and on demobilisation had moved to rheumatology and physical medicine, later taking his Diploma in Physical Medicine. He became consultant in the physical medicine and rheumatology department, holding this post until his retirement in 1979. He died in 1996.

In the later 1950s there were further discussions on extensions to the department. There were initial thoughts of siting this at Woodend but it was later decided to locate it at the City Hospital where there was vacant accommodation. The units at Stracathro and Woodend Hospitals were then closed and Ward 1 at the City Hospital, which had earlier housed diphtheria patients but was now empty, was, along with half of Ward 2, upgraded and converted for the department of physical medicine. Ward 1 housed the ward area, with 43 beds, whilst the space in Ward 2 was converted to house the physiotherapy department, offices and out-patient facilities.[42] The unit was formally and fittingly opened by Professor L. S. P. Davidson on 12 July

1960,[43] he having been the 'father' of the subject in Aberdeen, and it was to continue functioning here effectively for many years.

General Medicine

General medical patients were first admitted to the City Hospital about 1956 when Ward 4, which had previously housed tuberculous patients became under-utilised. At first, admission of emergencies was done on an ad hoc basis and mostly over the winter months when there was heavy demand on beds at Foresterhill and Woodend. This increased the number of admissions to the City Hospital by around 300 a year but had an adverse effect on the death rate. Thus, of 206 deaths at the hospital in 1956 and 1957, no fewer than 146 were in general medical cases as these patients were both older and more ill than the majority of infectious disease admissions.[44]

A formal general medical unit started in November 1959, regularly admitting emergencies, with its own day on the rota.[45] These patients were initially all looked after by Dr Chambers, but in 1961 half the beds were given to Dr John M. Stowers, who had been appointed consultant physician with a special interest in diabetes to succeed Dr Alexander Lyall in charge of the diabetic clinic. Fourteen beds in Ward 7 were also about then classified as general medical beds and used by Dr Walker. When Dr Bell retired in 1967 it was decided to replace his post by a general physician with interest in diabetes to assist Dr Stowers, and one of us (MJW) was appointed in April 1968. After refurbishment, the remaining portion of Ward 2 and half of Ward 3, again previously housing tuberculous patients, were converted to general medical use, giving 29 beds. Prior to Dr Williams taking up appointment, Dr J. S. Meredith, who had worked with the Colonial Medical Service in Tanganyika, acted as locum consultant.

With memories of the 1964 typhoid epidemic receding, the City Hospital was now very much a general hospital containing the infectious diseases unit. Of the 229 total beds only 49 beds were designated for infection, 27 of these being for children. Eighty-seven beds were designated as general medical, 43 were rheumatological, and the remaining 50 were used for other purposes. The hospital did its full share of acute medical receiving, apart from not taking patients with acute gastro-intestinal bleeding who might require surgical treatment. Total annual admissions to the City Hospital now increased to just over 3,000 a year, a very large proportion of these being general medical cases. Dr Walker and Dr Williams were also responsible for the monthly general medical clinics in

Orkney and Shetland. Patients from these northern islands requiring hospital admission were all admitted to the City Hospital wards. Apart from providing much interesting and indeed often exotic material for teaching purposes, this concentration in one site was of great benefit to the patients. There was an active islands visitors' association and visitors often knew more than one patient, and those without relatives in the city were soon befriended by others. Several of the nursing staff also visited the islands on holidays and became familiar with their patients' home surroundings and came to comprehend the local dialects!

Surgery and Gynaecology

As mentioned in Chapter 9, ENT surgery had been undertaken at times at the City Hospital since 1939. The initial operating theatre was located between Wards 3 and 4.[46] Wards 9 and 10, which opened in 1940, incorporated a new up-to-date and well-equipped operating theatre. This was originally intended for the performance of tracheostomy, which was often required in diphtheria cases, and for the treatment of throat abscesses which often then complicated scarlet fever. Occasional surgery for tuberculosis was also performed. The early mentioned problems, however, soon declined and the theatre was under-utilised. In 1949 regular operating lists for tonsillectomy and adenoidectomy (T&As) in children were arranged, two sixteen-case groups being dealt with weekly. This helped clear a large waiting list for this operation which had accumulated at the Sick Children's Hospital.[47] In 1951, however, for reasons not clear, it was deemed undesirable to continue this[48] and the theatre was again under-utilised for a period. In 1956 gynaecology lists for minor procedures were started, and fourteen beds in Ward 7 were used for this purpose, with lists again twice weekly. This continued for many years but had of course to cease during the time of the typhoid epidemic when the ward was early commandeered. Surgical work recommenced when this was over, and both general surgical and gynaecological cases were dealt with, as large waiting lists in both fields had accumulated during the typhoid outbreak, when all cold admissions to Foresterhill and Woodend had been halted. Between October 1964 and August 1965 a total of 960 surgical patients were treated.

Geriatric Medicine

Geriatric medicine first established itself, albeit temporarily, in the hospital in 1962, when Ward 6 was used to house geriatric patients whose accommodation elsewhere in the North-East was being refurbished. In 1965 Ward 6 was formally made into a permanent geriatric unit with 36 beds.

From this small beginning geriatric medicine steadily expanded, ultimately spreading throughout the whole hospital.

Nursing

The nurse training school, which specifically trained fever nurses, continued actively and had no problem recruiting staff. As well as training staff to work in the City Hospital it also recruited staff for Inverurie Hospital which had 80 beds designated for infection, although those mostly accommodated patients with TB. An arrangement was made to rotate student nurses from the Royal Infirmary to the City Hospital. This started in 1957. It was initially done on a voluntary basis although new entrants to training were then informed that this might be required. Student nurses from the City Hospital were also seconded for a period to the Royal Infirmary.

The 1964 typhoid outbreak placed great strain on nursing resources but many former fever-trained nurses who had left the profession answered an appeal and returned to help out. The same year the City Hospital was formally recognised as a training school for enrolled nurses, and a pupil nurse training school commenced the next year. Recruitment was good and the examination results achieved by trainees were as good as elsewhere.

The increasing general medical activity required increasing numbers of nursing staff and this posed accommodation problems at the hospital. Night staff had to stay in accommodation elsewhere and were bussed in and out daily.

In 1968 Miss V. Maltman who had been matron at the City Hospital for twenty years, retired. She was the second-longest serving in this post, her long period of responsibility being exceeded only by Miss M. Frater who had held the position for 32 years from 1896–1928. Miss Maltman was replaced by Miss A. C. Argo[49] (See Appendix 2).

Administrative Change

In late 1970, the Regional Board decided on a major administrative restructuring. They decided to amalgamate the Boards of Management of the Aberdeen General, Aberdeen Special and Kincardine Hospitals, and from 1 April 1971 the City Hospital became the responsibility of a new board, the Board of Management for the Foresterhill and Associated Hospitals. The Board of Management for the Aberdeen Special Hospitals held their last meeting on 9 March 1971.

References to Chapter Twelve

[1]   Northern Health Services Archives, North-Eastern Regional Hospital Board minutes (hereafter NERHB), 19 May 1948.

[2]   NERHB, 8 June 1948.

[3]   NERHB, 6 August 1948; NERHB, 16 June 1948.

[4]   NERHB, 8 June 1948.

[5]   NERHB, 5 July 1950.

[6]   NERHB, 6 September 1950.

[7]   Obituary, W. Chambers, *British Medical Journal*, 1963, vol. 2, pp. 939–40.

[8]   Northern Health Services Archives, Aberdeen Special Hospitals Board of Management minutes (hereafter ASHBOM), 31 May 1948.

[9]   Northern Health Services Archives, Annual Report of the Group Medical Superintendent to the Aberdeen Special Hospitals Board of Management (hereafter ASHBOM report) for 1967, pp. 1–2.

[10] ASHBOM report for 1959, p. 12; ASHBOM report for 1963, p. 5.

[11] NERHB, 8 June 1948.

[12] ASHBOM, 13 May 1952.

[13] NERHB, 6 May 1953.

[14] ASHBOM report for 1959, p. 9.

[15] R. Fraser, 'Memories of the City Hospital', unpublished manuscript, n.d., currently in the possession of Professor J. Friend.

[16] Ibid.

[17] J. Stowers, 'Regius Chair of Materia Medica', *Aberdeen Postgraduate Medical Bulletin*, January 1974, pp. 90–1.

[18] ASHBOM report for 1964, p. 3.

[19] Ibid., pp. 15–16.

[20] J. M. S., 'William Walker' (Obituary), *Aberdeen Postgraduate Medical Bulletin*, 1985, vol. 19, no. 2, pp. 38–9.

[21] ASHBOM report for 1969, p. 26.

[22] Fraser, op. cit.

[23] Ibid.

[24] NERHB, 14 February 1949.

[25] Obituary, Eric Gordon Barnes, *British Medical Journal*, 1996, vol. 2, p. 107.

[26] NERHB, 14 February 1949.

[27] Fraser, op. cit.

[28] Ibid.

[29] 'Hubert Watson Rutherford' (Obituary), *Aberdeen Postgraduate Medical Bulletin*, September 1988, vol. 22, no. 3, pp. 38–9.

[30] Annual reports of the Medical Officer of Health for the years 1948–70.

[31] Fraser, op. cit.

32 Ibid.
33 Ibid.
34 Ibid.
35 Obituary, Barnes, op. cit.
36 Fraser, op. cit.
37 Ibid.
38 NERHB, 5 October 1950.
39 'Frederick J. T. Bowie' (Obituary), *Aberdeen Postgraduate Medical Bulletin*, May 1974, p. 44.
40 I. D. Levack, and H. A. F. Dudley (eds), *Aberdeen Royal Infirmary*, London, Baillière Tindall, 1992, pp. 166–8.
41 NERHB, 14 February 1949.
42 ASHBOM report for 1959, p. 9.
43 ASHBOM report for 1960, p. 6.
44 ASHBOM report for 1956, p. 11; ASHBOM report for 1957, p. 21.
45 ASHBOM report for 1959, p. 9.
46 Fraser, op. cit.
47 ASHBOM, 13 September 1949.
48 ASHBOM, 8 May 1951.
49 ASHBOM report for 1968, pp. 3, 11–12.

Chapter Thirteen

Infections and the City Hospital 1949–72

The introduction of the NHS moved responsibility for the diagnosis and treatment of infections from the Medical Officer of Health to the general practitioner and hospital service. The MOH and Public Health Department (which was known officially as the Health and Welfare Department from 1948) remained responsible for the prevention and control of infection in the community. They were still therefore responsible for the maintenance of good standards of hygiene, the inspection of food processing and food handling premises, and the maintenance and encouragement of vaccination and immunisation programmes.

Dr Harry J. Rae continued as Medical Officer of Health to the new joint public health service of the North-East of Scotland until 1952. He should ordinarily have retired in 1951 but because of his outstanding service was kept in post by the Town Council for an additional year.[1] He was succeeded in Aberdeen by Dr Ian A. G. MacQueen.

Dr Ian A. G. MacQueen (1909–1992)

Ian MacQueen was born at Kirknewton and was brought up in Penicuik in Midlothian, his father becoming the headmaster of the local school. He was a bright pupil and after primary education locally went to George Watson's College in Edinburgh. His chosen career was to be in journalism and he obtained an MA (honours) at Edinburgh University.[2] He then, however, decided to study medicine and graduated MB ChB in 1937. He early focused on a career in public health medicine and obtained his DPH in 1939 and became assistant MOH for Barnsley. Subsequently, he became MOH for Mansfield, being at that time one of the youngest Medical Officers of Health in Britain.[3] He obtained his MD with commendation in 1949. Prior to his appointment in Aberdeen in 1952, he had been a medical officer at the Department of Health for Scotland since 1947. In Aberdeen he was particularly zealous in promoting and increasing the role of the health visitors in his department and came into conflict with anyone who had differing ideas or who in any way denigrated this service.

Dr MacQueen was to spend over twenty years as Aberdeen's MOH and events were to show that epidemic diseases could still pose a serious threat. With administrative re-organisation of the NHS, the post of Medical Officer of Health was dissolved, when the Health Boards took over in 1974.

For his final period of service, Dr MacQueen was appointed to a supernumerary post as specialist in community medicine, working in the Community Health Division offices at St Nicholas House. He retired in September 1975.

The various infections of note in this period will now be discussed sequentially as in Chapters 10 and 11. The data on the incidence of infectious diseases referred to in the text are taken from the annual reports of the Medical Officer of Health covering the period. The data, unless otherwise stated, apply to the city of Aberdeen.

MAJOR INFECTIONS

Smallpox

There were no further cases of this disease in Aberdeen although there was concern over its importation when there were outbreaks in Glasgow in 1950, in Brighton in 1950–1 and in Northern England in 1953.

Vaccination ceased to be compulsory with the introduction of the NHS but considerable numbers still underwent the procedure. Many who were not vaccinated in infancy, because their parents considered it unnecessary or were against it in principle, found that vaccination was compulsory if they were travelling abroad. Many countries required individuals to be vaccinated before entry. Vaccination was now done by general practitioners or medical officers at the child welfare clinics.

Under the stimulus of an Aberdeen graduate, Professor Allan Downie FRS (1901–88), professor of bacteriology at Liverpool and this country's leading expert on smallpox, the World Health Organisation (WHO) was persuaded to take on the project of global eradication of the disease by widespread vaccination.[4] Several technical advances in smallpox vaccination made this possible and by dint of great expenditure and effort, by May 1980 the WHO was able to declare that 'the world and all its people have won freedom from smallpox'. It is of coincidental interest that the main signatory of this declaration at the 33rd World Assembly in Geneva was Aberdeen graduate Dr A. R. A. Al-Awadi. After graduating in 1963 he had returned to his native Kuwait, where he became Minister of Health in 1975, and president of the World Health Assembly in 1980.[5]

OTHER COMMON ZYMOTICS

Diphtheria

The increasing use of immunisation proved its worth, soon leading to the disappearance of this disease. Between 1949–55 there were only ten cases, with just one fatality in 1950, and no cases occurred after 1955. There was still, however, a need for widespread immunisation to prevent the recurrence of diphtheria, and the immunisation programme was favoured by the development of combined vaccines which will be mentioned later.

Scarlet Fever

Although far less prevalent than before, this was still initially fairly common in this period with a peak of 513 cases in 1950 (Figure 26). From 1954 the incidence steadily declined and from 1960 onwards there were always less than 30 cases a year. The disease in this period appeared fairly mild and there was not a single death from this cause after 1948. The decline was in the main probably due to the early use of penicillin and other antibiotics in patients with sore throats rather than to effective immunisation. For reasons that are not clear, immunisation for scarlet fever had never become popular or widely used.

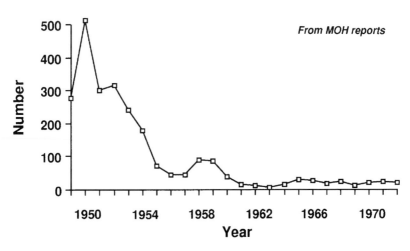

**Figure 26 Scarlet Fever
Incidence 1949–72**

From MOH reports

Typhoid and Paratyphoid Fever

These had become uncommon as a consequence of general improvements in food hygiene, but paratyphoid fever, which was notified under the same heading as typhoid, still occurred occasionally, although usually in small numbers. Between 1949–63 there were a total of 72 cases, but no fatalities. Twenty-five of the cases occurred in an outbreak of paratyphoid B in 1958. This affected a convent and a children's home which shared a common kitchen. The infection was traced to a female kitchen assistant who, it was discovered, had been a chronic carrier since having been infected during an outbreak in Dundee in 1941.[6]

The paratyphoid B of 1958 was a minor incident, however, compared with a major outbreak of typhoid fever six years later. The City Hospital returned to its early role as 'The Epidemic Hospital' in 1964 when it was overwhelmed by the notorious outbreak of typhoid fever known since as the 'Aberdeen Typhoid Outbreak'.

The Aberdeen Typhoid Outbreak of 1964

This had a small beginning. On 16 May two university students sharing accommodation were admitted to the staff ward at Aberdeen Royal Infirmary with a diagnosis of pyrexia of unknown origin. They had been unwell for a few days. Various investigations were arranged and on 19 May it was suspected on clinical grounds and from the early bacteriological results that they might be suffering from typhoid fever. They were transferred to the City Hospital that evening and the diagnosis was confirmed bacteriologically the next day. The Health and Welfare Department of the Town Council was then notified. There were already four patients from another family in the City Hospital, all of whom turned out to have the same disease, and other cases quickly emerged and were admitted. Numbers admitted thereafter showed a dramatic increase as seen in Figure 27 which shows the daily number of typhoid admissions between 16 May and 30 June.[7]

With this steady influx of increasing numbers, the officially designated 'infection wards' were soon filled, and other wards had to be successively commandeered, and the patients already there either discharged home or transferred elsewhere. The gynaecologists, who were using Ward 7, readily gave up their beds, as later did the rheumatologists in Ward 1. Douglas Bell was initially reluctant to give up Wards 2 and 3 but had to yield to the pressing need. Eventually, the whole City Hospital apart from Ward 9 and part of Ward 10, which were kept to deal with other infections in adults and children, were filled with cases of typhoid fever. Wards 3 and 7 were used for children with the disease and the few infants involved were admitted to Ward 10.[8] Later adult cases were admitted to the annexe at Woodend, then to Wards 7 and 8 there, and later to Tor-na-Dee Hospital. Forty children were admitted to the City Hospital and a further 46 cases presenting from 31 May onwards were treated in the Royal Aberdeen Hospital for Sick Children, where two wards with a total capacity of 60 beds had been cleared. Beds were also held in readiness in Dundee but it proved unnecessary to use this reserve.[9]

Figure 27 Typhoid
Admissions to hospital 1964

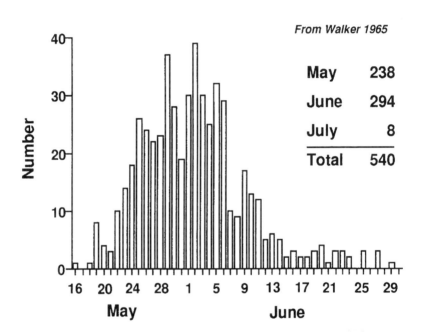

From Walker 1965

May	238
June	294
July	8
Total	540

Dr Fraser, the chest physician, had been covering the infection beds since Dr Chambers' illness. He was due to go on holiday to Switzerland in early June and offered to postpone this but the offer was declined.[10] Dr William Walker, who unbeknown to Dr Fraser had been appointed to Chambers' job, but was not due to take up the post until the end of the summer term, was released from his job at Dundee University and arrived to take overall clinical control of the typhoid patients. When he drove into the city to take up his new job, he realised with surprise that there was no traffic and very few people out in the streets. It was a lovely day and there were beautiful displays of flowers, but although it was a sunny city, it was also a dead city.[11] Aberdeen was in the grip of an epidemic. Dr Sandy Lyall, retired physician and head of the clinical chemistry department, returned to work to help. Additional junior medical staff and 56 additional nurses were also recruited.[12]

Medical Aspects: This account is largely based on the detailed report of the outbreak prepared jointly by many participants under the editorship of Dr William Walker.[13]

During the outbreak a total of 540 patients were admitted with suspected typhoid. A total of 507 patients were regarded as having the disease, of whom 86 were children under the age of twelve years. In 403 cases the diagnosis was confirmed bacteriologically and in 66 patients the diagnosis was made clinically. In 38 patients typhoid was not confirmed but could not be excluded. There were three deaths. An additional eight patients were known who contracted typhoid while visiting Aberdeen but were treated elsewhere; three in Glasgow, two in Newcastle, two in Dundee and one in Toronto.

The outbreak involved families. The 507 cases came from 309 households in the city and 33 in surrounding districts, fewer than 0.6 per cent of the 58,000 households in Aberdeen being involved. The outbreak took the form of a single wave with no proven secondary cases.

Great strain was put on the general practitioner service in the city by the outbreak. The first report of typhoid in Aberdeen was given in the evening of 21 May on radio and television but general practitioners then knew little more than their patients about the epidemic and its implications. On 24 May, all practices in the city were telephoned by the Health and Welfare Department indicating the probable source in a local supermarket and defining a 'typhoid contact'. Early diagnosis of cases and screening of contacts was the responsibility of the general practitioner. The following day, a letter from the City of Aberdeen Local Medical Committee was hand-delivered to all local general practitioners, informing them that large numbers of their patients who had been deemed to be 'contacts' by Dr MacQueen's staff, would, at the request of the latter, be attending their own doctors for blood tests. Headache and high fever were considered early features and the diagnosis could be virtually certain if a history of having eaten food from the relevant supermarket was obtained. A contact had been defined as 'any person residing in the same home as a known case or who had eaten food prepared or handled by a known case'. In the early days many blood samples were taken during the probable incubation period when no test was of actual value. This was rectified by a 'Notes for Guidance' circular produced by the Local Medical Committee, with specific advice from the City Hospital laboratory, which was sent to all practitioners. The later publication of names and addresses of patients in the local press also confused the issue. Many demanded tests although they were not contacts within the agreed definition. Surgeries became grossly overcrowded when groups of contacts appeared for tests and many practices set up special clinics outwith normal surgery hours. A special clinic was also later established to re-test those who had initially been screened too early. This was staffed voluntarily by general practitioners on a rota basis. Several retired practitioners offered help.

A special committee, consisting of representatives of all parts of the health service, was set up to aid liaison and communication, and practitioners in the city were kept informed of relevant developments by almost daily letters. The earlier admitted patients who had the heavier infection had an illness like gastro-enteritis coming on a few days after infection, with vomiting, diarrhoea, headache and usually high fever, while later patients had usually just headache and fever and more non-specific abdominal symptoms. Some patients had no symptoms or developed them only after admission, having had positive tests when checked as contacts. Inevitably, a number of patients admitted with suspected typhoid had a variety of other illnesses. The eleven different physicians involved in their care had to be very vigilant. Discussions among this group on common problems and projects were held regularly. All but eighteen of the adults treated initially were given the antibiotic chloramphenicol (chloromycetin) alone, it being of proven value in this disease. Ampicillin (a semi-synthetic penicillin) was used in a number of children and some patients were treated with both drugs. In a small number other antibiotics were used for specific reasons. A new broad-spectrum antibiotic cephaloridine, which it was thought might be of value, was tried in three moderately ill patients but seemed ineffective.[14]

Despite a full course of treatment, 86 patients suffered a relapse requiring further treatment. This was a well known event in this disease. Three patients died. Two were elderly with some incidental disease. One 60 year old lady died of a massive pulmonary embolism when being treated for a relapse.[15] Even after clinical cure had occurred, patients had to be detained in hospital to ensure full clearance of infection. It was known that about 30 per cent of patients still excrete *Salmonella typhi*, the infecting organism, immediately after completing treatment, and about three per cent became chronic carriers – they continue to excrete *S. typhi* continually or intermittently after a period of from six to twelve months following recovery from the acute stage.[16] These subjects are a considerable risk to others.

A 'clearance' regime was started four days after the end of treatment. This consisted of the examination of three paired specimens of stool and urine at four-day intervals. If three consecutive negatives were obtained the patient was discharged. The first victim was discharged on 19 June. An attractive 23-year-old woman, she was presented on discharge with a bouquet and sash declaring her 'Typhoid Queen – 1964'; a dubious title.[17]

A double blind trial of the antibiotic ampicillin was carried out in 114 early convalescent typhoid excretors. Half were given the active drug and half inert capsules. No conclusive benefit occurred, but a low incidence of chronic carriers – five out of the 469 confirmed cases – was found, and use of this drug may have contributed.[18]

Laboratory Aspects: Two blood cultures received at the City Hospital laboratory on 18 May yielded a growth of *S. typhi* on 20 May. On the same day the university department of bacteriology reported the isolation of *S. typhi* from the faeces and blood cultures of two patients. Between 19 and 23 May, thirteen cases of typhoid fever were confirmed on the basis of blood culture evidence.

This heralded the beginning of the Aberdeen Typhoid Outbreak, which put great stress not only on the hospital facilities, administrative services, public health staff and general practitioners, but also on the staff and facilities at the laboratories of the City Hospital and the bacteriology department of the university.

At the City Hospital extra laboratory staff had to be recruited, some voluntary, others as paid personnel. Two bacteriologists were seconded from the University of St Andrews, the technical staff was increased from nineteen to twenty-seven, the laboratory maids from nine to twelve, and the office staff from nine to twenty-four.

For many weeks the City Hospital laboratory was open from 6 am until 10 pm every day in order that the routine work as well as the massive number of specimens from the epidemic could be dealt with as quickly as possible. In all, from 20 May until 31 December 1964 the laboratory dealt with 70,304 investigations which included clot cultures, blood cultures, faeces and urine cultures and serological tests. A number of investigations on sewer swabs and food stuffs are included in this figure. Nearly 2,500 investigations were carried out by the university bacteriology department.

It was decided early on in the outbreak that the clot from bloods submitted for serological tests (Widal) should be cultured. From 11,043 such clot cultures, *S. typhi* was isolated from 153, and 122 cases of typhoid received their first bacteriological confirmation in this way. From faeces and urine specimens examined, 163 and six respectively were the first confirmatory tests made.

Of food stuffs examined, which included cooked and uncooked meats, unopened cans of meat and meat produce such as pies and bakery products, *S. typhi* was isolated from none. Swabs from slicing machines also failed to produce *S. typhi*. Of 453 sewer swabs examined by a variety of techniques, ten were positive for *S. typhi*.

There are many different strains of bacteria and the particular strain responsible for specific food poisoning incidents may be identified by a technique known as phage-typing. The phage-typing in connection with the Aberdeen typhoid outbreak was carried out on all isolates by the Enteric Reference Laboratory at the Central Public Health Laboratory, London. All cultures submitted were reported as being phage-type 34, a type not indigenous in the United Kingdom but found in South America and Spain.[19]

Public Health Aspects: The first notification of two suspected cases of typhoid was given to the local Health and Welfare Department on Wednesday 20 May. By midnight that day there were already twelve patients in the City Hospital suspected of having that disease and it was clear that there was a significant local outbreak. Questioning of these patients and their relatives by public health medical officers revealed three common food factors – milk from a large dairy, ice-cream from a particular shop and cold meat from a supermarket in the West End. Routine measures such as examination of water and milk, increase of water chlorination and notification of the Medical Officers of Health of adjacent areas and the Scottish Home and Health Department were implemented.

As further cases occurred and were interrogated it began to appear that the consumption of milk and ice-cream from the same source in some of the early cases had been coincidental, and suspicion increasingly converged on the cold meat department of the supermarket. On 21 May investigation of all the staff in the relevant shop was started and swabs taken from various sites. It had initially been thought that a typhoid carrier working in the shop was probably responsible but investigations on all the staff proved negative and by 23 May epidemiological evidence pointed specifically to sliced corned beef purchased from that supermarket. Of 41 patients admitted by that time, 38 could recall eating that specific product. The original tin considered to be involved had by then been destroyed, but on the same day, the Central Reference Laboratory at Colindale had typed the involved organism from the early cases and, as mentioned, had shown it was a strain unknown in Britain, but common in South America and Spain. Advice was given to those working in the shop on personal hygiene and on cleaning and disinfecting the premises. The shop was not then closed. This was later judged to have been an error, although in actual fact all those eventual sufferers were already incubating the disease.[20]

Up to 26 May the evidence still pointed to a limited outbreak, confined, unless secondary cases occurred, to persons who had eaten corned beef from a single infected six-pound tin, sold in slices between 7 and 9 May. The picture, however, then changed as later patients admitted simply gave histories of having eaten cold meats other than corned beef, purchased from the supermarket between 9 and 23 May. It then became clear that the slicing machine used for cutting cold meats must have been contaminated by the original infected corned beef and had then infected other cold meats. Multiplication of organisms then occurred when these lightly contaminated meats were stored in an uncooled display window exposed to sunlight. The shop was allowed to continue selling cold meat until 27 May and it was only on 1 June that the relevant counter was closed completely on the advice of Dr Betty Hobbs, an expert of the Public Health Laboratory Service.[21]

During the period 26–29 May it was realised that a large number of subjects may have been exposed to possible infection and there was a great fear of secondary outbreaks. No fewer than 23 patients worked in other food-handling institutions and the MOH estimated that as many as 35,000 citizens were potentially at risk.[22] Not all medical persons shared this view and later experts certainly considered the MOH's figure to have been a considerable over-estimate.[23]

Bill Walker, when returning to the hospital one day from his daily meeting with the MOH, stopped for coffee at a city cafe. The tables were beautifully laid out and there were waitresses standing around with nothing to do as there were no customers. Bill, in characteristic fashion, ordered a plate of cream cakes which, after corned beef, were the most avoided food in the city.[24]

Because of the MOH's belief that a very large number of people were at risk, several urgent discussions with the senior administrative medical officer of the Regional Hospital Board were held so that the hospitals could prepare for a probable influx of hundreds of patients; the laboratory service had to gear up for thousands of specimens and all leave for members of the public health service was cancelled. It was also decided to undertake health education through the mass media on an unprecedented scale and accordingly press conferences were held twice daily and numerous radio and television interviews and statements given. The later view of experts was that the MOH had over-estimated the communicability of the disease and created unnecessary alarm and induced panic.[25] The Health and Welfare Department was obviously put under great strain aggravated by staff shortages, which were then at their peak. Staff had to work exceedingly long hours and extra staff were drafted in to help.[26]

Publicity Aspects: The press, both local and national, had a field day! The matter first made headlines in the local *Press and Journal* (*P&J*) on 22 May: 'Aberdeen Outbreak Hits Families – 4, 4, 3: Typhoid Schoolboy Serious: 15 in Hospital – 14 Confirmed Cases'. According to a report of an interview with Dr MacQueen it was his view at this time that 'there was no need for alarm. Medical experts had identified the source. They had located all possible contacts and if there were to be any more cases they would be in the next few days'.

These views were to prove erroneous and Dr MacQueen was not himself to follow his own initial injunctions. The outbreak continued to occupy the headlines in the *P&J* for 33 days being displaced from prime position only three times in this period – on 24 May it was demoted by the report of the birth of triplets to a local woman and on 13 June by a report on the Queen's Birthday Honours List.

When later in the first week it became clear that the outbreak was to be much larger than first hoped, it was decided by the MOH to use the press, radio and television for a massive health education scheme to raise personal hygiene of all food-handlers, to secure voluntary temporary cessation of sale of all foods which might have been handled by a person incubating typhoid, and to discourage needless travel. It was also necessary to reduce public alarm. Many of the steps taken were draconian, however, and proved counterproductive.

On 25 May, at the request of the MOH, names and addresses of patients were published. As mentioned earlier, this led to innumerable friends and acquaintances requesting testing although they were not true contacts. City food shops and restaurants reported a slump in trade and several food production plants were closed. Many sporting fixtures and outings were cancelled. On 30 May, on the MOH's advice, all city schools were closed as was the College of Domestic Science. Dance halls in the town were also shut and the MOH later criticised 'selfish citizens' who were still attending dances out of town.[27] The city streets were all washed down with disinfectant. Attendances at cinemas slumped and hoteliers reported many cancellations of bookings by visitors. There were reports of Aberdeen citizens being denied entry or even turned away from hotels elsewhere in the country. The Ballater caravan site was closed. Tourists on a ship from Finland which called at Aberdeen harbour stayed aboard. Employees of a Perth firm who were working in Aberdeen were asked not to return home at weekends. Some travel agencies would only accept bookings from Aberdonians if they were immunised against typhoid.[28] This was irrational and created a risk of misdiagnosis in those individuals as if any recently immunised person developed a febrile illness or 'gastro-enteritis', he would certainly show on investigation a high or rising antibody titre which is ordinarily indicative of active infection. Most of the actions described in this paragraph were judged later by experts to have been unjustified and over-reactive.[29]

On 26 May the MOH reported to the press that the source of the infection had been identified in corned beef. 'Typhoid in Bully Tin' was the following day's headline. He reported later that the can involved had come from the government stockpile and had been manufactured in 1951 or 1953. This led to much government criticism in the press. This claim was later shown to be erroneous and had unfortunate effects.[30]

It was not until 10 June that the involved supermarket was specifically named although it had been known to the public health authorities since fairly early in the outbreak. This important diagnostic information had even been withheld for some time from general practitioners and hospital staff involved in diagnosis of the cases. This was one of several unfortunate schisms between the different medical groups involved that marred the handling of the outbreak.

Headlines in the local press tended to be factual and often reassuring. The tabloids and Sunday papers often reacted differently. On 1 June, the *P&J* reported that one Sunday paper had carried the headline 'City of Fear'. A week later the *The Sunday Times* was even more dramatic – 'Design For Epidemic: the Vulnerable City'.[31] It stated that the image of Aberdeen as the clean-swept granite city was erroneous. The reality was a town with poor sanitation and crowded housing – classic circumstances to favour the spread of typhoid. This was histrionic rubbish. The location of the involved supermarket in the West End on a main bus route was reflected in a higher concentration of patients from the more prosperous areas of the city and an excess of social classes I and II.[32] It must be stated that the involved supermarket had been an innocent victim of circumstances and was exonerated from any blame in the later expert report.[33]

The MOH criticised the outside press for their reporting. Dr MacQueen was quoted as saying 'WE'RE NOT A LEPER COLONY! End this hysteria outside'.[34] He seemed oblivious to the fact that it was his own actions and statements that had largely engendered these results. His words went unheeded. On 10 June the *P&J* reported that Speyside Council, on the advice of their MOH, had banned Aberdeen citizens from visiting their area. 'Panic Ban Lashed' shouted the *P&J*. Irrationality now prevailed. The university issued a circular to all outside examiners recommending that they wear cotton gloves when marking scripts from the city. An outside library also requested that a book which had been lent to Aberdeen University library be fumigated before being returned, and requested a certificate to certify that having been done!

All these actions were considered later by the expert enquiry to have been unjustified. They believed the MOH had over-estimated the communicability of the disease. It was not smallpox that was being dealt with! They also believed that the sensational publicity campaign was of little help in containing the spread of the disease.[35]

Relief, however, was on the horizon. The official 'All-clear' was given by the MOH on 17 June and the various bans imposed were removed.[36] The MOH was praised, but the very next day he issued an injunction for all to avoid paddling or swimming in the sea for the rest of the summer. 'Beach Bombshell' reported the *P&J*.[37] Final clearance to the city was provided by a surprise visit by the Queen on 27 June. A tiny number of patients were, however, still presenting. The last in the outbreak was admitted on 31 July.[38]

Epidemiological Conclusions: As mentioned earlier, the can which had contained the corned beef which seemed to be the source of infection had long been destroyed, but the epidemiological evidence regarding its responsibility was overwhelming. Records showed that the relevant supply had come from a canning establishment at Rosario in the Argentine. In the official report on the outbreak the whole canning process and possible methods of contamination were reviewed, and other similar outbreaks discussed. On further investigation it was discovered that at the time of production of the relevant can, the cooling of the cans after filling, sealing and sterilisation, was being done using unchlorinated water from the River Parana. The water was drawn off downstream from the town of Rosario from which untreated sewage was discharged into the river. It was assumed that there had been a small leak in one of the cans leading to the 'sucking in' of contaminated water and that typhoid bacilli could have then flourished and multiplied on the meat.[39]

Aftermath: The city suffered greatly through lost trade. Confidence was only slowly re-established. The involved supermarket soon closed down and the owning company never returned to the city. Even after the outbreak was finished and patients were being discharged home, much work remained. Sewer swabs had to be tested regularly in case any missed cases had become carriers.[40] One year after the outbreak, five known chronic carriers remained and had to be kept under surveillance. Dr MacQueen and the matron of the City Hospital, Miss Maltman, featured in the New Year's Honours List, both being awarded the OBE.

Aberdeen remained clear of typhoid fever until 1972 when two cases made their appearance. One of us (MJW), covering the Infection Unit in the temporary absence of Dr Walker due to illness, admitted a mother and daughter to the unit and having had clinical experience of typhoid in the earlier outbreak, suspected that these patients were suffering from this disease. This was confirmed bacteriologically. Both made an uneventful recovery. The source of their infection was never discovered but the strain of *S. typhi* involved was different from that responsible for the Aberdeen outbreak.[41]

Measles

The incidence of this disease during 1949–72 is shown in Figure 28A. There were significant outbreaks in 1951 and 1952, causing 824 and 801 cases respectively. Thereafter, for several years, the condition appeared to be uncommon but as the disease was not then compulsorily notifiable, the numbers reported may be an under-estimate. Fatalities were now unusual, there being only six reported deaths from this cause between 1949–60. This

**Figure 28A Measles
Incidence 1949–72**

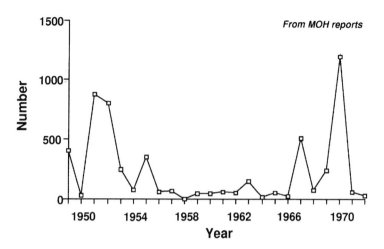

**Figure 28B Whooping Cough
Incidence 1949– 72**

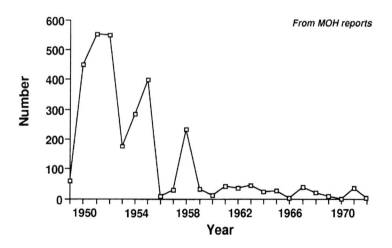

was because earlier deaths were usually due to infective complications which could now be controlled and cured by antibiotics.

After a lull of several years there was a significant outbreak in 1967 with 504 cases, and the following year measles was again made compulsorily notifiable. In 1970 the largest outbreak for many years occurred, with 1,199 cases, but the incidence thereafter steadily declined as supplies of an effective measles vaccine became available in 1969 and this was widely used after this last major outbreak.

Whooping Cough

This was made compulsorily notifiable in 1950 and the incidence during 1949–72 is shown in Figure 28B. It was initially fairly common but there were only seven reported deaths between 1949–55 because, as with measles, most of the earlier deaths were due to infective complications which could now be controlled.

Whooping cough vaccination was not earlier widely used, but in 1955 Aberdeen was involved with other centres in a research project using a combined vaccine giving protection against diphtheria, whooping cough and tetanus. This proved highly efficacious and came into routine use in 1957.[42] Thereafter the incidence of the disease markedly dwindled and after the 1958 outbreak it ceased to be a significant problem.

Poliomyelitis

This remained fairly common between 1949–58, as shown in Figure 29, with a total of 137 cases during this period, with significant epidemics in 1950 and 1954 when there were respectively 36 and 34 cases. It was mostly infants or young children who were affected and the majority of cases had the paralytic form. There were six deaths from this disease during this period. All cases were admitted to the City Hospital, which had been designated as the regional centre for the management of this disease. Special equipment had been obtained, including 'iron lungs' for the management of patients with respiratory paralysis. Patients of all ages with this disease were admitted to Ward 8 under Dr Chambers' care although Dr Galloway collaborated in the management of children with the disorder.[43]

Effective immunisation using Salk vaccine, which had to be given by injection, was developed in the USA and first became available locally in 1956. Supplies were initially very limited, and only 426 subjects were immunised in the first year, and 2,808 the following year. Thereafter supplies improved and the procedure became more widespread and there

Figure 29 Poliomyelitis
Incidence 1949–72

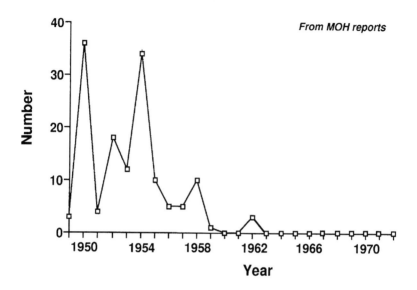

were only four further cases of polio notified between 1959–62. In 1962 oral polio vaccine (Sabin vaccine) was introduced and by the following year was in exclusive use as, apart from being easier to administer, it was also found to provide better and longer lasting protection. No further cases of this disease occurred after 1962. Poliomyelitis, however, remains prevalent in the Third World although in 1988 the World Health Organisation declared its commitment to the goal of global eradication of the disease by the year 2000 - an aim unfortunately not yet achieved.[44]

OTHER INFECTIONS

Puerperal Fever

This was initially still moderately common with 137 cases notified between 1949–53 and then only 37 cases from 1954–64 and none thereafter, consequent on effective preventative measures and early use of antibiotics for 'fever' in the puerperium. There were a total of six deaths from this cause between 1949–59.

Meningitis (Cerebrospinal Fever)

No differentiation was given in notifications for different types of meningitis but the majority were due to meningococcal infection (cerebrospinal fever). There were a total of 127 cases notified in the period 1949–72 of which 98 occurred in the first decade. With the effective use of antibiotics there were only seven deaths from this cause in the whole period. Virtually all these cases were admitted to the City Hospital.

Undulant Fever

This was not at this time common, with only a total of eighteen cases occurring between 1949–72, and there had been none during the thirteen-year period 1958–71. It was, however, to reappear, as will be discussed in the next chapter.

Erysipelas

There were a total of 387 cases of this skin disease notified between 1949–72 of which 270 cases occurred in the first decade. With early use of antibiotics there were only three deaths ascribed to this cause and none after 1956.

Infective Jaundice – 'Weil's Disease'

There were a total of 51 further cases of Weil's disease reported between 1949–55, nearly all in fish workers or those having some involvement in the fish trade with potential contact with the infection. The majority of these patients would have been admitted to the City Hospital. There were two deaths from this disease in 1951 and one of us (MJW) remembers that as a third-year medical student that year, the very first post-mortem he attended was on a fish worker who had died from this disease. He was deeply jaundiced and had succumbed to renal failure. When the head was opened the cerebrospinal fluid was also deeply icteric. Conjugated bile pigment does not ordinarily cross the blood-brain barrier but did in this situation because of concurrent meningeal inflammation. The disease virtually disappeared after 1955 because of the widespread adoption of the preventative measures earlier advocated by Dr John Smith.[45]

After 1956 no cases of Weil's disease were notified but from 1959 infective jaundice was increasingly notified and in 1968 all forms were made compulsorily notifiable. From 1959 onwards all cases were due to viral hepatitis in its different forms. Occasional cases of other less serious types of leptospiral infection still occurred but were not usually associated with jaundice.

Viral Hepatitis

Epidemic jaundice was first described by Hippocrates and large outbreaks have affected armies since the time of the Franco-Prussian War. In World War II huge epidemics occurred, particularly in the Middle East and Italy. Between wars it occurred in both sporadic and minor epidemic forms and gradually it was realised that there were two distinct types. One form, spread by the faecal-oral route had a short incubation period and became known as infective hepatitis – now Hepatitis A. The other form, with a long incubation period, was spread by blood transfusion or injections and became known as post-transfusion or serum hepatitis – now Hepatitis B. In America in 1965, Baruch Blumberg first identified a marker for Hepatitis B in the blood of an Australian aborigine so that it was initially known as the Australia antigen. The discovery of this marker greatly advanced knowledge, and markers for other types – there are now five – followed. It was then appreciated that blood in infective hepatitis (Hepatitis A) was also infective and that Hepatitis B could be spread by sexual contact. Specific tests are now available to diagnose the different types and to recognise carriers.[46]

Figure 30 Infective Jaundice
Incidence 1949–72

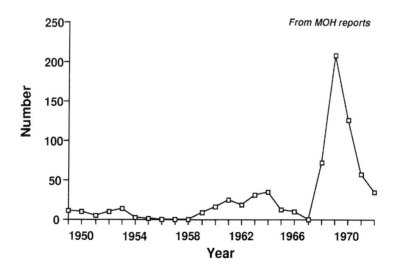

After infective jaundice had been made compulsorily notifiable in 1968 there was a considerable up-surge in numbers of cases, as shown in Figure 30. Most of these were probably cases of infective hepatitis but serum hepatitis among drug users also began to be encountered. In late 1971 and early 1972 there was also an outbreak associated with tattooing. Sixteen patients with jaundice were seen in Aberdeen and a further twelve patients were known who had probably also had the disease from the same cause. This outbreak was the subject of a separate medical report.[47]

Tuberculosis

Incidence: As shown in Figure 31 there continued to be around 200–300 new cases notified each year for the first decade of this period but the incidence thereafter fell strikingly and remained low, with only around 40–60 new cases of pulmonary TB being reported each year. The incidence of non-pulmonary TB was low throughout but also fell, from four to six cases a year to just one to three per year. The number of deaths from pulmonary TB also gradually fell from 40–60 a year to just one to seven a year.

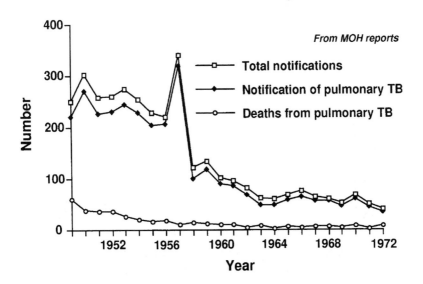

**Figure 31 Tuberculosis 1949–72
Total notifications, pulmonary notifications and deaths**

Most of these changes were related to the introduction and use of effective anti-tuberculous drug therapy. The gradual virtual disappearance of non-pulmonary TB was due to the control and eradication of bovine tuberculosis which was being actively practised.[48]

The use of anti-tuberculous drugs markedly reduced the duration of necessary hospital stay and later many patients were managed as out-patients. The need for artificial pneumothorax or pneumoperitoneum treatment rapidly declined and the A.P. clinic finally closed around 1960.[49] Surgical treatment was now also rarely needed. Other preventative measures were also being used.

BCG (Bacille-Calmette-Guérin) Vaccination: This had first been introduced in the 1920s but there was initial concern over its safety and efficacy and it was not widely used. Later developments produced products of proven value and it was introduced in Aberdeen in 1952. Initially only close contacts of TB patients were treated but by 1953 all school children were being tuberculin tested and BCG vaccine was given to any shown not to be resistant. BCG vaccination was initially performed only at the chest clinic by the chest physicians.

MMR Screening: It had been long known that many sufferers from pulmonary TB had minimal symptoms but were a considerable risk of infection to others. To facilitate the eradication of the disease, the Department of Health for Scotland decided in the 1950s to offer chest x-ray examination to everyone aged fourteen years and over, to assist the identification and diagnosis of early cases. The examinations were to be carried out initially by Mass Miniature Radiography units which were to operate in groups and visit the cities and towns throughout Scotland. Anyone with an abnormality found on MMR would then have a full-sized radiograph and if abnormal would be referred to the local chest clinic.

The MMR Unit commenced operation in Aberdeen in 1953 and 31,687 persons were x-rayed in the first year, with 92 or 0.3 per cent found to have TB, and in 1957 a major campaign was conducted when 78.6 per cent of the adult population were screened. There were 150 new cases of pulmonary TB detected, explaining the marked rise in notification rate that year as shown in Figure 31.

The campaign markedly increased the chest physicians' workload. It was stipulated by the Health Department that those with an abnormal miniature film had to have a full-sized x-ray taken within a week, and if this was abnormal the patient had to have their clinical examination within a further week. To cope with this large extra load, all staff, medical, nursing, radiological and clerical, had to do many extra evening clinics, for no additional recompense.[50]

SOME NEW DISEASES

Several new diseases emerged as problems during this time. Viral hepatitis has already been described.

Malaria

This is due to infection by one of four species of protozoa of the genus Plasmodium (*P. vivax*, *P. ovale*, *P. malaria* and *P. falciparum*) and is transmitted to man by the bite of an infected Anopheles mosquito. The first three species of Plasmodium give rise to a relatively benign form of disease – benign tertian or benign quartan malaria. *P. falciparum* infection, however, gives a serious illness – malignant malaria – which has a high mortality rate unless rapidly diagnosed and effectively treated.

Malaria existed in Britain in the past but is now confined to tropical and sub-tropical countries and remains a common cause of mortality and morbidity in the world. Cases were seen in Aberdeen after the war as a result of increasingly frequent foreign travel. Between 1949–72, 38 cases were notified and admitted to the City Hospital. No record is available as to number of deaths. Interestingly, between 1945–48 there had been 36 cases, this large number being due to no less than 23 cases notified in 1946, presumably in returning servicemen or POWs from the Far East.

Infantile Gastro-Enteritis and E. Coli

Large numbers of infants with diarrhoea were admitted annually to the paediatric ward in Ward 10 of the City Hospital where they were under the charge of Dr Hugh Galloway. As it was not a notifiable disease no specific figures are available. In a report, however, on epidemic gastro-enteritis of infants in Aberdeen during 1947, John Smith and others reported that 415 infants with diarrhoea were admitted that year, of whom 240 were diagnosed as having infective gastro-enteritis of uncertain aetiology. There was a significant mortality rate, no fewer than 105 or 50.6 per cent having died. It mainly occurred in bottle-fed babies and had a peak incidence in the summer. Institutional outbreaks were common. Coliform organisms were frequently cultured from the stools, but its relationship to the disease was then inconclusive.[51] John Smith later showed it was specific strains of coliform bacilli which were involved and he named these the α and β types and he and his clinical colleagues later confirmed the relationship of these different types to the disease.[52] Different strains occurred in outbreaks in different years and in later years the illness was mild in form.[53]

This was important original work by John Smith for which the Royal College of Physicians of Edinburgh awarded him the Lister Fellowship in 1954, and published a monograph by him on this subject.[54]

References to Chapter Thirteen

[1] Aberdeen Central Library, Town Council Minutes (hereafter TCM), 16 November 1950.

[2] Mrs S. Innes, personal communication.

[3] Dr G. Innes, personal communication.

[4] J. Howie, 'Professor Allan Downie FRS' in *Portraits from Memory*, (The Memoir Club), Cambridge, The University Press, 1988, pp. 131–4.

[5] F. Fenner, D. A. Henderson, I. Arita, Z. Jezek and L. D. Ladnyi, *Smallpox and its Eradication*, Geneva, World Health Organisation, 1988, pp. 1138–40.

[6] Annual Report of the Medical Officer of Health for Aberdeen for 1958, pp. 105–6.

[7] W. Walker, 'The Aberdeen Typhoid Outbreak of 1964', *Scottish Medical Journal*, 1965, vol. 10, pp. 466–79.

[8] W. H. Galloway, personal communication.

[9] Walker, 1965, op. cit.

[10] R. Fraser, 'Memories of The City Hospital', unpublished manuscript, n.d, currently in the possession of Professor J. Friend.

[11] Mrs M. Walker, personal communication.

[12] Walker, 1965, op. cit.

[13] Ibid.

[14] W. Walker, 'Cephaloridine in Typhoid', *British Medical Journal*, 1964, vol. 2, pp. 1529–30.

[15] Walker, 1965, op. cit.

[16] E. M. Russell, A. Sutherland and W. Walker, 'Ampicillin for Persistent Typhoid Excretors including a clinical trial in convalescence', *British Medical Journal*, 1966, vol. 2, pp. 555–7.

[17] *The Press and Journal,* June 20 1964.

[18] Russell et al., op. cit.

[19] Walker, 1965, op. cit.; Scottish Home and Health Department, *The Aberdeen Typhoid Outbreak 1964*, Edinburgh, HMSO, 1964.

20   Scottish Home and Health Department, op. cit.
21   Ibid.
22   Annual Report of the Medical Officer of Health for Aberdeen for 1964, p. 11.
23   Scottish Home and Health Department, op. cit.
24   Mrs M. Walker, personal communication.
25   Scottish Home and Health Department, op. cit.
26   Walker, 1965, op. cit.
27   *The Press and Journal*, 1 June 1964.
28   Walker, 1965, op. cit.
29   Scottish Home and Health Department, op. cit.
30   Scottish Home and Health Department, op. cit.
31   *The Sunday Times*, 7 June 1964.
32   Walker, 1965, op. cit.
33   Scottish Home and Health Department, op. cit.
34   *The Press and Journal*, 8 June 1964.
35   Scottish Home and Health Department, op. cit.
36   *The Press and Journal*, 18 June 1964.
37   *The Press and Journal*, 19 June 1964.
38   Walker, 1965, op. cit.
39   Scottish Home and Health Department, op. cit.
40   Walker, 1965, op. cit.
41   Annual Report of the Medical Officer of Health for Aberdeen for 1972, p. 60.
42   Annual Report of the Medical Officer of Health for Aberdeen for 1957, pp. 102–3.
43   W. H. Galloway, personal communication.
44   J. Chander and S. Subrahmanyan, 'Mass Polio Vaccination', *British Medical Journal*, 1996, vol. 312, pp. 1178–9.
45   J. Smith, 'Weil's Disease in the North-East of Scotland', *British Journal of Industrial Medicine*, 1949, vol. 6, pp. 213–20.
46   S. Sherlock, 'Viral Hepatitis', in *Diseases of the Liver and Biliary System*, Oxford, Blackwell, 1975 (5th edition), pp. 305–39.
47   N. A. G Mowat, P. Brunt, F. Albert-Recht and W. Walker, 'Outbreak of Serum Hepatitis Associated with Tattooing', *The Lancet*, 1973, vol. 1, pp. 33–4.
48   J. Smith, 'Review of the progress of dairy science. Section F. Milk-Borne Diseases', *Journal of Dairy Research*, 1950, vol. 17, pp. 93–6.
49   R. Fraser, op. cit.
50   Ibid.
51   C. Giles, G. Sangster and J. Smith, 'Epidemic Gastro-Enteritis of Infants in Aberdeen during 1947', *Archives of Disease in Childhood*, 1949, vol. 24, pp. 45–53.

52   J. Smith, 'The Association of Certain Types (α & β) of *Bact Coli* with Infantile Gastro-Enteritis', *Journal of Hygiene*, 1949, vol. 47, pp. 221–6.

53   J. Smith, H. Galloway and A. L. Speirs, 'Infantile Gastro-Enteritis with Special Reference to the Specific Serological Type O 55 B 5 H 6 (*Beta* Type) of *Bacterium Coli*', *Journal of Hygiene*, 1950, vol. 48, pp. 472–83; J. Smith, 'The Sensitivity to Antibiotics of Strains of Bact Coli Associated with Infantile Gastro-Enteritis', *Archives of Disease in Childhood*, 1953, vol. 28, pp. 30–3.

54   J. Smith, *The Aetiology of Epidemic Infantile Gastro-Enteritis*, Edinburgh, The Royal College of Physicians of Edinburgh, 1955.

Chapter Fourteen

The City Hospital and Infections 1972–97: the Final Years

The next twenty-five years saw several changes in the administrative control of the City Hospital, and, latterly, the steady transference to the Foresterhill site of most of the services which had evolved there. Ultimately, the hospital was no longer to serve the function for which it had originally been built in 1877 and was to lose the many other specialties which had been developed there.

Administration

The newly-formed Board of Management for the Foresterhill and Associated Hospitals first met on 1 April 1971.[1] They were to have a short reign. Interestingly, it was early appreciated that the hospital's role would change considerably in future years. It was thought likely that the City Hospital would eventually be retained predominantly for geriatric beds, or the wards perhaps used for decanting purposes while wards or units elsewhere were being altered or upgraded, or perhaps utilised for general practitioner beds.[2] It was, however, to be many years, and there were indeed to be further changes in the interim, before this came to pass. Early consideration was also given to the transfer of the isolation unit for children to the Children's Hospital, while retaining that for adults, but because of cost implications, this proposal was not to be implemented for a considerable time.[3]

In 1972 the NHS (Scotland) Act was passed, requiring major administrative re-organisation. All Regional Hospital Boards and Boards of Management were to be dissolved and many of the health functions and staff of local authorities transferred to the responsibility of new Area Health Boards which had to be set up.[4]

The Board of Management for the Foresterhill and Associated Hospitals was not finally dissolved until the end of March 1974.[5] However, the new Grampian Health Board first met on 18 June 1973 as there was much preliminary re-organisation to arrange.[6] The Board decided to organise their area into three districts: Moray, later known as the West District; Banff, Buchan and Gordon, later known as the North District; and Aberdeen City, Kincardine and Deeside, later known as the South District. The City Hospital then became administered by the South District. Dr J. P. Sexton, who had previously been Group Medical Superintendent, continued under the new title of District Medical Officer until he left in 1976 to become postgraduate dean to the Aberdeen University's medical faculty. District Medical Officers were appointed to administer medical matters in the individual districts and Dr Ian G. Simpson and Dr Ian A. McDonald held the South District post successively from 1976–83. Ian Simpson was to leave hospital administration and later become chief executive and secretary to the Medical and Dental Defence Union of Scotland while Dr McDonald went on to become Chief Administrative Medical Officer to the Borders Health Board.

The year 1977 was the centenary of the opening of the original Epidemic Hospital which had soon become the City Hospital. Grampian Health Board marked the event on 1 September of that year, although this was two months after the hundred-year anniversary of admission of the first patients. Celebrations commenced in the morning with a thanksgiving service. In the afternoon an invited audience of 150, including Lord Provost William Fraser and his wife, attended the City Hospital where they were addressed by Mr W. S. Crosby, then chairman of Grampian Health Board. He paid tribute to the devotion of the staff and the hospital's reputation for kindness and compassion. He then planted a cherry tree beside the nurses' home, adjacent to the old croquet lawn. In the evening a barbecue was held for the staff.[7] The tree still flourishes, flowering bountifully in the spring, but its significance is unrecorded by any plaque. Matthew Hay and the other several distinguished medical superintendents who had looked after 'their hospital' with devotion and loving care, might well have recorded the event in more concrete form. Times had changed, however, and the City Hospital was now just a peripheral part of a large administrative organisation.

In October 1982 there was a minor administrative restructuring when the Board agreed to change from districts to a unit-based system,[8] although this was not to be implemented until 1984. The next major change occurred with the introduction of general management in 1986. On the recommendation of outside business consultants who had been engaged at great expense, new unit structures were devised and unit management quickly followed. The groupings decided upon ran contrary to medical advice and the City Hospital found itself placed in the Geriatric and Specialist Services Unit, with its administrative base at Woodend. This resulted in many of the City Hospital consultants having to flit between units in the same working day, as their busy schedules took them from wards or clinics at the City Hospital to the same at the Royal Infirmary at Foresterhill or Woolmanhill which were both in the domain of the Acute Services Unit. Finally in 1992, all this expensively set up structure was dismembered when trust status was granted, unsupported by the vast majority of medical staff, and the City Hospital then came under the Grampian Healthcare NHS Trust, now the Grampian Primary Care NHS Trust.

Structural Changes

Although these repeated changes in administration might have led to confusion, they overall led to considerable improvements and changes, probably due to new individuals having different viewpoints on long-standing problems.

Early in the period under consideration, an expensive extension to the laboratory was agreed to, the hospital lighting was improved, the heating and electrical services were upgraded and a new nurse-call system installed. In 1973 a new teaching unit was constructed between Wards 3 and 4.[9] This proved immensely useful for both undergraduate teaching and small postgraduate meetings, and was also used by others.

In the ensuing years, many other costly changes had to be made as services were redeployed but these will be discussed under the relevant clinical service headings.

THE CLINICAL SERVICES

General Medicine

It is appropriate to discuss this specialty initially as the general medical beds were to be the first to move from the City Hospital to Foresterhill.

Active general medical units continued in Wards 2, 3 and 4 under respectively Dr Williams (Wards 2 and 3), Dr Stowers and Dr Walker (Ward 4). Dr Walker also admitted many general medical patients for investigation to his officially-designated infection beds in Wards 8 and 9. The first group of wards admitted both emergency cases and list admissions for investigation, the latter coming from the diverse out-patient clinics served by these three consultants – diabetic, endocrine, general medical and haematological. Patients were also admitted from the Orkney and Shetland Islands medical clinics which were visited by Drs Walker and Williams, and from 1972 for a year by Dr Williams on his own.

In 1973 Bill Walker left the City Hospital on being appointed to the regius chair of therapeutics in Aberdeen. Dr Stowers then for a period shared the medical beds in Ward 4 with Dr Alan Johnston. The latter, who had been a consultant physician for some years, had earlier had charge of medical beds at both Woodend Hospital and Foresterhill, sharing the Infirmary beds with Dr Ian Gordon, the senior physician. On Dr Gordon's retirement, however, the ward at Foresterhill had been given over to the renal physicians to establish a medical renal unit, and the beds in Ward 4 at the City Hospital were given to Dr Johnston to offset his loss of beds. He, however, found it impractical to work in two such widely separated sites and later withdrew from Ward 4, at which time the administration took the opportunity to reorganise the hospital's bed distribution.

Dr C. C. Smith was appointed a consultant general physician with interest in infection to replace Bill Walker. Dr Smith was born and schooled in Barbados and still retains a Caribbean lilt in his talk. He graduated and had his postgraduate training in medicine in Edinburgh, covering a wide range of sub-specialties, and trained in infection with the late Dr James Murdoch. Known as Chris to his friends but 'C. C.' to his juniors and patients, he is a complete general physician and a rumbustious, larger-than-life character. He quickly established harmonious relations with his City Hospital colleagues and lasting friendships developed.

On his arrival in December 1973, he was, with just cause, vexed to discover that his general medical beds in Ward 4 had been 'removed' between the time of his interview and arrival, without his having been in any way privy to the discussions. Strong representations to the administration were made, and it was decided that Ward 7, which had been unused since early that year when the gynaecologists had ceased their operating lists at the City Hospital, should be refurbished and re-opened.[10] This was done, and Chris managed to work as a general physician, admitting both emergency and list cases to Wards 7 and 8, although the working conditions for the staff were far from ideal for dealing with ill patients. About the same time as C. C. Smith was appointed, Dr James Friend was appointed consultant chest physician to replace Dr Eric Barnes and shared some of the beds in Wards 7 and 8. On Dr Fraser's retirement, Dr J. S. Legge was appointed consultant chest physician and was given the beds in Ward 4 that Dr Johnston had relinquished.

The management of all medical problems at the City Hospital had in fact become increasingly difficult. Medical technology had made great advances. Patients, for their proper diagnosis and treatment, commonly required ready access to new radiological techniques such as ultrasonography and echocardiography, and imaging procedures using the CT (computerised tomography) scanner, and isotope procedures developed by the medical physics department. These facilities were all on the Foresterhill site and involved City Hospital patients in long, rather uncomfortable journeys by ambulance. Furthermore, work in the latter years was periodically disrupted by a series of unfortunate industrial actions involving, at different times, telephonists, laundry staff, portering and catering staff, and – most disruptive of all – ambulance staff. Contrary to the repeated claims of union officials, patients were unquestionably harmed.

A move of the general medical beds to the Foresterhill site then became highly appropriate, although the consultants involved had reservations over exchanging their workplace in the friendly open-air atmosphere at the City Hospital for the more anonymous factory-like complex at Foresterhill. The move was in fact first proposed in 1976, but because of sundry problems was delayed for several years. Ward space, however, eventually became available with the translocation of the professorial medicine and therapeutic units from Wards 1 and 4, which were juxtaposed in the medical block at Foresterhill, to new accommodation in the Infirmary's Phase II development. The involved consultants at the City Hospital, however, 'held out' until the empty wards had been fully upgraded, and, in particular, demanded the installation of piped oxygen, an important facility which they had had at the City Hospital for many years, but which was still then absent from the older Infirmary wards. These improvements were made and the units finally moved in March 1980, Drs Stowers and Williams into Ward 4 (later Wards 27 and 28) and C. C. Smith with the chest physicians into Ward 1 (later Wards 25 and 26). Several of the ward sisters, staff nurses and auxiliary nurses accompanied them, but many found the rather impersonal frenetic atmosphere at Foresterhill alien to their tastes and gradually left for other posts. Many of those involved could vouch for the rather more relaxed, friendly atmosphere of the small hospital they had left, where everybody knew everyone else. This was strikingly lacking in the large complex. One of us (MJW), shortly after moving, was accosted one day in the main hospital corridor by a porter who thought he was the painter!

No longer could the rose beds be sniffed while moving between wards; missing also were the harsh background cries of seagulls or, on stormy days, the sound of waves crashing on the nearby beach. No longer could one pause, before heading for home in the autumn dusk, to watch the nightly influx of starlings to their tree roosts where they wrought havoc on the night staff's cars parked beneath. All this and much more became distant memories. One chapter in the history of the City Hospital had closed.

The Paediatric Infection Unit

As this was the second specialty to leave the City Hospital site, it will be considered next.

Dr Hugh Galloway continued in charge of Wards 3 and 10, which remained active and well occupied. Ward 3 admitted young children with diverse infections such as measles, chickenpox and whooping cough, especially those from poorer homes or with complicating features. Children who were in-patients in the Children's Hospital for investigation or treatment and who then developed any of the common exanthemata, were also transferred to the City Hospital for isolation.[11] Ward 10 admitted ill infants. There were a few cases of suspected meningitis, but the common problem was diarrhoea due to gastro-enteritis or salmonellosis or other bowel infections.

Measles was still at that time prevalent, with a mean of 460 cases a year from 1972–90, but only once exceeded 1,000 cases per year, there being 1,053 cases in 1974.[12] The incidence of whooping cough declined due to effective immunisation and only twice exceeded 200 cases per year in the period 1972–90. There were 254 cases notified from Grampian region in 1978 and 296 cases in 1982.[13] Scarlet fever had also become uncommon, and cases were rarely admitted.

Hugh Galloway retired in 1980 and was replaced by Dr Peter Smail. Dr Smail was brought up at Harrow in Middlesex, and graduated in medicine at Oxford but did his postgraduate training in paediatrics in Dundee.[14] On his appointment as consultant in medical paediatrics in Aberdeen, he took charge of the paediatric infection unit and also of the children's diabetic and endocrine clinics at the Children's Hospital. Shortly after his arrival, the paediatric beds in Ward 3 were closed, as their occupancy rate had considerably fallen consequent on the decline in incidence of the common childhood exanthemata. All children with suspected infections were thereafter admitted to Ward 10. The incidence of the common exanthemata was later to decline further when a combined measles, mumps, rubella (MMR) vaccine became nationally available from 1 October 1988.[15]

The provision of adequate out-of-hours cover for the sick children at the City Hospital became increasingly difficult and was intensified by the departure of the general medical beds in 1980. The children's beds were covered at middle-grade level by a doctor on duty at the Children's Hospital, who could be fully occupied there when required to visit a sick child at the City Hospital. The paediatricians had been anxious for many years to have their infection beds moved to the Children's Hospital site, but financial stringencies made this impractical until 1990, when a new purpose-designed unit was built and opened adjacent to, but separate from, the other ward pavilions.

In the few years before their move, some new problems in the field had emerged and merit brief consideration.

Campylobacter Infection: Initially considered to be only animal pathogens, these organisms had become recognised as an important cause of gastro-enteritis and occasionally systemic infection. The genus campylobacter (meaning curved rod) involves several different species. The commonest is *C. jejuni*. Most farm animals, meat sources and pets harbour the organisms, and transmission to humans occurs by ingestion of contaminated food, especially undercooked poultry, or from drinking unpasteurised milk or untreated water. It most commonly causes an acute gastro-enteritis but can cause systemic infection, and various complications have been reported. Young children and adolescents and young adults are most at risk. The diagnosis can be confirmed by culture or serological tests. The infection responds well to treatment with the antibiotic erythromycin,[16] and became a well-recognised problem in the paediatric infection unit.[17]

Kawasaki Disease: First reported by a Japanese paediatrician, after whom it is named, this condition has been increasingly recognised worldwide and appears to be increasing in frequency. It was the subject of a major BBC Panorama report in November 1996. The cause remains unknown, with no specific diagnostic test, and so the condition has to be recognised on clinical grounds. It causes a constellation of clinical features and the presence of several leads to the diagnosis. These are sustained fever, conjunctival injection, inflammation of the mouth and throat, a variable rash often mimicking measles, swelling and redness of the hands and feet, and enlargement of the lymph nodes in the neck. Accompanying this is an important inflammation of the coronary and major limb vessels and, if not diagnosed and effectively treated, is becoming a major cause of acquired heart disease. The condition responds dramatically to intravenous gamma globulin which must be given during the active febrile phase.[18] Four to five such cases were seen in the paediatric infection unit each year although since 1990, for unknown reasons, the incidence has considerably decreased.[19]

E. Coli (0157:H7) and the Haemolytic–Uraemic Syndrome: The recognition of strains of *E. coli* as an important cause of infantile gastro-enteritis by Dr John Smith and his colleagues at the City Hospital in the later 1940s was recorded in Chapter 13. Since then other strains of *E. coli* had been identified as pathogenic. In the early 1980s workers in the USA identified a specific strain known as 0157:H7. This is a common harmless commensal in the gut of domestic animals and is transmitted to humans through undercooked meat and unpasteurised milk. Infection gives rise to acute gastro-enteritis, often with bloody stools. The organism also elaborates a toxin, which when absorbed, causes endothelial cell injury. The kidney blood vessels in particular are involved, leading to renal failure. Characteristic blood changes also occur, the red blood cells being damaged as they pass the altered vasculature, and platelets are depleted as they adhere to the damaged blood vessels. This is known as the Haemolytic–Uraemic Syndrome. Although all age groups may be affected, it most commonly affects infants and young children. It is the most common cause of acute renal failure in childhood. The condition achieved notoriety with the huge outbreak in Wishaw in Lanarkshire in November–December 1996.

The condition is most often encountered in the summer months and seems to be increasing in frequency. From about four cases a year in Aberdeen, the frequency has increased to around twelve a year.[20] A high proportion of affected children require renal dialysis in treatment but fortunately most recover normal renal function.

It is a point of justified pride that there there were no deaths in the paediatric infection unit at the City Hospital after 1980.[21]

The Adult Infection Unit

Dr Chris Smith arrived in December 1973, bursting with zeal, to take charge of the adult infection unit. There were theoretically 37 beds designated for adult infectious diseases, but in practice only 26 were useable. Ward 9, opened in 1940, was the most recently built part of the hospital, and the ground floor had two four-bedded wards and fourteen isolation cubicles. Each cubicle had a separate elbow-tap wash-hand-basin, an extractor fan and vinyl working surfaces, making cleaning and disinfecting easy. The ward had communal toilets and so was not suited for patients with suspected infective diarrhoea. Such patients had initially to be admitted to the out-dated rooms adjacent to Ward 8 – the 'out-houses'. There was accommodation there for four patients, and each room had its own toilet, with special sluicing equipment. Diarrhoea was in practice the most common presenting symptom necessitating admission to the infection unit, and this put great pressure on these few beds.

In 1985 C. C. Smith and his colleagues published an informative analysis of twelve months' admissions to the unit between April 1980 and March 1981. There were a total of 605 patients admitted during this period and in 134 (22 per cent) diarrhoea was the presenting complaint. Of this 134, only 58 turned out after investigation to have infective disorders, the remainder having miscellaneous medical or surgical problems.[22] When patients were found to be non-infectious, they could be transferred to the other accommodation in Ward 8, which consisted of two small six-bedded wards and several two-, three- or four-bedded rooms. The same situation pertained for many admitted with jaundice as suspected cases of infective hepatitis. Of 76 such patients admitted during the time of the survey, only 21 proved to have viral hepatitis on testing. The remainder turned out to have a miscellany of different types of liver or biliary tract disease.

Structural Changes

As already mentioned, the accommodation in the out-houses was out-moded and unsatisfactory. This had been appreciated by the administration, and demolition of the ward was suggested in 1978, but pressure on the beds and financial constraints prevented action.[23] Following the move of the general medical beds to Foresterhill in 1980 the situation altered, and a year or two later, Wards 7 and 8 were demolished and replaced by a new 'Portakabin type' construction linked to Ward 9, providing three high-risk isolation rooms, each suite having its own toilet, wash-hand-basin and shower.[24]

Dr Smith had also been anxious to develop an out-patient facility at the City Hospital, to review patients discharged from the infection unit. This was refused initially in 1983,[25] but later, common sense prevailed. The operating theatre and its adjacent facilities attached to Ward 9 had been lying empty and largely unused since the gynaecologists had ceased their twice-weekly operating sessions at the hospital in early 1973.[26] This area was later altered to provide teaching and out-patient rooms with office accommodation which proved their worth.[27]

For the first thirteen years of his time in Aberdeen, C. C. Smith had to cover his units single-handed and depended on the generosity of friends (many) for cover in his absence. In 1986 Dr J. Graham Douglas, a Yorkshireman who had also graduated and trained in Edinburgh, was appointed to a new post, to work a third of his time in infection and the remaining two-thirds in chest medicine.

To complete the discussion of structural changes, it is necessary at this point to refer to AIDS (acquired immunodeficiency syndrome), which will be discussed in more detail later. This first appeared as a 'new' disease in the USA in 1981 and soon spread worldwide and appeared in Scotland in 1984. An explosion of cases was feared, but it was not until 1990 that the Health Board agreed to the need for special accommodation for such patients. With the departure of the paediatric infection beds, Ward 10 was now empty and the accommodation there was altered, and a lift installed. This led to a loss of some beds in Ward 9, so that when the new accommodation opened in April 1991, the total number of infection beds was unaltered.[28]

Workload

This was consistently heavy. The unit operated an 'open door' admission policy and served a population that increased from 400,000 in 1980–81 to more than 500,000 in 1991.[29] It admitted patients from the city of Aberdeen, rural Grampian, the off-shore North Sea oil installations and the Orkney and Shetland Islands. In Dr Smith's and his colleagues' early survey of a year's admissions already referred to, there had been a total of 605 patients.[30] He and his colleagues published a second similar analysis of all patients admitted during 1991.[31] The total by then had increased to 900. Whereas in the first survey, 40 per cent of patients were found after investigation to have a non-infectious condition, this had dropped by the time of the second analysis to 28 per cent.[32]

The four most common presenting symptoms in both studies were diarrhoea (22 per cent and 36 per cent), jaundice (13 per cent and 3 per cent), headache with meningeal irritation (suspected meningitis, 12 per cent and 13 per cent) and sore throat (8 per cent and 18 per cent of total admissions). Miscellaneous reasons for admission included malaria, varicella-zoster infection, soft tissue infections, and pulmonary tuberculosis (patients with this disease who were considered infective being admitted by the chest physicians to Ward 9). Twenty-two patients with AIDS were also admitted in 1991.[33] Cross-infection in the unit, both to patients and staff, was never a problem because of careful strict adherence to basic guidelines.[34]

The overall problem of infectious diseases in the period 1972–94 will now be considered and certain of the infections discussed in more detail.

INFECTIOUS DISEASES AND THE CITY HOSPITAL 1972–94

The major infections of the past – cholera, smallpox and typhus – were now forgotten, and poliomyelitis and diphtheria had disappeared as a result of effective immunisation programmes. Several problems, however, remained, and some new ones emerged.

Infective Diarrhoea

As already mentioned, diarrhoea was the most common presenting symptom requiring admission. In C. C. Smith's 1980–81 survey, a specific aetiological agent was isolated in 20 per cent of the 134 such patients. Salmonella gastro-enteritis was the most common.[35] At the time of the 1991 survey, the number of patients with salmonella infections was similar, but some new pathogens causing infective diarrhoea had been recognised and were identified. Campylobacter enteritis, which was mentioned in the paediatric section, increased from seven cases in 1980–81 to 27 in 1991.[36] This probably reflected the increased consumption of 'chicken bits' and take-away foods. Several other less common new pathogens were also represented.

Typhoid Fever

Aberdeen was to be spared a further major outbreak, but between 1972–94 a total of fifteen cases were identified from the Grampian area. There were also five cases of paratyphoid fever.[37] There were never more than one or two cases of typhoid in individual years, with ten separate years in this period without any. The majority of patients were infected abroad, having been travelling either on holiday or business.

One of us (IAP) has, however, knowledge of a rather unusual case in this period. A nurse working in a psycho-geriatric unit in the North-East was admitted after investigation of her acute diarrhoea and fever had revealed the presence of *S. typhi* in her stools. She had not been abroad and gave no history of recent consumption of unusual foods. All patients and staff at the hospital where she worked had specimens of faeces and urine examined, and all were clear apart from one elderly demented lady who was excreting *S. typhi*.

Relatives were consulted and it was discovered that she had suffered from the 'Fever' during the First World War. Old records were examined and it was ascertained that she had been a known typhoid carrier. Somehow this information had been mislaid or forgotten. The interesting aspect of this case was the fact that she had been indoctrinated well and truly in personal hygiene. She had brought up a family of five children and there was no evidence that any infection had occurred during this time. In her demented state, however, she had become occasionally incontinent, and this is when the nurse had been infected. While in her isolation room the patient was discovered hiding her faeces under the linoleum which covered the floor. It seemed that even in her demented state she was aware that her faeces were dangerous and had to be properly disposed of. An interesting piece of public health detective work!

Streptococcal Throat Infection

Scarlet fever, as already mentioned, had become rare. In adults, however, sore throat, which was most commonly due to streptococcal infection, was a common cause of admission. Numbers of these patients also had peritonsillar abscesses (quinsy) requiring surgical drainage. Thus in the 1991 survey, C. C. Smith and his colleagues reported 166 admissions from the total of 900 due to sore throat. Nearly two-thirds of this group had bacterial tonsillitis and 59 required surgical drainage.[38] Glandular fever often emerged as an alternative diagnosis in this group of patients.

Viral Hepatitis (Infective Jaundice)

Viral hepatitis was only specifically made notifiable in 1975, having been previously recorded along with some other conditions as infective jaundice. Leptospiral jaundice was also made officially notifiable the same year and in the period under review there was only a single case recorded locally, in 1980.[39]

The number of cases of viral hepatitis notified from Grampian region each year for the period 1973–94 is shown in Figure 32A. Figure 32B shows the number of positive tests for Hepatitis B obtained in the Aberdeen virus laboratory from 1978–94 and the number of positive tests for Hepatitis A from 1982, testing for the latter virus having only started in the laboratory at this time.[40]

Figure 32A Viral Hepatitis
Cases notified from Grampian Region to SHHD 1973–94

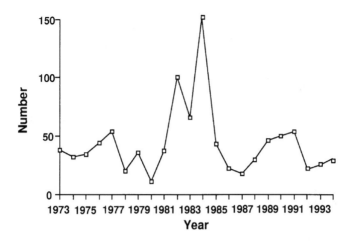

Figure 32B Hepatitis A 1982–94, Hepatitis B 1978–94
Positive tests obtained in Aberdeen Virus Laboratory

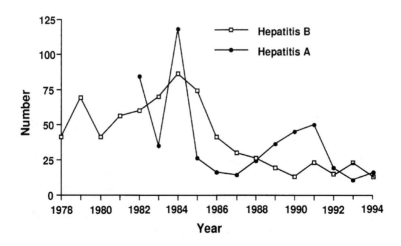

The marked increase in incidence of viral hepatitis between 1982–5 is probably in part due to increased diagnostic precision following the introduction of specific testing for Hepatitis A, but in the early years of this period there were also several outbreaks of Hepatitis A on off-shore oil installations, involving a total of 22 patients.[41] Hepatitis B was most frequently encountered in intravenous (IV) drug abusers but occasional cases occurred in homosexuals or from heterosexual contact.[42] As shown in Figure 32B, the incidence of Hepatitis B in the area fell considerably after 1984. This was due to the active publicity which, following the appearance of AIDS, was given to the dangers of needle-sharing, as well as the ready provision of free needles and syringes to registered addicts who were the main at-risk group.

AIDS

It is appropriate to discuss this new disease at this stage because of its close relationship with Hepatitis B, consequent on the similar manner of spread.

This first emerged as a new syndrome in Los Angeles in California, USA in 1981, when there was a report of five cases of pneumocystis pneumonia in young men. This protozoa had been known for many years to be a rare cause of pneumonia in patients whose immune mechanisms were defective as a result of disease or chemotherapy. It was very rare and this concentration of cases in a short period was most unusual. All the patients affected were active homosexuals. Very shortly afterwards, workers in both California and New York reported 26 cases of a rare form of widespread skin malignancy – Kaposi sarcoma – again in homosexuals who showed evidence of depressed immune mechanisms. Other unusual infections were also common in these patients, and the number reported rapidly escalated as the occurrence of this new syndrome became recognised. By September 1982, 593 cases had been reported and by August 1985 this figure had climbed to 12,932. There was a very high mortality rate. Thus in this last group 50 per cent had died, while in those diagnosed before January 1983 the mortality rate was even higher at 75 per cent. While the early reports of this disease were all in homosexuals and exclusively gay men, it soon became appreciated that the disease was also found in IV drug abusers. It was later found that it could also be transmitted by heterosexual contact, by blood transfusion or by injection of blood products as in haemophiliacs, and also affected the children born to sufferers.[43] The condition soon spread worldwide and by mid-1995, an estimated eighteen to nineteen million persons were estimated to have become infected.[44] This number has since escalated to 33.6 million.[45] It is clearly the modern pandemic.

In 1983 workers in France and the USA simultaneously isolated the causative virus from patients. Known initially as HTLV, it is now known as HIV (human immunodeficiency virus). Several types have since been described and serological tests introduced.[46] Tests for HIV infection were introduced in Aberdeen in 1985. Figure 33 shows the total number of cases of AIDS reported in Scotland between 1984–94, with the number of male cases and the number of fatal cases. The predominance of males and the high mortality rate are clearly shown.

Figure 33 AIDS
Total cases, male cases, fatal cases in Scotland 1984–94

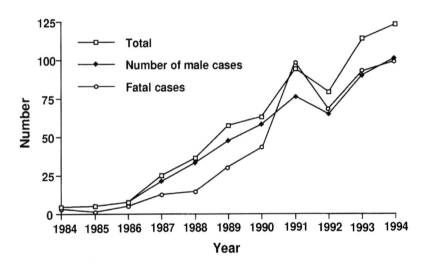

Aberdeen was relatively spared compared with the cities in the Scottish central belt. In C. C. Smith's and his colleagues' survey of admissions in 1991, five women and seventeen men who were HIV antibody positive required a total of 35 admissions. There were twelve homosexual men, eight IV drug abusers and two who had contracted infections through heterosexual activity.[47] There has been no major increase since, but with modern treatment sufferers now live longer and require frequent re-admissions for the management of the different infections to which they are prone. In 1997 there were 52 patients under care.[48]

Meningitis (Meningococcal Infection)

Previously notified as cerebrospinal fever, the term was changed to meningococcal infection for official statistical purposes in 1975.[49] The number of cases notified from Grampian in the period 1973–94 is shown in Figure 34.[50] The numbers fluctuated, with two apparent small peaks and a trough lasting about seven years.

**Figure 34 Meningococcal Infection
Cases notified from Grampian Region to SHHD 1973–94**

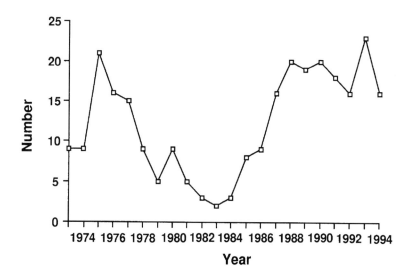

Headache with or without vomiting and neck stiffness leading to the suspicion of meningitis was a common cause of admission. In the survey of 1980–81 there were 73 such patients (12 per cent of the total) and in the 1991 analysis 121 patients (13 per cent of the total).[51] In the first survey 39 of the 73 cases proved on investigation to have meningitis and 28 in the second analysis. This was more often viral than bacterial. With aggressive anti-microbial therapy there were no recorded deaths from bacterial meningitis from 1973 but overwhelming meningococcal infection is still an occasional and tragic cause of death, affecting as it does otherwise healthy and previously fit young persons.

Malaria

A total of 111 cases were notified from the Grampian area to the Scottish Home and Health Department in the period 1973–94.[52] This, however, is clearly an underestimate as C. C. Smith and his colleagues gave two separate reports of the condition seen in the infection unit, recording 31 cases seen in the period 1974–8[53] and 110 patients admitted between 1980–91,[54] giving a total of 141 cases for a lesser period. In the latter analysis the majority of patients were male (80 per cent) and under 40 years of age (84 per cent). Most were either Caucasians born in the UK (69 per cent) or native Africans (25 per cent) who were students recently arrived for further education or returning from visiting their home countries on holiday. The British residents acquired the infection either while on oil-related business in Africa (46 per cent) or after travelling on holiday (30 per cent).[55]

No patients died in the unit from this infection but we have knowledge of at least one patient who died elsewhere in the city from overwhelming infection which had been delayed in diagnosis, as the victim had refused earlier hospital admission.

Undulant Fever (Brucellosis)

In Dr Smith's early years in charge of the infectious diseases unit brucellosis was still a common referral diagnosis. It was almost invariably due to *Br. abortus* infection, and was primarily an occupational disease, affecting those in frequent contact with cattle or dairy products. Veterinary surgeons, abattoir workers, farmers, butchers, workers with meat or dairy products and also laboratory workers handling specimens from sufferers were those most at risk. Non-occupational exposure occasionally occurred by ingestion of unpasteurised milk or milk products. One of us (MJW) had experience of a case of *Br. melitensis* infection, the patient having acquired this from drinking goat's milk.

Patients with acute or chronic brucellosis were admitted to the unit while Dr Smith was besieged for years by innumerable patients with 'imagined chronic brucellosis' referred to his out-patient clinic. Most of these subjects had psychiatric disorders, but assessment was difficult as most were fully aware of the usual symptoms of the disease, and as the condition was registered as an industrial compensational disease, the diagnosis had financial and litigious implications.[56]

No official annual record of notifications was kept but the adult infection unit admitted fourteen patients in 1980–81,[57] while none were recorded in 1991.[58] This was due to the fact that in the 1970s a brucellosis eradication scheme had been agreed to eliminate the disease in cattle. This took several years to implement, by the testing of all cattle and slaughter of those infected, and during that period vets and abattoir workers were at increased risk. The disease has now been eradicated in North-East Scotland.

Departure

After the departure of general medicine, followed by the paediatric infection unit, the adult infection unit was left somewhat in isolation at the City Hospital, chest medicine and rheumatology being the only other acute disciplines then on site. A large number of the patients admitted were acutely ill, needing the highest standard of care and attention. Many of those who turned out to have non-infective illnesses also required the full panoply of modern diagnostic facilities for their proper investigation and management, requiring frequent ambulance trips to Foresterhill. The situation further worsened with the departure of the laboratory services to Foresterhill in December 1991. Despite the best endeavours of laboratory colleagues, the service was clearly less good than before. All specimens had to be sent by hospital van or taxi to Foresterhill with resultant delay. Transfer of the adult infection unit to Foresterhill became a pressing necessity but did not prove possible until 1994. Accommodation in the east block of Aberdeen Royal Infirmary became available when the blood transfusion service moved into new spacious accommodation on the west of the site. Considerable structural alterations were required but the adult infection unit was finally moved into its new purpose-designed accommodation in February 1995. The unit contains only twenty beds and in the next five years annual admissions averaged 1,200 per year.[59]

The original Epidemic Hospital had opened in 1877 to provide isolation facilities for infectious diseases to protect the town's citizens. With the departure of the adult infection unit this activity at the City Hospital now ceased.

Chest Medicine and the Chest Clinic

After many years of sterling service, retirement beckoned for the earlier chest physicians, or phthisiologists as they sometimes called themselves. Dr Eric Barnes was due to retire in mid-1973, and in advance, meetings were held to discuss the attributes required of his replacement. Wide experience in the diagnosis and management of tuberculosis was no longer a prerequisite, but a widely-trained thoracic physician with knowledge of respiratory physiology and experience in modern diagnostic procedures was required, and so neither of the local somewhat more junior staff could be considered.[60] Dr James Friend was appointed. James came from Edinburgh and, after doing his pre-clinical training in Cambridge, he graduated in medicine in Edinburgh. He then did his initial clinical training in that city, latterly training in chest medicine under the famous Sir John Crofton, and then worked in Oxford for five years before coming to Aberdeen.

As mentioned earlier, he was given some chest beds in Wards 7 and 8, sharing with C. C. Smith. He also had charge of beds at Tor-na-Dee and responsibility for several peripheral clinics. Dr Robert Fraser retired in late 1976, and Dr Joe Legge was appointed and took up post in early 1977. Joe was an Aberdeen graduate who had received his postgraduate training in thoracic medicine in Aberdeen and Dundee. He was given chest beds in Ward 4, the administration having re-designated what were formerly general medical beds when Dr Alan Johnston withdrew from working there. John Young, who was mentioned in Chapter 12, had returned to work in the chest clinic in 1973, but had to retire on health grounds in 1976. Douglas Kay continued to work at Tor-na-Dee and in the chest clinic until his retirement in 1986. He was replaced by Dr J. Graham Douglas in a new consultant post. As previously mentioned, Dr Douglas was to spend one-third of his time in infection as a colleague to C. C. Smith, and two-thirds of his time in chest medicine.

A major redeployment of beds for chest medicine occurred coincidental with the move of the general medical beds to Foresterhill in 1980. All three chest physicians shared half the beds in Wards 1 and 2 (later 25 and 26) at Foresterhill with C. C. Smith, replacing the beds they had had at the City Hospital in Wards 4, 7 and 8. Ward 2 at the City Hospital was then structurally altered and upgraded, the chest beds at Tor-na-Dee were cleared and male patients from there admitted to Ward 2 at the City Hospital. The chest physicians also took over nine beds for female chest cases from the rheumatologists in Ward 1, as the latter's need for beds had declined.

Workload

Tuberculosis was no longer the dominant problem. As mentioned in the previous chapter, the incidence of new cases had been declining since 1958 and this downward trend continued, apart from some exceptional years. The numbers of new pulmonary cases per year ranged from 20–26 per year during 1993–7, while the numbers of new non-pulmonary cases, which were often managed by the chest physicians, were from two to six during the same period.[61]

There was, however, no shortage of other clinical material. Increasing numbers of patients with chronic bronchitis, asthma or pulmonary fibrosis were seen, and numerous out-patients referred for investigation of persistent cough, chest pains or breathlessness. Many patients were also referred after some abnormality had been noted on a chest x-ray done at their general practitioner's request.

A special asthma clinic had first been started at Woolmanhill by Dr K. N. V. Palmer, reader in the department of medicine, who had a special interest in pulmonary disease, and on his retirement this was taken over and extended by the chest physicians.[62] They also set up and developed a weekly bronchoscopy clinic at Foresterhill, taking this load over from the thoracic surgeons who were being increasingly occupied with cardiac surgery.

Additional appointments were required to help with the increasing workload. Dr Steven Watt, a lecturer in the department of medicine, who was involved in the Aberdeen Hyperbaric Unit, was made an additional consultant, and helped with both in-patient care and out-patient clinics. Professor Anthony Seaton, professor of occupational and environmental medicine, who had special interest and expertise in occupational lung diseases, also did some chest clinics. In 1993 Dr David Godden, who was also a lecturer in medicine, was appointed an additional consultant to work half-time in the hyperbaric unit and half-time in the chest clinic. His post was created by special Scottish Office funding to develop the special adult cystic fibrosis clinic.[63] Sufferers from this genetic disorder, who usually present in infancy or early childhood, are now surviving into adult life as a result of effective antibiotic treatment of the repeated chest infections to which they are prone, and require skilled multi-disciplinary follow-up and care.

Work for the chest physicians with their in-patients split between Foresterhill and the City Hospital became increasingly difficult. The thoracic surgery department and the pulmonary function laboratory, imaging facilities, and facilities for bronchoscopy and other invasive investigations were all based at Foresterhill, and amalgamation of the chest unit on that site was clearly desirable. This became possible in 1993, and then finally in 1994 they were able to move all their beds from the City

Hospital into Wards 1 and 2 at Aberdeen Royal Infirmary when the ENT surgeons who had previously occupied that floor moved elsewhere.[64] The chest physicians' beds were now all on the Foresterhill site.

The chest clinic, where most of their out-patient activity was centred, initially remained at the City Hospital, but was moved to Foresterhill in March 1997. From that date, patients with probable or suspected TB would no longer pass the portals to the hospital in Urquhart Road, and from that date, the City Hospital relinquished the last remnant of work related to its earlier 119 years of existence.

Physical Medicine (Rheumatology)

This specialty, based on Ward 1, was still then known as the department of physical medicine and rheumatology. Dr Logie Bain remained in charge, supported by Dr Hubert Balch, who had become a consultant in rheumatology. They were also helped by Dr J. M. R. Wetherly, an Aberdeen graduate and general practitioner who worked part-time as a medical assistant. Out-patients were seen both at the City Hospital and Woolmanhill, the clinic at the latter being conveniently adjacent to the physiotherapy department. The earlier facilities and clinic at the Justice Mill Lane Baths had been closed.

Logie Bain was a man of great charm and integrity, and his warm sense of humour and always optimistic outlook did much to alleviate the suffering of those unfortunates with painful chronic arthritis. He was the main driving force behind the establishment of Lovat Lodge in Nairn, and a mobile home in the caravan site at Strachan, near Banchory, where arthritis sufferers could have a heavily-subsidised break, away from their usual environment.[65]

This period saw the introduction of a wide range of new anti-inflammatory agents and other drugs of great value in the management of chronic rheumatic diseases. Physical methods of treatment, using wax baths, splinting and local heat from diverse sources, had a diminishing therapeutic role, and so Logie sought to change the title of his department to just the department of rheumatology. He was, however, frustrated in this objective until after his retirement. Dr Wetherly retired in November 1976 and his post was replaced by a senior house officer appointment.[66] Logie Bain, followed soon by Hubert Balch, retired in early 1979. It was agreed then that the department would become the department of rheumatology, and two new consultants in this specialty were appointed – Dr J. A. Norris Rennie and Dr Cliff Eastmond.[67] Norris, who took up his post in January

1979, was an Aberdeen graduate who had received his postgraduate training at the Centre for Rheumatic Diseases in Glasgow, while Cliff was an Edinburgh graduate who had had his postgraduate training in Liverpool and Leeds. He took up post in June 1979.

The management of rheumatoid arthritis and the other chronic rheumatic disorders had become more effective, and the prolonged in-patient stays often needed in the past disappeared, with a decline in need for hospital beds. As mentioned earlier, when the chest beds moved from Tor-na-Dee to the City Hospital in the early 1980s, about half of the female end of Ward 1 was taken over for chest cases, and later major structural alterations were made, formally sub-dividing that ward. At the same time a new sun-lounge, funded by Arthritis Care, was added.[68]

In 1986 an additional consultant post was created, part-funded for ten years by the Arthritis and Rheumatism Council, and Dr David Reid was appointed. An Aberdeen graduate, he had trained in his specialty in Edinburgh. His particular remit was to organise teaching in rheumatology and to initiate research. He had a particular interest in the problem of osteoporosis, a major source of disability and predisposition to bone fractures in the elderly and other groups. He was the driving force behind the appeal by the north-east branch of the National Osteoporosis Society for funds for two state-of-the-art bone mineral scanners. A total of £83,000 was raised locally and the new bone mineral scanning unit was opened on 14 February 1991 by Fiona Kennedy, the local singer and actress.[69]

The scanners were initially housed in the administration block at the City Hospital before moving into the old Ward 9 Portakabins which had been altered and moved to a site adjacent to Wards 1 and 2. In 1995 the unit moved to empty accommodation at Woolmanhill.[70] A most useful additional clinical service has been provided and productive research in the field undertaken.

In 1994 the department of rheumatology moved to Aberdeen Royal Infirmary, thus ending 34 years' happy and fruitful association with the City Hospital.

Physiotherapy and Occupational Therapy

A physiotherapy department had been established at the City Hospital as an integral part of the department of physical medicine and rheumatology in Ward 1, when this opened in 1960. The main out-patient base for the department at Woolmanhill was also sited in juxtaposition to the out-patient facilities for rheumatology. For many years indeed the majority of out-patient referrals for physiotherapy had to be directed through the consultants in physical medicine. The Aberdeen School of Physiotherapy opened at Woolmanhill in 1962 making recruitment of staff easier. A related department of occupational therapy opened in Ward 1 at the City Hospital in 1964.

Initially, most of the work in these departments was with in-patients in the rheumatology unit, but later increasing numbers of patients in the general medical wards were treated, and the staff numbers had to be steadily increased. Following the opening of the school of physiotherapy, both junior and senior students worked at the City Hospital under supervision.

Both departments at the City Hospital closed with the transfer of the rheumatology beds to Aberdeen Royal Infirmary.

The Radiology Department

Activity in the radiology department was to decline markedly following the departure of the general medical beds in 1980, and this coincided with a time of rapid staff changes in this specialty. Before this occurred, however, there was a brief period of increased activity.

The administration were anxious to close the Chest Radiography Centre in King Street which provided x-ray facilities for general practitioners. It was decided to move this to the City Hospital and approval was given as early as 1972.[71] As with many of the administrative plans, this, however, took some years to implement and the move did not occur until 1979. Extra accommodation was required and a number of structural alterations made. The radiology department had previously occupied three sides of a square, surrounding a small central courtyard where staff, on sunny days, could relax during their coffee or tea breaks, albeit at danger from over-flying seagulls! This open area disappeared, being covered over to provide an additional x-ray room, increasing the number of x-ray machines from two to three. An adjacent chest secretary's room was requisitioned for office accommodation.[72]

In 1978, shortly before the removal of general medicine, Dr Mike Allen resigned to become medical officer to the Jockey Club. This allowed him more time for another great pastime – golf at the Royal and Ancient Golf Club at St Andrews. He has also been the medical officer supremo at recent Open Championships. Mike was the most friendly and obliging of colleagues, always ready to aid anyone in need.

At its peak, the x-ray department at the City Hospital employed four radiographers, one darkroom technician, one nurse, one secretary, and one ambulance driver to transport the patients from the separate wards.[73]

With the decline in workload, a full-time radiologist was no longer justified and after Dr Allen's departure consultants from Foresterhill visited as required. Drs John Cantley, Elizabeth Robertson and Shona Campbell successively filled this role, with intervening periods of cover by senior registrars. This arrangement ceased in February 1995, and x-ray films taken at the City Hospital since that date have been sent to Woodend for reporting. Following the move of the chest clinic to Foresterhill in March 1997 the activity in the x-ray department further declined. They do, however, provide an out-patient service for x-rays to general practitioners in the surrounding area and it is envisaged that this will continue.[74]

Geriatric Medicine

This was the sole specialty which was to expand greatly, as the other units left the site, freeing accommodation. As recorded in Chapter 12, geriatric medicine had first gained a toehold in the City Hospital in 1962, and a permanent geriatric unit was established there in 1965. As mentioned at the beginning of this chapter, the administration, as early as 1971, envisaged the hospital becoming almost entirely a geriatric hospital.[75] It was to take over twenty years, however, for this to come about. Initial developments were slow. Following the departure of general medicine in 1980, Ward 4, which then lay empty, was used to accommodate the patients from Ward 6, while this ward was upgraded. This coincided with a time of great pressure on beds in the geriatric service which was based at Woodend. There were not nearly enough hospital beds to meet demand. Many patients had to be left at home and were often then admitted to the acute medical wards, where they languished for months, blocking the acute beds. Peripheral hospitals were utilised, and many Aberdeen citizens were placed for long-term care in Maud Hospital. This was a constant source of complaint because of difficulty in visiting, and much adverse publicity was generated. The Board were forced to act. In 1978 they decided to build as quickly as possible several new 30-bed units.[76] One of these was to be located at the City Hospital on the site of Wards 7 and 8 which were to be demolished. These new units were so planned that they could accommodate either geriatric or psycho-geriatric patients, the latter service also being under great pressure. Final decision on usage was not to be made until completion, depending on the individual needs at that time. The first unit at the City Hospital was not in fact completed until 1982 and was initially used for geriatric patients, but after a few years was changed to psycho-geriatric use. Wards 3 and 4 had earlier been altered and upgraded and were also used for geriatric patients, with accommodation for 58 patients. So the number of geriatric beds available at the City Hospital had steadily increased from 48 in 1982 to around 120 in 1984. That same year Aberdeen patients in Maud Hospital were able to be transferred to the City Hospital.[77]

New 60-bed units were completed on the site in 1987 and 1991. One, known now as Jasmine Park, is run by a private healthcare organisation – the Community Health Services Limited – whilst the other unit, again a two-storey building, sited alongside Wards 9 and 10 but known as Wards 7 and 8, was entirely run by Grampian Healthcare NHS Trust. Because of the changing demand on long-stay beds, this ward closed in March 1997.

References to Chapter Fourteen

[1]   Northern Health Services Archives, Board of Management for Foresterhill and Associated Hospitals minutes (hereafter FBOM), 1 April 1971.

[2]   FBOM, 4 November 1971.

[3]   FBOM, 1 April 1973.

[4]   NHS (Scotland) Act 1972, *The Public and General Acts and Measures of 1972*, London, HMSO, pp. 1645–1713.

[5]   FBOM, 31 March 1974.

[6]   Northern Health Services Archives, Grampian Health Board minutes (hereafter GHB), 18 June 1973.

[7]   *The Press and Journal*, 2 September 1977.

[8]   GHB, 6 October 1982.

[9]   FBOM, 24 July 1973.

[10]   FBOM, 7 March 1974.

[11]   W. H. Galloway, personal communication.

[12]   *Scottish Health Statistics*, Edinburgh, HMSO, 1972–91.

[13]   Ibid.

[14]   P. Smail, personal communication.

[15]   *Scottish Health Statistics*, op. cit.

[16]   S. Ashkenazi and T. G. Cleary, 'Campylobacter' in R. E. Behrina, R. M. Kliegman and A. M. Arvin (eds), *Nelson: Textbook of Paediatrics*, London, Saunders, 1996 (15th edition), pp. 800–802.

[17]   W. H. Galloway, personal communication.

18 S. Ashkenazi and T. G. Cleary, 'Kawasaki Disease' in R. E. Behrina, R. M. Klicgman and A. M. Arvin, op. cit., pp. 678–80.
19 P. Smail, personal communication.
20 Ibid.
21 Ibid.
22 M. E. Ellis, J. Burnett, C. McGrath and C. C. Smith, 'An analysis of 12 month's admissions to a regional infection unit with an 'open door' admission policy', *Journal of Infection*, 1985, vol. 10, pp. 4–16.
23 GHB, 30 August 1978.
24 Ellis et al., op. cit.
25 GHB, 1 December 1983.
26 FBOM, 9 January 1973.
27 C. C. Smith, personal communication.
28 Ibid.
29 R. S. Dykhuisen, R. J. Trent, D. P. Pacitti, T. M. Reid, J. G. Douglas, and C. C. Smith, 'An analysis of 900 consecutive admissions to a Regional Infection Unit', *Journal of Infection*, 1994, vol. 29, pp. 189–93.
30 Ellis et al., op. cit.
31 Dykhuisen et al., op. cit.
32 Ibid.
33 Ibid.
34 Ibid.
35 Ellis et al., op. cit.
36 Dykhuisen et al., op. cit.
37 *Scottish Health Statistics*, op. cit.
38 Dykhuisen et al., op. cit.
39 *Scottish Health Statistics*, op. cit.
40 T. Brown, principal clinical virologist, personal communication.
41 Ibid.
42 Ellis et al., op. cit.
43 A. B. Christie, *Infectious Diseases*, vol. 1, Edinburgh, Churchill Livingston, 1987 (4th edition), pp. 24–32.
44 D. Goldberg, B. Davis, G. Allardice, J. McMenamin and G. Codere, 'Monitoring the spread of HIV and AIDS in Scotland 1983–1994', *Scottish Medical Journal*, 1996, vol. 41, pp. 131–8.
45 'Global Survey of HIV/AIDS Epidemic', *WHO AIDS Epidemic Update*, December 1999.
46 Christie, op. cit.
47 Dykhuisen et al., op. cit.

48 A. R. Mackenzie, R. B. S. Laing, S. J. Urbaniak, P. J. Molyneaux, J. G. Douglas and C. C. Smith, 'Epidemiology and Outcome of HIV Infection in North-East Scotland (1985–1997)', *Journal of Infection*, 1999, vol. 38, pp. 107–110.

49 *Scottish Health Statistics*, op. cit.

50 Ibid.

51 Ellis et al., op. cit.; Dykhuisen et al., op. cit.

52 *Scottish Health Statistics*, op. cit.

53 M. Taylor, C. C. Smith, R. R. Khaund and A. Basu, 'Malaria in the North-East of Scotland. A review of 31 cases (1974–78)', *Scottish Medical Journal*, 1979, vol. 24, pp. 296–8.

54 D. Nathwani, R. Badial, R. R. Khaund, J. G. Douglas and C. C. Smith, 'Malaria in Aberdeen: An Audit of 110 patients admitted between 1980–1991', *Scottish Medical Journal*, 1992, vol. 37, pp. 106–110.

55 Ibid.

56 Ibid.

57 Ellis et al., op. cit.

58 Dykhuisen et al., op. cit.

59 C. C. Smith, personal communication.

60 R. Fraser, 'Memories of the City Hospital', unpublished manuscript, n.d., currently in the possession of Professor J. Friend.

61 *Scottish Health Statistics*, op. cit.

62 Professor J. Friend, personal communication.

63 Ibid.

64 Ibid.

65 J. R. S. Innes, 'Logie Samuel Bain' (Obituary), *Aberdeen Postgraduate Medical Bulletin* 1988, vol. 22, no. 2, pp. 39–40.

66 GHB, 6 October 1977.

67 GHB, 13 November 1978.

68 H. Norton, Divisional Operational Services Manager, Aberdeen General Hospitals Division, personal communication.

69 *The Press and Journal*, 15 February 1991.

70 Professor D. Reid, personal communication.

71 FBOM, 1 April 1972.

72 Mrs N. E. McKay, superintendent radiographer, personal communication.

73 Professor L. A. Gillanders, personal communication.

74 H. Norton, personal communication.

75 FBOM, 4 November 1971.

76 GHB, 30 August 1978.

77 GHB, 2 February 1984.

Chapter Fifteen

The City Hospital Laboratory

Reference has been made in several preceding chapters to the establishment of the Laboratory at the City Hospital. Such a facility, although talked about for many years, did not materialise in a permanent form until 1920. It provided a service for the City Hospital and all the peripheral hospitals in the North-East of Scotland, for Aberdeen Town Council's Public Health Department and for all general practitioners in Aberdeen and the neighbouring counties.

In the early years of the City Hospital, pathological and bacteriological examinations were performed, as required, in the university's department of pathology, which had been established in 1882. The first incumbent of the chair of pathology was D. J. Hamilton (1849–1909), whose main interest and expertise were in the emerging field of bacteriology. His department provided a pathological service for the Royal Infirmary. Professor Hamilton also co-operated closely with Matthew Hay, and in 1894 a scheme began whereby, at no cost to the general practitioners of Aberdeen and a number of neighbouring burghs, 'throat brushings from suspected cases of diphtheria' could be examined. From 1896 sputum could be examined for tubercle bacilli, and the diagnosis of typhoid confirmed or refuted by a serological test. From 1898 a bacteriological diagnosis of cholera was possible.[1] Thus, a bacteriological service was developed, available for the patients of the doctors in Aberdeen and the North-East as well as those patients in the City Hospital and the Royal Infirmary, although no records are available to confirm the extent of its use. This service continued to be provided by the university department of pathology until 1920.

As early as 1898, in a report to the Public Health Committee, Matthew Hay had raised the question of the provision of a municipal laboratory sometime in the future.[2] Such a laboratory would be available to undertake investigations, as required, in the bacteriological investigation of water, milk and food. However, at that time Hamilton was still willing and anxious to carry on this public health work, provided money could be raised to cover the salary of a special assistant and the outlays involved. The question of a laboratory was again raised in 1908 when Professor George Dean (1863–1914) was appointed to the chair of pathology. He entered into agreement with the Town Council to continue to undertake the bacteriological examinations required.[3] It is abundantly clear that vigorous efforts were being made by the Medical Officer of Health for Aberdeen and by the professor of pathology to provide every facility for the bacteriological examination of appropriate specimens. The aim was to assist in the diagnosis and prevention of disease, and in this endeavour they had the active support of the Town Council. There can be detected, however, a suggestion of disappointment in one sentence in the MOH's annual report for 1908:

> There is still room for a more extensive utilisation of the bacteriological laboratory by the medical practitioners of the city, some of whom rarely have recourse to the valuable assistance which it is capable of rendering them in the diagnosis of doubtful cases.[4]

In 1910, as recorded in Chapter 5, a small room in one of the pavilions at the City Hospital was altered and equipped as a modest laboratory for bacteriological purposes at a cost of £15. There are no records of the amount of work carried out there by the resident physicians. In 1913, however, when the number of specimens examined by the university department of pathology amounted to 3,293, it was stressed that this number did not include those specimens examined at the City Hospital.[5]

The death of Dean and the outbreak of World War I in 1914 contributed to the delay in establishing, under the local authority, the proposed laboratory for bacteriological examination of materials of public health significance. Dean's successor, Professor Theodore Shennan (1869–1948), agreed to continue the arrangement made by his predecessor.[6] However, during the course of the war, Shennan approached the Medical Officer of Health with a view to making a fresh arrangement. Shortage of staff, space and equipment, and the increasing demands being made on his department had made the public health work burdensome.

The Development of the City Hospital Laboratory

In 1914 a proper small clinical laboratory for resident medical staff at the City Hospital was established. This was situated on the first floor of the Tuberculosis Institute (See Chapter 5). All concerned were satisfied that the time had come for the establishment of a laboratory with a permanent staff to provide facilities for the various activities of the public health departments in the city of Aberdeen and adjacent counties. In 1915, when 2,942 examinations were made in the university (lower than the figure for

1913, quoted above), it was stated that 'a large number of examinations were made in the laboratory at the City Hospital'.[7]

Gradual enlargement of this laboratory facility occurred until four rooms on the first floor of the Tuberculosis Institute were being used for purely laboratory purposes. Two of these rooms were set aside and furnished for routine bacteriological work and two were reserved for research purposes. A trained technician from the department of pathology was appointed, and a maid allocated for cleaning purposes. Senior medical students who assisted with the clinical work of the hospital were permitted access to the laboratory to help with the simpler tests. An x-ray machine had also been installed on the same floor and it was part of the duties of the laboratory technician to develop the plates and films for the chest physician.[8]

In 1919 the Public Health Committee agreed to submit to the Town Council, a recommendation by the MOH for more extensive laboratory facilities to be made available, so that the public health work carried out by the department of pathology could be transferred to the City Hospital. Such an arrangement would necessitate the appointment of a suitably qualified medical graduate to work at the expanded laboratory. The Town Council approved the proposals and the MOH was authorised to make the arrangements for the transfer.[9] The Council also agreed that the bacteriological services provided for the diagnosis of acute infectious diseases for the local authorities of the counties of Banff, Kincardine, Moray and Nairn could also be transferred to the City Hospital laboratory. Dr J. Parlane Kinloch, deputy MOH, was put formally in charge of this work while the local authorities also agreed to appoint a full-time medical officer to work in this field under his supervision. Matthew Hay recommended Dr John Smith for this new post, and he was appointed in 1920.[10] Smith was to hold this position until 1958 and made major contributions to the running of the City Hospital. He also established both a national and international reputation as a bacteriologist of distinction.

Dr John Smith (1892–1976)

The son of a farmer, John Smith was born on 24 July 1892 at Bogs of Enzie, near Buckie. He received his education at Buckie High School, and enrolled as a medical student at Aberdeen University in 1910. He became an expert billiards player to the detriment of his studies during his first year at medical school, and failed his first professional examination. Thereafter, he concentrated on his work and never failed another examination, although he retained his expertise with the cue! He graduated in 1915, joined the Royal Army Medical Corps, and served in military hospitals in France. He was invalided from the Medical Corps in January 1919, after a year in hospital recovering from burns caused by mustard gas shells.

On his return to Aberdeen, John Smith took his DPH in 1919 and the following year was appointed to the new post at the City Hospital. He obtained his MD with honours in 1927, his thesis being 'The serological classification of diphtheria bacilli'. He was also awarded the degree of DSc in 1927 for his thesis 'Etiological and immunological studies in scarlet fever'. He was elected MRCP (London) in 1931 and became FRCP in 1939. He was a Foundation Fellow of the College of Pathologists in 1964 and the following year Aberdeen University bestowed on him the honorary degree of LLD.

In 1931 Dr Smith received the Nicholls Prize of the Royal Society of Medicine for his researches on 'The causes and prevention of death in childbirth from septicaemia'. He was awarded this prize a second time in 1934 for 'A further investigation into the source of infection in puerperal fever'. He also won the Katharine Bishop Harman Prize in 1932 for his work on the causes and prevention of puerperal fever. A further honour came to him in 1954 from the Royal College of Physicians, Edinburgh, namely that of a Lister Fellowship for his bacteriological researches into infantile gastro-enteritis.

Dr Smith's knowledge and experience of infectious diseases and their causative agents were recognised by official bodies, who appointed him to a number of national committees dealing with infectious diseases and food hygiene. He published more than 80 scientific papers during his working life and many of these were of great importance, contributing much to an understanding of diseases and their causative agents. He retired in 1958, devoting himself to reading, billiards and horticultural pursuits, particularly the cultivation of orchids. He died on 19 June 1976 while visiting his son, a consultant obstetrician, in England.[11]

When John Smith was appointed to his new post at the City Hospital, Professor Shennan (of the university department of pathology) agreed to act as consultant pathologist to the City Hospital and the Public Health Department generally. Thus, on 1 January 1920, the bacteriological services previously provided to the city of Aberdeen and to the counties of Banff, Kincardine, Moray and Nairn by the department of pathology of the university were all transferred to the laboratory at the City Hospital.[12]

Aberdeen County Council did not initially join the laboratory scheme. The county analyst, who had a laboratory in Aberdeen and a son who was medically qualified, proposed that the latter should carry out all the bacteriological examinations required by the county authority.

A new era in the provision of bacteriological and other laboratory disciplines in the North-East of Scotland had begun. The scope of the City Hospital laboratory was never precisely defined, but its main purpose was to provide help in the diagnosis and prevention of infectious disease for doctors in public health, in general practice, and in hospitals. Veterinary practitioners submitted specimens of animal origin from farms and slaughter houses for the diagnosis of tuberculosis, brucellosis and salmonellosis in cattle, and sanitary inspectors submitted water and milk samples. Thus the City Hospital laboratory examined all specimens presented to it which had a bearing on the diagnosis and prevention of infectious diseases in North-East Scotland, with the exception of those specimens from the Aberdeen Royal Infirmary, which were dealt with by the clinical pathologists there. The capital cost of the City Hospital laboratory was provided by Aberdeen Town Council, but the annual laboratory costs were divided among the local authorities participating in the scheme. The total laboratory costs divided by the number of specimens examined during each financial year gave an average specimen cost. Each authority involved then paid according to the number of specimens received from their area.

The first complete bacteriological report submitted by Dr John Smith for the City Hospital covered the period from 1 June 1920 to 31 May 1921.[13] A total of 11,300 laboratory examinations had been required by the City Hospital, while the total examinations requested by the town amounted to 6,984. In addition, 1,767 examinations were carried out for the North-Eastern counties participating in the laboratory services scheme. During the first year, the vast majority of the specimens examined from the City Hospital were swabs for diphtheria – over 8,100. No separate breakdown of the number of specimens examined for the City Hospital and the rest of the town is given in the annual reports provided by the laboratory after 1921. In 1922 14,785 specimens for the city of Aberdeen (including the City Hospital) were examined and 1,768 specimens for the North-Eastern counties.[14]

Because of the increasing demand for laboratory services since his appointment in 1920, Dr John Smith, who had originally given part of his time to clinical tuberculosis, had to devote his whole time to bacteriology and clinical pathology.[15]

By the early years of the 1920s, the science of biochemistry had made marked progress and the newer knowledge could now be applied to the study of nutrition and to the diagnosis and treatment of diabetes, nephritis and metabolic diseases. Medical practitioners now required access to a laboratory that could provide the necessary analyses for such cases to be properly diagnosed and managed. In 1923 the public analyst, Mr Jamieson, who held a part-time appointment with the Town Council, wished to retire. Under the provision of the Food and Drugs Act, his main function was to prevent adulteration and fraud, and in his last year of office he had examined 530 samples. The MOH recommended that a whole-time analyst and biochemist be appointed. This suggestion was approved and Mr Alex B. Weir, BSc, AIC, was appointed to this post from 21 August 1923.[16] In order to provide more laboratory accommodation, the diagnostic x-ray facilities were transferred to rooms on the ground floor of the Tuberculosis Institute, freeing two first-floor rooms which were then furnished for analytical and biochemical work.

Matthew Hay, incapacitated by ill-health, retired in 1923 and was succeeded by Dr J. Parlane Kinloch, who became MOH for Aberdeen and lecturer in public health at the university. Dr John Smith became director of the City Hospital laboratory, a post he retained until his retirement in 1958. The interest and enthusiasm with which Dr Kinloch viewed the laboratory services is apparent from his annual report for 1924, in which he stated 'The enormous advantage of having the Public Health Laboratories of the City in physical association with the City Hospital need not be emphasised'. In the section of his report dealing with the City Hospital services it was made clear that the hospital services permeated every department of public health activity and this was due largely to the laboratory services. He remarked 'If advance is to be made, experimental medicine and clinical medicine must go hand in hand' and continued:

> The conception of the function of municipal laboratories as being confined to the diagnosis of infections and to the work of the public analyst is entirely antiquated, and modern municipal laboratories are required to provide not only the bacteriological and biochemical services required for the diagnosis, treatment, and prevention of disease in its widest sense, but to be essentially experimental in nature and fundamental in their physico-chemical basis, having for their essential aim research into the ultimate causes of disease and its prevention, the conditions of health, and all the problems of rehabilitation and resistance.[17]

In order to publicise the extent to which the Town Council had made available, free of charge, laboratory services and supplies of vaccines, sera and other therapeutic substances to medical practitioners within the city of Aberdeen, a summary of the facilities available was prepared and issued in 1924. This was well received. Doctors in general practice were provided with suitable equipment for the collection of specimens and the necessary containers or packages to post them to the laboratory. The laboratory also became the centre from which vaccines, anti-bacterial sera, diphtheria antitoxin and agents used in diphtheria prevention, and insulin could be obtained on demand.[18]

The number of laboratory examinations carried out over succeeding years rose steadily as medical practitioners came to appreciate the value of laboratory investigations in assisting them in the diagnosis of their patients' illnesses. The annual report of the MOH for 1930 revealed a marked increase in the number of examinations made.[19] This was due at least in part to the establishment of a sub-laboratory at Woodend General Hospital, about which some comment should be made.

Woodend Hospital Sub-Laboratory

The Aberdeen Parish Council was originally responsible for the care of the destitute and sick poor. To provide accommodation for them an institution known as Oldmill had been built at a cost of £130,000 and opened in 1907 (See Chapter 8). It consisted of two sections: a hospital for the sick poor comprising 200 beds, a special hospital of 146 beds partially used for cases of tuberculosis, and the third section which housed the destitute and unemployable.

In 1915, during World War I, the whole institution had been evacuated and used as a military hospital (the 1st Scottish General Hospital). It reverted to the Parish Council in 1919, but the special hospital section lay empty, the Public Health Department of the city preferring then to send cases of pulmonary tuberculosis to the City Hospital. As recorded in Chapter 8, in 1924 Dr Kinloch urged the Town Council to absorb the medical work of Oldmill Hospital. After lengthy discussions, this was agreed, and the official transference of the hospital blocks from the Parish Council to the Town Council took place in 1927. These blocks were renamed Woodend General Hospital and immediately provided beds for cases of pulmonary and surgical tuberculosis, greatly relieving pressure on the bed situation at the City Hospital.[20]

After various alterations Woodend General Hospital, comprising 350 beds, was soon fully occupied, and it became essential to provide a laboratory for immediate and routine investigations. A large side-room and ante-room on the first floor of the main hospital building were equipped for laboratory work. A science graduate and a trained technician were transferred from the City Hospital laboratory to this sub-laboratory. Most of the specimens for bacteriological examination were transported by ambulance to the main laboratory at the City Hospital.

Expansion of the City Hospital Laboratory

Inclusion of the Aberdeen County service: As recorded in Chapter 9, Dr Harry J. Rae became MOH to the city of Aberdeen in 1929 following J. Parlane Kinloch's resignation the previous year. Dr Rae had been MOH to Aberdeen County Council, and in 1930 the city and county authorities decided to organise a regional public health service. Dr Rae was then appointed MOH to both Aberdeen Town Council and Aberdeen County Council, and shortly afterwards Kincardine County was admitted to the combination. This led to a more complete co-operation between Aberdeen's local authority hospital services and those of the counties. However, the other activities of the different public health departments were never fully co-ordinated with the exception of the laboratory services.

At a meeting of the Town Council on 15 January 1934, it was reported that a letter had been received from the clerk of Aberdeen County Council indicating that the county bacteriological services were to be ended and suggesting that the City Hospital laboratory should undertake the work. Sub-committees were set up and in due course recommended that the councils of both authorities should approve an arrangement whereby the County Council would pay £800 per annum to Aberdeen Town Council for these laboratory services.[21] This was agreed and the arrangement came into operation on a year-to-year basis from 16 May 1934, and continued until the councils had to transfer their laboratory services and hospitals to the North-Eastern Regional Hospital Board, upon the formation of the National Health Service in 1948.

Laboratory examinations for venereal diseases: When the main VD clinic was first established at Woolmanhill as described in Chapter 7, the bacteriological and serological tests necessary for the control and treatment of these diseases were performed by Dr George M. Duncan, the hospital clinical pathologist. Following his death in 1935, the specimens for laboratory examination from the VD clinic, numbering many thousands annually, were examined at the City Hospital laboratory.[22] Whereas the number of such specimens examined at the City Hospital in 1924 had been 733 and in 1934 had increased to 6,326, the number examined in 1936 was 14,995, largely due to the additional specimens from the main VD clinic.[23]

Laboratory Developments 1935–48: By 1935, the number of examinations being carried out had increased to such an extent that it was no longer possible to continue without extra staff. Permission was obtained for the appointment of a full-time medical assistant and two additional technicians. Dr G. Batty-Smith, who had previous pathological experience, was appointed, together with one fully-trained male technician and one female trainee technician. The clerical and domestic staff were also increased to deal effectively and efficiently with the compilation of records and reports, the preparation of postal packets and general domestic duties in the laboratory.

When the laboratory was first instituted the only building available as an animal house was the old stable, which had housed the horse used for ambulance haulage. A new building to house laboratory animals was designed and erected on a site adjacent to the main laboratory building. This animal house, constructed of granite, was completed in 1937. The chief reason for animal experiments on guinea pigs was to aid the diagnosis of human infections due to the tubercle bacillus and also to test milk samples for the presence of bovine tubercle bacilli. Prior to the establishment of tuberculosis-free dairy herds and the pasteurisation of milk, much human illness was caused by the transmission of this disease from cattle to man.

The constant increase in the work of the laboratory, due partly to appreciation of the help which could be given, and partly to rapidly advancing medical knowledge, made it necessary to provide increased accommodation. After discussion, it was agreed that the tuberculosis clinic and x-ray departments should be transferred to the main administrative building thus freeing the whole of the ground floor of the building in which the laboratory was already housed. It was found possible to retain all members of staff throughout the war years, and to maintain a satisfactory service throughout the region, although certain items of equipment, culture media and chemicals had to be obtained from the central stores of the Department of Health for Scotland. During this time, in addition to its normal commitments, the laboratory undertook the examination of specimens submitted by units of the armed forces stationed within the region.

In 1946 Dr Batty-Smith decided to give up laboratory medicine and his post was filled by Dr Christopher Giles in December of that year. Dr Giles gave valuable service until the end of January 1948, when he was appointed to take charge of the laboratory associated with the general hospital in Stoke-on-Trent. He was succeeded by Dr James A. F. McLean, pathologist at Stracathro Hospital, near Brechin.

In 1945 it became evident that further accommodation was required if the laboratory was to continue functioning efficiently. Ward 5, a building consisting of a number of small wards used partly for the treatment of patients with venereal diseases and partly for the treatment of patients with infective skin disorders, lay at the rear of the laboratory. After discussion with the MOH and Dr F. J. T. Bowie, who was in charge of the venereal diseases unit, it was decided that all cases of VD should be treated at the centre established in the out-patient department of the Royal Infirmary. Accommodation for patients with infective skin disorders was found elsewhere in the City Hospital. A corridor was built, linking the main laboratory building and a portion of Ward 5, making urgently needed space available. The clerical staff was then able to transfer to more spacious quarters, and other rooms were utilised as a staff room and a stationery store for the preparation of postal packets. Apparatus was also installed for the sterilisation of infected equipment, for the preparation of culture media and distilled water. As a result of these changes, a third room became available for analytical work within the main laboratory building.

Additions to staff also became necessary. This was increased to three medically qualified persons, one chief technician, three senior technicians, three junior technicians, three typists, six female domestic workers, and one animal house attendant. The staff employed at the sub-laboratory at Woodend Hospital consisted of one science graduate, one trained technician and one female domestic worker.

Immediately prior to the changes brought about in 1948 by the introduction of the NHS, the City Hospital laboratory provided services for the following:

1. The Public Health and Sanitary Departments of Aberdeen, Aberdeenshire, Banffshire, Moray & Nairn, Kincardineshire and the Orkney and Shetland Islands.
2. General practitioners and consultants in the above areas.
3. Certain hospitals in these areas, amounting in all to 40 establishments, large and small.

4. The veterinary services in the area, when their work impinged on public health and until the veterinary investigation laboratory of the North of Scotland College of Agriculture was established at Craibstone in 1947.

For the last full year (1947), prior to the introduction of the NHS, the total number of examinations carried out by the laboratory was 70,463. In addition 647 samples were examined under the Food and Drugs Act.[24]

The Laboratory under the National Health Service

During the years 1948–58 there were few changes of note in the general administrative arrangements of the regional laboratory service. During this period, however, medical research made immense progress and every aspect of laboratory medicine shared in this. Advances of great significance were made in bacteriology, virology, immunology, biochemistry, haematology and pathology, resulting in the introduction of additional laboratory procedures with a consequent increase in the complexity of the work. To some extent, the situation was helped by the fact that standardised reagents, such as culture media, serological reagents and apparatus for the more rapid determination of chemical constituents of body fluids, became available from commercial sources. However, the end result was a large increase in the number of laboratory examinations requested, with the consequent need for additional staff and more up-to-date accommodation and facilities.

The city analyst and biochemist, Mr Alex Weir, who had been appointed in 1923, retired in May 1955. His successor, Mr Thomas M. Clark, OBE, BSc, FRIC, was appointed that year to hold the official post of city analyst under the jurisdiction of Aberdeen Town Council, and biochemist at the City Hospital laboratory under the North-Eastern Regional Hospital Board. In January 1963, Mr John Ritchie, Aberdeen County's analyst retired. Mr Clark, with the concurrence of Aberdeen Town Council and the Regional Hospital Board, became county analyst as well, and supervised the work done in the analyst's laboratory at 41½ Union Street, Aberdeen, for the counties of Aberdeen, Banff, Kincardine, Caithness and Ross and Cromarty.

Dr John Smith retired as director of the City Hospital laboratory in 1958, after 38 years' service. He had been the sole bacteriologist appointed when the laboratory was instituted in 1920 and he had seen it grow from small beginnings. In the first year of its existence 19,000 examinations had been made from materials submitted from the city of Aberdeen and the surrounding counties, while the total examinations made in 1957, the last full year under Dr John Smith's jurisdiction, numbered 64,925.[25]

Dr James Brodie (1913–81)

James Brodie was appointed consultant-in-charge of the City Hospital laboratory in 1958, to succeed Dr John Smith. This was not an easy post to take over. John Smith was well-known and appreciated by the medical practitioners and many others locally to whom he had given help and guidance on all aspects of laboratory medicine. He had also built up an international reputation as a bacteriologist. However, over the twenty years that Dr Brodie was in charge of the laboratory, he established his own reputation as an efficient and competent bacteriologist who maintained the highest standards in providing a diagnostic service to the community of North-East Scotland.

James Brodie was born in Dundee in 1913 and received his schooling in that city. He graduated in medicine at St Andrews University in 1937. He had several spells in general practice and served as resident medical officer in Arbroath Infirmary. He obtained the DPH in 1940 and then joined the university department of bacteriology in Dundee under Professor W. J. Tulloch. In 1943 Dr Brodie received the degree of MD with a gold medal. He was senior lecturer in the department for seven years prior to his appointment to the City Hospital laboratory. During his tenure of office in Aberdeen, Dr Brodie published over 40 papers on different infectious diseases, including salmonellosis, gastro-enteritis and staphylococcal infections, as well as hospital cross-infection and hand-hygiene. However, it was during the Aberdeen typhoid outbreak in 1964 that James Brodie excelled. He controlled the laboratory with its dedicated and efficient staff and coped with the sheer volume of work which emanated from over 500 cases of typhoid and the testing of suspects. The laboratory played a major role, with the physicians, in the diagnosis and treatment of victims.

Following the typhoid outbreak, brucellosis was Brodie's chief interest. He published a number of papers on this subject and made an important contribution to controlling and eliminating this disease in North-East Scotland. His department at the City Hospital was designated as the Scottish National Reference Laboratory for Brucellosis.[26]

Many were the demands made by Dr Brodie for improved accommodation for his laboratory which, for most of the time he served there, was quite unsuitable for a modern laboratory. Nonetheless, although the accommodation was poor, this did not prevent the staff from coping, year after year, with increasing workload, nor did it prevent the work being accomplished at a very high standard. Nor did the laboratory stick to out-of-date methods and techniques – it was always at the forefront with the latest advances in technology. In later years Dr Brodie suffered from ill health, but always returned to the laboratory full of interest in the new technology. He worked hard and well and played a significant part in improving the health of those in the North-East of Scotland.

A local review of the scope of laboratory services in the region, covering bacteriology, virology, pathology, blood-grouping and the public health analytical service laboratory services in the North-East, took place shortly before Brodie's appointment. Certain recommendations were made, but decisions were deferred until the Dunlop Committee Report on laboratory services was available.[27] Decisions were later made as to which of the several laboratories in the area would deal with material from the various hospitals.[28] The general laboratories concerned, in addition to that at the City Hospital, were the university laboratories, the Woodend Hospital laboratories and two other smaller laboratories in the university department of medicine and the Blood Transfusion Service, which dealt with special types of work. Virology for the region was carried out in the university laboratory at Foresterhill as was the bacteriology for Aberdeen Royal Infirmary.[29] All pathological specimens were dealt with in the university department of pathology at Foresterhill. In addition to the work for the various hospitals throughout the region (except Aberdeen Royal Infirmary), the laboratory at the City Hospital dealt with all public health work and material for examination submitted by general practitioners throughout the whole of the Regional Hospital Board area. The presence of the city analyst at the City Hospital was recognised as increasing the efficiency of the service because many specimens, such as milk, water, food, etc which emanate from public health services, require chemical as well as bacteriological examination. The Board of Management for the Aberdeen Special Hospitals was made responsible for all day-to-day matters connected with the administration of the City Hospital laboratory.[30]

Laboratory Extensions

In 1959 it was decided that the entire building associated with the old Ward 5 should be incorporated into the laboratory, with internal reconstruction to suit the requirements of laboratory work.[31] However, it was made clear at that time in the annual report of the Group Medical

Superintendent to the Board of Management of the Aberdeen Special Hospitals, that

> ... the end result will be a laboratory the premises of which will not comply, by any means, with recognised modern design. This fact has been recognised and the present reconstruction, which will be completed early in 1960, is of a minimum character pending further consideration by the Regional Board of the possibilities of establishing the laboratory in another location outside the City Hospital. The main structural faults in the existing premises are that they really consist of what was an ordinary house with extensions reached through long and winding corridors. Most of the rooms are very small and the whole layout prevents any effective attempt at organising the activities on a streamlined basis which would satisfy the views of a modern Work Study team.[32]

Whatever further consideration may have been given to the problem of space for the laboratory no change materialised and no plans were announced to ease the situation at that time. In consequence the laboratory had to work on under these out-of-date conditions for many more years.

Work of the Laboratory

The annual report of the laboratory for 1963 showed 228,997 examinations had been performed compared with 126,814 in 1959. This increase occurred despite the fact that from October 1962 the bacteriological work for Woodend Hospital had been transferred to the university department of bacteriology at Foresterhill.[33] However, with the increase in laboratory space gained by incorporation of Ward 5 in 1960, and by some increase in staff numbers, it was possible to deal with the additional workload.

The upsurge in work involved all sections of the laboratory. In biochemistry, for example, the number of toxicological tests had increased, especially in relation to drug overdosage. The development of general medical units and the rheumatology unit at the City Hospital also led to a marked increase in demand for bacteriological, biochemical, haematological and serological tests. The range of tests carried out for venereal diseases was also extended and the techniques used were brought into line with those performed at the Venereal Diseases Reference Laboratory.[34]

An arrangement was made whereby the laboratory at the City Hospital would continue to carry out for Aberdeen's general hospitals a number of tests not done in the university laboratories at Foresterhill. These included antibiotic sensitivity tests on cultures of *Mycobacterium tuberculosis* as well as animal inoculations for this organism, leptospirosis investigations, anti-streptolysin O levels, thyroid antibody tests and certain toxicological investigations.

When appropriate, new tests were added to the armamentarium of the laboratory. Sometimes this enabled well-established tests to be replaced by more up-to-date, more efficient or cheaper methods. In 1963, for example, the then current pregnancy diagnostic test performed in the laboratory was the Hogben test, which involved the use of female *Xenopus laevis* toads.[35] The female African toad was injected in the back with 2 ml of suspected pregnancy urine or 1 ml of an extract. A deposit of six or more eggs within 4–12 hours indicated pregnancy. A comparison of the toad technique with four commercially available haemagglutination pregnancy tests was carried out, in the hope that one of these tests might prove to be a satisfactory, reliable and economical substitute. This involved 500 urine specimens submitted to the laboratory.[36] From the results obtained it was possible to discontinue the Hogben test and introduce a haemagglutination tube test by the beginning of June 1964. Thus the colony of *Xenopus laevis* toads became redundant and was dispensed with. Space freed in the animal house became available for a breeding unit for guinea pigs.[37]

The total number of tests performed in the laboratory during 1964 reached a record number of 337,545, largely, but not entirely, accounted for by the many specimens from typhoid or suspected typhoid patients from the outbreak that year (See Chapter 13). However, in 1965, the number of tests performed exceeded even that carried out during the 'typhoid year', amounting to 341,162.[38] This was in no way a freak year for in each succeeding year up to 1970 the number of tests carried out rose steadily, so that in 1970 the total was 426,204. These increases involved all sections of the laboratory.

Laboratory Accommodation – Again!

It had been apparent for some time that additional accommodation was urgently required to deal with the increasing workload. Hopes of a move to a new laboratory at Foresterhill in 1967 were dashed, but the suggestion was made that accommodation might be made available in the adjacent laundry, which had closed down. Agreement on this was reached in 1968, but it was stated that financial considerations could delay completion of these new premises for up to two years.[39] This reconstruction of part of the laundry would accommodate the biochemistry and haematology sections of the laboratory. The space thus freed would permit additional accommodation for the bacteriology section, as well as allowing much needed extensions to the general office, post room and packaging room, and the provision of proper staff rooms for technicians, typists and maids. The new biochemistry laboratories were completed in 1970 and the haematology laboratories in 1971.

In 1967 the Home Office had demanded that the animal house be modernised and it was the responsibility of the Regional Hospital Board to finance this.[40] The alterations were completed in 1969, after a year during which temporary premises were used, a situation that greatly restricted the number of animal inoculations the laboratory was able to perform, as well as preventing the breeding of guinea pigs. The modernised animal house, although providing less space for breeding of guinea pigs, was now much better proportioned and provided quarantine, inoculation and breeding rooms, as well as a post-mortem room and other facilities. 'Anyone knowing the old premises would not recognise the new. Indeed, the conditions of housing of the laboratory animals is palatial when compared with the premises occupied by the human population of the laboratory!'[41]

Staff Changes

Miss Nora Davidson, who had joined the technical staff of the laboratory in January 1920 and had been chief technician for many years, retired in 1962. She was succeeded by Mr Harry Mellis, who, in turn, was followed in 1974 by Mr Edward Macpherson, who held the post of senior chief technician until his retirement in 1995. The number of scientific and technical staff in the three divisions of the laboratory (bacteriology, chemical pathology and toxicology, and haematology), eventually reached 36, a great increase when compared with the two in post in 1920.

The number of staff in the laboratory office and post room also increased, particularly during the 1970s as the volume of laboratory reports increased and the amount of mail received and dispatched became greater. Replacement specimen outfits were sent out with each report forwarded to general practitioners or hospital ward. Miss Lily Philip, who had worked at Woodend Hospital, was appointed to take charge of the laboratory office in 1946 and held this post until 1974 when she retired. She was succeeded by Mrs M. Christie, who held the post until 1989 and saw many changes in the organisation of the office work. One of the most important of these changes was the introduction of photocopying machines, which made the preparation of duplicate reports much easier.

Scottish National Reference Laboratory for Brucellosis

A comprehensive investigation of the problem of brucellosis in the Orkney Islands as it affected the human and bovine populations was undertaken in 1965 at the request of the Scottish Home and Health Department (SHHD).[42] In the first year 39 isolations of *Br. abortus* were made from 479 milk samples. Over the next few years the investigation was stepped up and extended to other areas, and many infections were revealed in the human and cattle populations using both old and new techniques.

The results of these examinations were notified to the Medical Officer of Health of the appropriate local authority so that the necessary action could be taken to prevent the spread of the disease to humans. This was one of the most important measures taken in the North-East of Scotland to prevent the spread of brucellosis, particularly where milk might be consumed unpasteurised, before the advent of the national campaign for the eradication of brucellosis in cattle.

In 1969 laboratory examinations revealed that there was a continuing spread of *Br. abortus* infection in dairy herds in the North-East. In the human population, since the beginning of the local campaign, 518 individuals had serological responses consistent with a clinical diagnosis of brucellosis, while another 1,182 had antibody responses that indicated exposure to the causative organism.[43] As long as brucellosis in cattle was allowed to persist, it would continue to be a disease in humans.

On 1 April 1973, the SHHD set up the Scottish National Reference Laboratory for Brucellosis at the City Hospital laboratory with Dr J. Brodie as its director.[44] All isolates of *Br. abortus* obtained from milk samples and other sources could be sent to the reference laboratory for biotyping, which was a useful adjunct in the epidemiological investigation of this condition. Thus, the Reference Laboratory at the City Hospital played an important and significant part in the elimination of this disease in cattle and humans in Scotland as a whole.

Administrative Control

Following the introduction of the NHS in 1948, the City Hospital laboratory was initially administered by the North-Eastern Regional Hospital Board and became known as the Regional Laboratory. Thereafter, control passed, as mentioned earlier, to the Board of Management for the Aberdeen Special Hospitals, and in 1958 the name was officially changed to 'The Laboratory at the City Hospital'.[45] When the latter Board was dissolved in 1971, administrative control of the laboratory passed to the newly-constituted Board of Management of Foresterhill and Associated Hospitals. With re-organisation of the NHS in 1974, a further change in administrative control took place, the laboratory then coming under the jurisdiction of the South District of Grampian Health Board. In 1984 re-organisation in the NHS led to the laboratory being administered by the Geriatric and Specialist Services Unit based at Woodend.

Special Treatment Centre Laboratory

Over the years the consultant and other staff at Woolmanhill in the Special Treatment Centre (STC, previously known as the VD clinic), had stained and microscopically examined smears of discharges from attending patients. This procedure was helpful in that it often allowed immediate confirmation of the diagnosis. Specimens from these patients had, of necessity, to be sent to the laboratory for culture and antibiotic sensitivity tests. Blood specimens had also to be sent for the various serological tests then in use.

It became increasingly urgent in the period 1979–80 that some changes should be made at the STC to improve the laboratory facilities available. Accordingly, a room was set aside for laboratory work, additional equipment provided, and a trained technician from the City Hospital laboratory posted there to carry out the necessary microscopical and other work. A consultant bacteriologist from the City Hospital laboratory visited the STC laboratory at least twice a week to confirm smooth running of the service provided.

This arrangement was of great assistance to the medical team at the STC, relieving them of necessary tasks such as preparing and staining slides, and it ensured that patients were provided with an efficient bacteriological service.

Working Party on Laboratory Services

In 1969 the Regional Hospital Board set up a working party to examine the present and future needs of laboratory medicine in the region.[46] Rationalisation of the laboratory services was clearly required and the suggestion was made that new purpose-built laboratories for bacteriology, biochemistry and haematology should be built on the Foresterhill site. These would undertake all the clinical pathological investigations required by all the hospitals, general practitioners and public health departments in North-East Scotland. Such laboratories would be independent of the university laboratories, but would co-operate and work closely with them. The university laboratories would benefit by being relieved of their routine hospital commitments and would be able to carry out their prime functions of teaching and research. The ideas were not acceptable to several of the staff involved, however, and the working party's deliberations did not result in any clear future policy.

The problems facing the administration of the NHS at this time were the same as those that had existed in all previous years, namely competing priorities and lack of money. The difficulty facing the laboratory at the City Hospital was one of accommodation. It was far from desirable and allowed little room for expansion, a necessity in view of the ever increasing demands made on its services. It was to be nearly two further decades before a final solution was achieved.

'Fifty Years of Service (1920–70)' [47]

The year 1970 saw the completion of fifty years of service by the City Hospital laboratory and this was the subject of an article in the *Aberdeen Postgraduate Medical Bulletin*. Apart from the City Hospital itself, the laboratory had served many smaller hospitals, public health authorities and general practitioners in the North-East region from St Cyrus to Unst. Its activities covered bacteriology, haematology, clinical biochemistry and toxicology. In its early years it had also given a limited service in pathology and virology, but these services were later entirely provided by the respective university departments.

In the first year of its existence the laboratory carried out 11,300 tests for the City Hospital, while in its fiftieth year 403,370 tests were performed. When this latter figure is broken down, 54.5 per cent of the tests were done for general practitioners, either for patients in their own practices or from one of the smaller peripheral hospitals that they looked after.

The review gave full details of the number of specimens received and the tests done by the different sections of the laboratory over recent years, and some data back to 1920. The test/specimen ratio showed that not only had the number of tests done increased over the years but so also had the number of specimens. In the early days of the laboratory almost all specimens received had had only one test performed but later several tests were often carried out. For instance, serum might be tested for antibodies to a range of different organisms.

The massive increase in workload in the 50-year period is clearly evident and this growth continued year by year.

Staff Changes 1964–91

Bacteriology: Dr James McLean, who had been appointed as a second bacteriologist in 1948, resigned in 1963 on being appointed to a post in London. He was succeeded by Dr Peter Callaghan, who was previously lecturer in bacteriology in the Welsh National School of Medicine in Cardiff. He did not settle in the area, however, and resigned in 1968 to return to his native Wales. One of us (IAP) was then appointed consultant bacteriologist at the City Hospital and became consultant in administrative charge on Dr Brodie's retirement in 1978. At this same time Dr Tom M. S. Reid, a local graduate who had trained in bacteriology in the university department of microbiology, became consultant bacteriologist at the City Hospital and, later, consultant-in-charge on Dr Porter's own retirement in 1983.

Dr Ian Gould, an Edinburgh graduate joined the staff as second consultant bacteriologist in 1983, and both he and Dr Reid continued at the City Hospital until the department, as will be recorded, moved to Foresterhill in 1991.

Chemical Pathology and Toxicology: Mr Thomas Clark, chemical pathologist and toxicologist at the City Hospital laboratory, and public analyst for Grampian Region, retired in August 1981 after 26 years' service. The dual appointment that he had held was then discontinued, and thereafter the public analyst for the Grampian Region, who had his laboratory at 41½ Union Street, had no connection with the City Hospital laboratory.

Mr Clark was not replaced at the City Hospital. Mr Laughlan Charles, a senior scientific officer already on the staff in the clinical pathology section, took over supervision of this work. He remained in post, being responsible for all the clinical biochemical and toxicological tests with the existing staff until early 1989, when this section of the laboratory was transferred to Foresterhill and amalgamated with the university department of chemical pathology.

Haematology: Measurements of haemoglobin concentration, white blood cell and platelet counts, examination of blood films, and other simple haematological tests had been in the repertoire of the laboratory from its inception. This work was initially done by Dr John Smith and later by Dr McLean. The latter was also responsible for the limited amount of histopathology done at the City Hospital laboratory until 1963 when this work was all transferred to the university department of pathology at Foresterhill.[48]

The haematological workload had steadily increased, both from general practitioner referrals and, from 1956, from the general medical wards at the City Hospital. In 1964 an additional post in clinical pathology was created and Dr R. J. L. Davidson was appointed to take charge of this work.

Ron Davidson was born in Arbroath and graduated in medicine at St Andrews University. After house officer posts in Dundee Royal Infirmary, he spent two years on national service in the RAMC in Malaya. He had had initial thoughts of a career in obstetrics but, pending the availability of a post, became lecturer in pathology in Dundee with Professor Lendrum. After three years, having abandoned thoughts of obstetrics, Dr Davidson returned to clinical medicine as registrar in medicine for two years before becoming senior registrar in clinical pathology at the Western Infirmary, Glasgow. A year later he came to Aberdeen. The laboratory service in haematology was quickly expanded to include microbiological assays for folic acid and vitamin B12, special serological tests for glandular fever, and other diagnostic procedures. Close collaboration was quickly established with Dr Bill Walker who had come to Aberdeen some months earlier, and an excellent service was provided. If samples submitted by general practitioners for haematological examination suggested or indicated a diagnosis of leukaemia or some other blood disorder requiring hospital investigation and treatment, immediate admission could be arranged to the beds at the City Hospital in Bill Walker's charge, and further diagnostic tests performed in collaboration.

During the 1960s, the workload of the haematology section increased five-fold, and additional staff were clearly required. In 1964 consideration was given to appointing a registrar in haematology, but this proved unsuccessful, there being no applicants, and so in 1968 a medical assistant post was established and Dr A. Basu appointed. A graduate of Calcutta University, he had been working in Manchester before coming to Aberdeen.

In 1973 Ron Davidson left the City Hospital on being appointed senior lecturer in haematology to take charge of the university department of haematology at Foresterhill. He was replaced as consultant at the City Hospital laboratory by Dr Rathin Khaund. He had graduated in Assam in India, and had come to the UK in 1963, and after obtaining additional qualifications in London, had worked in the haematology department at Glasgow Royal Infirmary.

The workload in haematology continued to increase although fewer haematological cases were admitted to the City Hospital wards following the departure of Dr Walker in 1973. Cases of acute leukaemia were still admitted for a period to the cubicles in Ward 9, however, where they were jointly managed by Dr C. C. Smith and Dr Audrey Dawson, then senior lecturer in clinical haematology.

Over the years the number of specimens from general practitioners and peripheral hospitals steadily increased until 1990 when Dr Khaund, Dr Basu and the entire technical staff moved to the department of haematology at the medical school, Foresterhill.

Research Work at the Laboratory

The work of the laboratory referred to in this chapter so far has been mainly concerned with specimens from patients or from samples of milk, water or food, submitted for bacteriological, haematological, biochemical or toxicological examination. After the laboratory had been established in 1920 and was functioning satisfactorily, Dr John Smith turned his attention to some of the problems facing bacteriologists and clinical pathologists at that time. That decision led to the gathering of a rich harvest of research work emanating from the laboratory over the years. The pattern of research established in the 1920s persisted during the lifetime of the laboratory, until it closed its doors in 1991.

In the early years, accounts given by Medical Officers of Health and their medical staffs often revealed that investigations into some outbreak of disease left doubts about the original sources of disease. At that time serological classification of streptococci, pneumococci, salmonellae, shigellae (and other enterobacteria) had not been developed and bacteriophage typing of *Salmonella typhi* and of staphylococci was unknown. It was only in the decades which followed that it became possible with certainty to establish that isolates from an outbreak of (say) gastro-enteritis belonged to the same serological group or belonged to the same phage type.

Many such investigations were carried out and the results published in medical and scientific journals. Sometimes these were published as purely personal contributions by Dr Smith, but often in conjunction with administrative and clinical colleagues engaged in public health. Dr Smith himself published over 80 scientific papers on a variety of diseases and their causative organisms. These included publications on scarlet fever, diphtheria, typhoid and paratyphoid fever, bacillary dysentery, Weil's disease, undulant fever, gastro-enteritis in children, and salmonella food poisoning. The causative organisms in two instances of salmonella food poisoning were new serotypes first isolated at the City Hospital laboratory: *Salm. aberdeen* and *Salm. rubislaw*. His contributions on the causation and source of infection in puerperal fever were of outstanding importance and were recognised by the award of the Nicholls Prize, as mentioned earlier.

During Dr James Brodie's tenure of office in charge of the laboratory the flow of contributions to medical journals was maintained, papers on salmonellosis, gastro-enteritis and staphylococcal infections being among those published. Important publications included accounts of the Aberdeen typhoid outbreak of 1964 with particular reference to the serological findings, the epidemiology of brucellosis in Orkney and North-East Scotland, the method of isolating *Br. abortus* from milk samples and on the serology of human brucellosis. Dr R. J. L. Davidson, while at the City Hospital laboratory, published a number of papers on infectious mononucleosis, haemolytic anaemia and haemoglobinuria.

One of us (IAP) published a number of papers, including one on boric acid preservation of urine samples, a technique introduced into routine use particularly for urine specimens subject to delay before examination. Other publications during the period 1968–83 with colleagues, laboratory and clinical, included reports on shigellosis, the antibiotic spectinomycin, a milk-borne outbreak of campylobacter infection, and a cost-benefit study of a milk-borne outbreak of salmonellosis.

Dr T. M. S. Reid and Dr I. M. Gould, in keeping with the pattern established, wrote a large number of papers on many aspects of laboratory work over the years from 1983 until 1991, along with clinical and other colleagues. These included papers on the use of different antibiotics and their efficiency and application to different clinical conditions, on food poisoning, on salmonella carriers, reactive arthritis, Lyme disease and the application of the Malthus analyser in a diagnostic microbiology laboratory.

The Closure of the Laboratory at the City Hospital

During the final twenty years of its existence, the staff working at the City Hospital laboratory felt it was inevitable that the laboratory there would ultimately cease to exist. As mentioned earlier, a working party on laboratory services set up by the Regional Board in 1970 had failed to reach any definite conclusions. The final stimulus to change came from the university authorities.

The pathology and bacteriology services for the main Aberdeen hospitals had initially been developed in university departments. Similarly, the university had established a department of clinical chemistry in 1925 with Dr A. Lyall as part-time lecturer, and he was to remain in charge for 35 years. In 1962 a chair of chemical pathology was established and was held by Professor Sam Fraser until his retirement in 1983, when the chair lapsed because of funding problems, and Dr Iain Ross, a senior lecturer, was given charge. The haematology department had likewise been university based, having been developed within the department of medicine in the early 1950s.[49]

The university provided all the staff for these different departments and was responsible for the running and the upkeep of the areas involved in the medical school at Foresterhill. However, the Regional Board and, later, Grampian Health Board paid a significant annual contribution for the services provided. In the early 1980s the university was subjected to considerable financial restraint, and pressure was put on staff to be more involved in research than in fulfilling NHS commitments. The university then indicated to the Health Board that they would have to reduce their involvement in the laboratory services and in other fields. Accordingly, in 1985, a joint working party of the Board and university was set up to consider the problem of laboratory rationalisation.

This group reported in April 1986 and their report was endorsed by the Board in December 1986.[50] It was proposed that certain laboratory services (clinical chemistry/chemical pathology, haematology and bacteriology) should all be provided at Foresterhill, and that all university staff whose duties related in the main to service provision should transfer to Health Board employment. It was also proposed that all the laboratory disciplines at the City Hospital be transferred to Foresterhill and amalgamated with the relevant departments there. Extensive negotiations with staff then occurred and, because of various problems, the transfer took place in staggered fashion, clinical chemistry (chemical pathology) moving in early 1989, haematology in early 1990 and finally bacteriology in the spring of 1991.

Thus, after 71 years, the laboratory at the City Hospital ceased to exist. Over its long history, however, it had played an important role in the proper function of the City Hospital and in the medical services for the North-East of Scotland.

References to Chapter Fifteen

1   Annual Report of the Medical Officer of Health for Aberdeen for 1898, pp. 3–4.
2   Aberdeen Central Library, Town Council Minutes (hereafter TCM), 17 January 1898.
3   TCM, 19 April and 21 June 1909.
4   Annual Report of the Medical Officer of Health for Aberdeen for 1908, p. 34.
5   Annual Report of the Medical Officer of Health for Aberdeen for 1913, p. 51.
6   Annual Report of the Medical Officer of Health for Aberdeen for 1914, p. 63.
7   Annual Report of the Medical Officer of Health for Aberdeen for 1915, p. 127.
8   Annual Report of the Medical Officer of Health for Aberdeen for 1914, p. 61.
9   TCM, 7 July 1919.
10 TCM, 19 January 1920.
11 I. A. Porter, 'John Smith' (Obituary), *Aberdeen Postgraduate Medical Bulletin*, January 1977, pp. 54–6.
12 Report of the Medical Officer of Health for Aberdeen for the years 1916–21, p. 176.
13 Report of the Medical Officer of Health for Aberdeen for the years 1916–21, pp. 176–9.
14 Annual Report of the Medical Officer of Health for Aberdeen for the years 1922–3, pp. 167–70.
15 Ibid., p. 165.
16 TCM, 22 October 1923.
17 Annual Report of the Medical Officer of Health for Aberdeen for 1924, p. 171.
18 Ibid., pp. 171–4.
19 Annual Report of the Medical Officer of Health for Aberdeen for 1930, pp. 104–6.
20 N. J. Logie, 'History of the Aberdeen Joint Hospital Scheme and Site' in G. P. Milne (ed.), *Aberdeen Medico-Chirurgical Society. A Bicentennial History 1789–1989*, Aberdeen, Aberdeen University Press, 1989, pp. 155–78.
21 TCM, 19 March 1934.
22 TCM, 2 December 1935.
23 Annual Reports of the Medical Office of Health for Aberdeen for: 1924, p. 175; 1934, p. 62; 1936, p. 62.
24 Annual Report of the Medical Officer of Health for Aberdeen for 1947, pp. 58–61.
25 Report of the Medical Office of Health for Aberdeen for the years 1916–21, pp. 176–9.
26 A. M., 'James Brodie' (Obituary), *Aberdeen Postgraduate Medical Bulletin*, 1981, vol. 15, no. 2, pp. 29–30.

27 Northern Health Services Archives, North-East Regional Hospital Board minutes (hereafter NERHB), 4 September 1957.
28 NERHB, 6 May 1959.
29 NERHB, 5 February 1958.
30 Northern Health Services Archives, Annual Report of the Group Medical Superintendent to the Aberdeen Special Hospitals Board of Management (hereafter ASHBOM report) for 1958, p. 1.
31 NERHB, 4 November 1959.
32 ASHBOM report for 1959, p. 11.
33 ASHBOM report for 1963, p. 21.
34 ASHBOM report for 1960, p. 20.
35 ASHBOM report for 1963, pp. 21–2.
36 J. Brodie and H. Mellis, 'A comparative study of pregnancy tests', *Practitioner*, 1966, vol. 196, pp. 821–5.
37 ASHBOM report for 1964, p. 27.
38 ASHBOM reports: for 1965, p. 21; for 1967, p. 24.
39 ASHBOM report for 1968, p. 26.
40 ASHBOM report for 1967, p. 24.
41 ASHBOM report for 1969, p. 18.
42 ASHBOM report for 1965, p. 22.
43 ASHBOM report for 1969, pp. 18–19.
44 'Scottish Brucellosis Reference Laboratory', *Aberdeen Postgraduate Medical Bulletin*, September 1973, p. 85.
45 NERHB, 5 February 1958.
46 NERHB, 5 February 1969.
47 J. Brodie, R. J. L. Davidson, I. A. Porter, and T. M. Clark, 'Born 1920 .....', *Aberdeen Postgraduate Medical Bulletin*, October 1970, pp. 3–11.
48 ASHBOM report for 1963, p. 21.
49 I. D. Levack and H. A. F. Dudley (eds), *Aberdeen Royal Infirmary*, London, Baillière Tindall, 1992, pp. 154–89.
50 Northern Health Services Archives, Grampian Health Health minutes, 4 December 1986.

Epilogue

What of the City Hospital today? A visit to survey the scene showed much new, but also many relics of the past. Pleasant memories were evoked. The surrounding high stone walls remain, with the entrance on Urquhart Road unchanged. The attractive granite lodge, which in bygone years housed the head porter, still stands. No such uniformed gentleman has occupied it since the 1960s, and it now provides staff accommodation. The spacious grounds continue to be well maintained and the open lawns are interspersed with trees, flower- and rose-beds. Half-way across the grass, between the nurses' home and former doctors' residence, and the site formerly occupied by old Ward 7 and 8, bordering what was previously the croquet lawn, is a 25-yard stretch of four to six foot high old stone wall. This must be part of the original boundary wall which would have bordered the reception house (Figure 1, Chapter 3).

Many of the granite-walled wards with their distinctive squat two-storey towers at the ends nearest Urquhart Road remain. Wards 1, 2, 3 and 4 were all built in 1910 but have been much altered by additions and appendages. The original function of the upper storey of the towers is obscure. They are now closed off, the stairs being unsafe[1], and the upper windows are boarded up. The entrance area to what was formerly Ward 1, along with the old physiotherapy department, the rheumatology out-patient area and offices, along with parts of old Wards 1 and 2 now houses a community health centre opened in 1996, providing chiropody, physiotherapy and other services. For several years it was also the city base for the Grampian Doctors On Call Services (G-Docs) started in 1996.[2] Their four gleaming white cars with green stencilled trim and adorned with sundry logos, could be seen resting in the car park, awaiting the evening's and night's activity. In April 2000, however, this service was relocated to new purpose-built accommodation within the Primary Care Resource Centre in the Liberty Health and Research Park on the Foresterhill site. The accommodation was recently named the David Anderson Building, in memory of the late Dr David Anderson, former senior partner in the Oldmachar medical practice in King Street. When chairman of G-Docs, Anderson was much involved in planning the move to the Foresterhill site. Much of old Wards 1 and 2 lie empty and unused but after refurbishment will house the Links Medical Practice, currently at 144 King Street, and the Marischal Medical Practice of 187 King Street. These practices have recently merged and the converted wards will provide much improved more spacious accommodation.

Wards 3 and 4 have been joined by a central extension and are known as the Links Unit and have been extensively altered to provide 58 continuing care beds for geriatric patients. These come mainly from the surrounding areas of the city. With the decreasing need for such beds consequent on the increasing number of private nursing homes, Grampian Health Board announced plans in 1998 to close this facility. However, following an active campaign by patients' relatives, staff and local councillors, the Board revised their plan. Half was closed in May 1998 but the other part retained.

There are also currently plans to open some general practitioner beds in this area and possibly to create an Aberdeen City Community Hospital. This would provide beds for use by local practices to provide an appropriate mode of care for suitable patients and decrease pressure on the acute medical beds at Aberdeen Royal Infirmary.[3] The exact site for these developments remains unclear as the patients in the Links Unit are due to move this year into the block known as Jasmine Park.

The site formerly occupied by Wards 7 and 8 is now filled by an attractive modern single-storey block with roughcast walls and flat roof. Known now as Ward 5, this housed 30 psycho-geriatric patients until its closure in June 2000 when the patients were transferred to one of the new developments at Royal Cornhill Hospital or to private nursing home care. Nearby, where old Ward 6 formerly stood, lies a new ward, known as Jasmine Park, a two-storey building with roughcast walls and pitched tiled roof. Opened in 1991, this is one of the newer 60-bed geriatric units and for the past ten years, although housing NHS patients, has been run by a private company. Their contract, however, comes to an end in the year 2001, and the Links Unit is to be relocated there to provide a flexible care scheme for the elderly.[4]

The other 60-bed unit, now known as Ward 6, lies adjacent to Wards 9 and 10 and is of similar design. Although completed in 1987 it was for a period half-empty and was closed completely in 1997 but has since been occasionally re-opened to house patients decanted from other hospitals when wards there were being refurbished. Wards 9 and 10 lie deserted and empty, the Portakabin extension mentioned earlier having been removed. The kitchen and laundry are also closed. The ovens and ranges in the kitchen were finally damped in October 1994, and all hot meals for patients are now prepared at Royal Cornhill Hospital and transported down by heated van. The nurses' home was closed in September 2000. There are now no resident doctors.

The main laboratory building lies empty, the granite walls becoming mildewed and grimy. The laboratory extension, which formerly housed the haematology and clinical biochemistry departments, was latterly the base for the Grampian Reprographics Department. The adjacent boiler house and workshops remain. The administration block, or clinic block as it is known to the administrators, remains unchanged, the clock in the central tower facing Urquhart Road still keeping perfect time. Part of this block, along with the chapel, mortuary and store which lie on the other side of the internal road from the main laboratory, were all built in 1880. and are the only parts of the original hospital remaining. The radiology department remains under the clock tower, providing a service for nearby general practitioners. For a two-year period it was reduced to part-time working but is again open for the whole working day although its long-term future is unclear.

The chest clinic moved to the Foresterhill site in early 1997. Part of the block facing the nurses' home, having been affected by subsidence, was demolished. This area has been replaced by an attractive gravelled section with seats and flower containers. The upper portion of the remaining block has since December 1999 housed the Rapid Response Team of social workers and social care services which operated during the winter months to relieve pressure on the stressed medical beds in the Aberdeen Royal Infirmary.

Although the level of clinical activity on the site is greatly reduced, it was noteworthy that the car parking spaces were nearly all full! There appeared to be only one doctor on site at the time of a day-time visit.

There are still many around who retain happy memories of their working days at the City Hospital. The friendly atmosphere which pertained has been perpetuated in two specific ways.

The City Hospital Golf Outing

C. C. Smith's energies extend into areas beyond medical practice. In 1977, along with Dr Logie Bain and Mr Sandy Burgess, he launched the annual City Hospital Golf Outing. The late Sandy Burgess was a drug representative firstly for Wyeth and then for MMM Inc. He and his wife had respectively been patients of Dr Smith and Dr Bain, and Sandy had earlier spent a period in the City Hospital with TB.[5] The outing was originally held at Aboyne Golf Club moving shortly for a period to Deeside and was then regularly held at Banchory. The 'field' was initially small, being restricted to those who had worked or were working at the City Hospital, those consultants who visited frequently for consultations and those general practitioners who regularly referred patients. With the passage of time and the renowned popularity of the event, the criteria for invitation relaxed. Even some lady golfers attended! Only those who had been at some time offensive to C. C. Smith (a few) were declined an invitation. Several friendly drug representatives and their companies gave generous support. Various trophies were competed for. Each year, a captain for the day was selected and wore a chain of office bearing the names of all former captains. All those who could wield golf clubs and who specifically worked at the City Hospital have held this honour. An unusual trophy, known originally as the S. B. (Silly Buggers) trophy, became the Sandy Burgess Quaich in memory of his involvement over so many years. Logie Bain, who was the inaugural captain, generously provided a silver salver, and Hugh Galloway a cup for the lady golfers. There was also an Infection Unit Cup and sundry other lesser trophies.

The round of golf was followed by mild libations and high tea, and a good day was had by all attending. In recent years the field consisted of around 40 individuals, and in 1994 the event was appropriately named THE CITY HOSPITAL MEMORIAL GOLF OUTING. In recent years, however, there have been constraints on the pharmaceutical industry in funding such events. Consequent on this and other factors it was decided that last year's event which was held at Edzell Golf Club would have to be the 'final round'. The trophies are now displayed in a cabinet in the infection unit.[6]

The City Hospital Tie

This was the joint brainchild of Drs Joe Legge and Norris Rennie in 1995. Produced by RAM Leisure, it consists of oblique bands of navy-blue and green, the navy-blue stripes bearing the faint outline of a flying seagull while this is highlighted in light blue on the broad bottom segment, and below the bird's feet, the logo CHAFF also in light blue. This stands for the CITY HOSPITAL AT F... FORESTERHILL. The F... is open to different interpretations!

The Future

The long-term future of the site is still uncertain. With increasing emphasis on private care for the elderly, the demand for long-stay hospital beds has declined. As mentioned earlier, many of the wards built or altered for this purpose lie empty. Empty wards have, however, to be maintained sound and weather proof and this costs money without generating income. Recent press reports indicate that the Grampian Primary Care NHS Trust, who have been responsible for the site since re-organisation of NHS trusts on 1 April 1999, wish to sell about 75 per cent of the site within the next two years. None of the buildings are listed and so it is not inconceivable that the site may ultimately be cleared and redeveloped.

Whatever happens, the City Hospital can be proud of its past.

References to Epilogue

[1] H. Norton, personal communication.

[2] Ibid.

[3] Sister Rosemary Nixon, personal communication.

[4] Ibid.

[5] C. C. Smith, personal communication.

[6] Ibid.

APPENDICES

The information in these appendices is taken either from the City Hospital Staff Register or from the Town Council Minutes.

Appendix 1

Aberdeen's Medical Officers of Health

1868–1880	Francis Ogston (Title MOH only introduced 1881)
1881–1886	William J. R. Simpson
1886–1888	Theodore Thomson
1888–1923	Matthew Hay
1923–1929	J. Parlane Kinloch
1929–1952	Harry J. Rae
1952–1974	Ian A. G. MacQueen

Appendix 2

Head Nurses and Matrons at the City Hospital 1885–1974

Year	Name	Title
1885–1887	Mrs M. Thomson	Head Nurse
1887–1896	Miss M. Bothwell	Head Nurse Matron from 1889
1896–1928	Miss M. Frater	Matron
1928–1941	Miss M. D. Frater	Matron
1941–1946	Miss H. Paterson (Mrs Kirk)	Matron
1946–1948	Miss M. E. Scott	Matron
1948–1968	Miss V. Maltman	Matron
1968–1974	Miss A. C. Argo	Matron

Appendix 3

Resident Physicians at the City Hospital 1894–1913

Date Appointed	Name	Salary	Date of Resignation
1 Oct 1894	W. E. G. Duthie	£50	Sept 1895
1 Oct 1895	J. Fletcher	£50	Sept 1897
1 Oct 1897	J. A. Rose	£50	Jan 1898
14 Feb 1898	J. S. Laing	£75–100	Died 29 Dec 1901
27 Jan 1902	H. Fraser	£100	Aug 1902
15 Sept 1902	W. E. Taylor	£100	May 1904
20 June 1904	G. A. Mavor	£100	March 1906
16 April 1906	A. G. Anderson	£100	Oct 1908
21 Dec 1908	G. Banks	£100 £120–£150 from 1911	Aug 1913 (as Asst. MO)

Appendix 4

Junior and Senior Medical Officers at the City Hospital 1913–25

	Junior MOs		Senior MOs
1913–15	B. T. Saunders	1913–15	J. Chalmers (Resigned to join RAMC)
1915–17	Vacant	1915–17	J. P. Kinloch (Temporary appointment)
1918–22	Isabella Ferguson	1918–20	J. Chalmers
1921–23	J. Moir	1920–21	V. Yule N. Maclennan
1923–25	E. R. Sorley	1921–25	J. S. Anderson

Appendix 5

Senior Resident Medical Officers at the City Hospital 1925–48

1925–1927	John S. Taylor
1928–1930	A. M. Fraser
1930–1934	Robert G. Henderson
1934–1937	Douglas Bell
1937–1938	J. H. Stephen
1938–1943	Unfilled; latterly because of the war
1943–1945	Austin Clay
1945–1948	W. Chambers

Appendix 6

Junior Medical Officers in the VD Department 1920–30

1920–1921	Robert Ferguson
1921–1923	Burton Yule
1923–1926	George Matthew Fyfe
1926–1930	F. J. T. Bowie

Appendix 7

Residents at the City Hospital 1925–45 (in alphabetical order)

F. Bowie	H. Dawson	A. G. Emslie	Dr Fettes
A. Forrest	A. M. Fraser	R. Fraser	J. Gammie
W. Gapper	W. Gorrod	S. Gray	D. Harkins
J. Harper	J. Hay	J. Hogg	J. Innes E.
Johnstone	Dr Johnston	C. Liddell	J. Lobban
R. Macdonald	A. Maclennan	R. Michie	E. Morrison
H. Morrison	W. Morrison	Dr Petrie	J. Pickles
N. Ross	C. Russell	M. Schultz	G. Stephen
R. Stuart	J. Webster	A. Wilkins	Dr Will

Appendix 8

Nursing Officers and Nursing Services Managers at the City Hospital 1974–2001

Year	Name	Title
1974–1988	Miss A. E. Munro	Senior Nursing Officer
1976–1990	Mrs J. Mackenzie	Nursing Officer
1986–1988	Mrs P. Cullary	Nursing Officer
1988–1989	Mrs K. Hallam	Nursing Officer
1989–1991	Mrs M. Forrester	Nursing Officer
1991–1994	Mr J. Forrest	Nursing Services Manager (Acute Services)
1991–1994	Mr M. Gray	Nursing Services Manager (Care of Elderly)
1994–1999	Mrs C. Ledingham	Nursing Services Manager (Care of Elderly)
1999–Present	Mr C. Stewart	Manager for Service in Transition

INDEX

Blumberg, Baruch, 190
Boards of Health, 10, 11
body louse, 64
Boer War, 67
Bothwell, Miss, 41, 48
Bowie, Fred J. T., 111, 122, 143,
146, 155, 165, 171, 233, 257,
258
Br. abortus, 152, 213, 240, 246
Br. melitensis, 152, 213
Bretonneau, Pierre, 81
British Medical Association, 28, 32,
51, 54, 56, 85, 97
British Red Cross Society, 94, 146
Brodie, James, 235, 236, 240, 243,
246, 248, 249
Buckley, Dr, 119
Budd, William, 3, 67
Burgess, Sandy, 252

Callaghan, Peter, 243
Calmette, Albert, 90
Campbell, Shona, 220
campylobacter, 203, 207, 221, 246
Cantley, John, 220
carriers, 83, 135, 150, 179, 185,
190, 246
Cash, John Theodore, 45, 55
centenary of the City Hospital, 198
cephaloridine, 178
Chain, Ernest, 126, 132
Chalmers, James, 52, 256
Chambers, William (Bill), 156,
157, 158, 167, 170, 176, 187,
257
Charles, Laughlan, 7, 40, 55, 64, 90,
243
chemotherapy, 78, 131, 146, 160,
210
chest clinic, 157, 163, 164, 166,
192, 214–5, 216, 217, 220, 252
chest medicine, 206, 214–5, 215
chickenpox, 159, 202
China, 1, 124

chloramphenicol (chloromycetin),
178
cholera, 3, 5, 9–12, 18, 22, 28, 50,
60, 67, 207, 224
cholera hospital, 12, 28
Christie, John F., 95, 122
Christie, M., Mrs, 239
City analyst, 53, 102, 234, 236
City Hospital Golf Outing, 252
City Hospital laboratory, 130, 224–
49
City Hospital laboratory, closure,
246
City Hospital Scandal, 37–42
City Hospital Tie, 253
Clark, Norman S., 160
Clark, Thomas M., 234, 243
Clay, Austin C., 124, 257
Collins, E. Godfey, 5, 123
combined vaccine, 174, 187, 202
Community Health Services
Limited, 221
Copeman, W. S. C., 119
Corynebacterium diphtheriae, 81
cowpox, 13, 14
Craig, John, 155, 160
Cran, Margaret, 125
Crofton, John, 163, 215
Crosby, W. S., 198
Cuninghar-Hill Hospital, 31
cystic fibrosis, 216

David Anderson Building, 250
Davidson, Alexander Dyce, 45
Davidson, L. Stanley P., 106, 119,
125, 149, 150, 153, 166
Davidson, Nora, 239
Davidson, R. J. L., 244, 246, 249
Dawson of Penn, 108
Dawson, Audrey, 245
Dawson, Colonel A., 123
Dean, George, 224, 225
Department of Health for Scotland,
109, 120, 172, 192, 232

Gillanders, L. A., 164, 223
glandular fever, 159, 244
Godden, David, 216
gonococcus, 94
gonorrhoea, 95, 96, 117, 132, 148,
    165
Gordon, Alexander, 77, 86
Gordon, Ian, 200
Gospels, 1
Gould, Ian M., 243, 246
Gowar, F. J. Sambrook, 146
Grampian Health Board, 197, 198,
    221, 241, 247, 251
Grampian Healthcare NHS Trust,
    199, 221
Grampian Primary Care NHS Trust,
    199, 254
Grampian Reprographics
    Department, 252
Guérin, Camille, 90
gynaecology, 168

haematology, 108, 159, 160, 234,
    239, 241, 242, 244, 245, 247,
    252
Hamilton, D. J., 6, 156, 224
Hay, Matthew, 32, 42, 44–56, 58,
    61, 64, 68, 69, 72, 74, 76, 78, 83,
    85, 86, 91, 93, 95, 97, 99, 103,
    198, 224, 226, 229, 255, 258
Health and Welfare Department,
    172, 175, 177, 180, 182
heliotherapy, 144
Henderson, Robert G., 114, 115,
    128, 257
hepatitis, 159, 189–91, 193, 205,
    208
Hepatitis A, 190, 196, 208, 210
Hepatitis B, 190, 208, 210
herpes zoster, 159
Hill, Ian, 106
Hippocrates, 67, 190
Hobbs, Betty, 181
Hogben test, 238

Holmes, Oliver Wendell, 20, 77
Horder, Lord, 119
human immunodeficiency virus
    (HIV), 211

immunisation, 4, 83, 84, 85, 131,
    133, 135, 143, 157, 172, 174,
    187, 202, 207
immunity, 7, 80, 109, 130, 131
Inada, 148
infantile gastro-enteritis, 193, 196,
    204, 227
infective diarrhoea, 207
Innes, Elizabeth, 105
Innes, John A., 106
iron lung, 114–5, 128, 157, 187

Jamieson, Mr, 229
Jasmine Park, 221, 251
Jenner, Edward, 13, 14
Jenner, William, 67
Johnston, Alan, 97, 128, 200, 215,
    258
Justice Mill Lane Baths, 120, 166,
    217

Kaposi sarcoma, 210
Kawasaki disease, 203–4
Kay, Douglas, 163, 164, 215
Keers, Dr, 163
Kennedy, Fiona, 218
Khaund, Rathin, 223, 244, 245
Kilgour, Alexander, 11, 19, 20, 29
Kinloch, J. Parlane, 51, 52, 53, 98,
    99–111, 112, 122, 130, 131, 140,
    142, 143, 226, 229, 230, 231,
    255, 256
Klebs, Edwin, 81
Koch, Robert, 4, 12, 88, 93, 131

laboratories, 5, 49–51, 52, 53, 95,
    99, 100, 102, 104, 108, 114, 116,
    120, 155, 160, 165, 178, 179–80,